LEVEL
2

HEALTH AND SOCIAL CARE

ALISON HETHERINGTON
ELIZABETH RASHEED

HODDER
EDUCATION
AN HACHETTE UK COMPANY

In order to ensure that this resource offers high-quality support for the associated BTEC qualification, it has been through a review process by the awarding body to confirm that it fully covers the teaching and learning content of the specification or part of a specification at which it is aimed, and demonstrates an appropriate balance between the development of subject skills, knowledge and understanding, in addition to preparation for assessment.

While the publishers have made every attempt to ensure that advice on the qualification and its assessment is accurate, the official specification and associated assessment guidance materials are the only authoritative source of information and should always be referred to for definitive guidance.

BTEC examiners have not contributed to any sections in this resource relevant to examination papers for which they have responsibility.

No material from an endorsed textbook will be used verbatim in any assessment set by BTEC.

Endorsement of a textbook does not mean that the textbook is required to achieve this BTEC qualification, nor does it mean that it is the only suitable material available to support the qualification, and any resource lists produced by the awarding body shall include this and other appropriate resources.

Orders: please contact Bookpoint Ltd, 130 Milton Park, Abingdon, Oxon OX14 4SB. Telephone: (44) 01235 827720. Fax: (44) 01235 400454. Lines are open from 9.00 - 5.00, Monday to Saturday, with a 24 hour message answering service. You can also order through our website www.hoddereducation.co.uk

If you have any comments to make about this, or any of our other titles, please send them to educationenquiries@hodder.co.uk

British Library Cataloguing in Publication Data

A catalogue record for this title is available from the British Library

ISBN: 978 1 444 1 8656 7

Published 2013

Impression number   10 9 8 7 6 5 4 3 2 1

Year   2016 2015 2014 2013

Cover photo © Jason Todd/Getty Images

Illustrations by Barking Dog Art

Typeset by Integra Software Services Pvt. Ltd., Pondicherry, India.

Printed in Italy for Hodder Education, an Hachette UK Company, 338 Euston Road, London NW1 3BH

Contents

How to use this book

This book will give you all of the knowledge you will need for the BTEC Level 2 First Certificate and Extended Certificate in Health and Social Care. The layout and language is aimed specifically at Level 2 students and each Learning Aim is clearly set out so that you can find the information that you need.

Tick boxes ✓

Tick the boxes to track your progress through each topic.

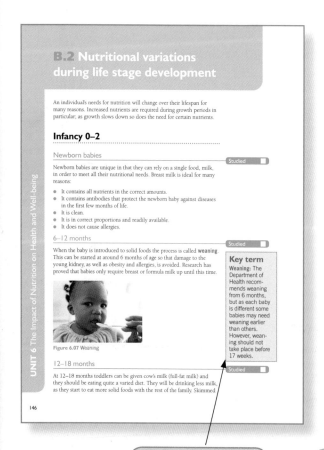

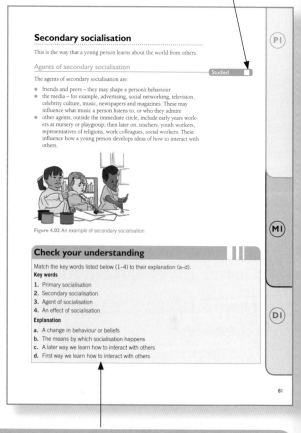

Key terms

Check important words and what they mean

Check your understanding

Use these questions at the end of each topic to make sure that you have understood the main points.

Real life connections

Find out more about different job roles in health and social care.

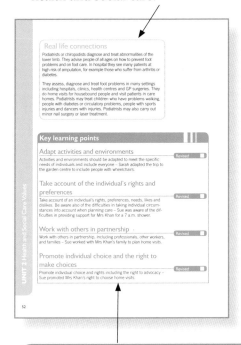

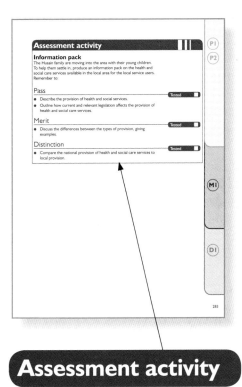

Key learning points

Summaries of all of the main knowledge for each Learning Aim, with tick boxes for you to check off which subjects you have revised.

Assessment activity

Test your understanding of the subject with activities which give you examples of what you need to know to meet pass, merit and distinction criteria.

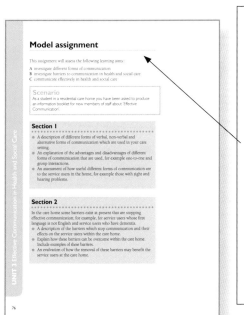

Model assignment/ sample assessment

At the end of each unit you'll find either a Model Assignment that will give you the opportunity to generate the evidence you need or a Sample Assessment that will test your knowledge ready for the exam.

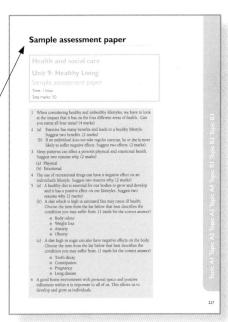

Acknowledgments

Photo credits

The authors and publishers would like to thank the following for permission to reproduce material in this book:

p. 15 (top left) © Blend Images / Alamy; (top right) © Leila Cutler / Alamy; (centre left) © Imagestate Media; (centre right) © Nick Kennedy / Alamy; (bottom left) © Image Source / Alamy; (bottom centre) © Cultura / Alamy; (bottom right) © UpperCut Images / Alamy; p. 33 © yanlev – Fotolia.com; p. 41 © blickwinkel / Alamy; p. 84 © Jacek Chabraszewski – Fotolia.com; p. 108 © Jeffrey Blackler / Alamy; p. 109 (left and right) © Crown Copyright; p. 110 © Libby Welch / Alamy; p. 131 (left) © Morgan Lane Photography/ iStockphoto.com; (right) © a4stockphotos - Fotolia.com; p. 132 (left) © Monika Adamczyk - Fotolia.com; (right) © Julián Rovagnati – Fotolia.com; p. 134 © Maria Brzostowska - Fotolia.com; p. 135 © Nancy R. Cohen/Photodisc/Getty Images/ Eat, Drink, Dine 48; p. 146 © Monkey Business – Fotolia.com; p. 165 © Jose Luis Pelaez Inc/Blend Images/Corbis; p. 169 © Ed Maynard; p. 188 © picamaniac - Fotolia; p. 219 (top) © Yuri Arcurs – Fotolia.com; (centre) © Science Photo Library / Alamy; p. 267 (left) © JOSE OTO/ SCIENCE PHOTO LIBRARY; (centre) © ADRIENNE HART-DAVIS / SCIENCE PHOTO LIBRARY; (right) © PAUL WHITEHILL/SCIENCE PHOTO LIBRARY; p. 276 (top) © auremar – Fotolia.com; (bottom) © mangostock – Fotolia.com; p. 277 © Lisa F. Young – Fotolia.com; p. 314 (top left) © cycreation – Fotolia.com; (top centre) © sjhuls – Fotolia.com; (top right) © Kevin Wheal / Alamy; (centre left) © JERRY MASON/SCIENCE PHOTO LIBRARY; (centre right) © LARRY MULVEHILL/ SCIENCE PHOTO LIBRARY; (bottom) © WILLIAM GAGE/CUSTOM MEDICAL STOCK PHOTO/ SCIENCE PHOTO LIBRARY; p. 327 © David Humphreys / Alamy; p. 331 (left) © John Birdsall/ Photofusion; (centre) © michaeljung – Fotolia.com; (right) © bst2012 – Fotolia.com; p. 346 © micromonkey – Fotolia.com.

Every effort has been made to trace and acknowledge ownership of copyright. The publishers will be happy to make suitable arrangements with any copyright holders whom it has not been possible to contact.

Unit 1

Human Lifespan and Development

This unit provides the opportunity to investigate how humans grow and develop and the impact of the four aspects of human growth and development: physical, intellectual, emotional and social. It also looks at how different events, both expected and unexpected, have an impact on growth and development and the support mechanisms which are available to help manage them.

Learning aims

In this unit you will:

✓ explore human growth and development across life stages.

✓ investigate factors that affect human growth and development and how they are interrelated.

Learning Aim A

A.1 The different life stages people pass through during the life course

Life stages that all humans should pass through during normal **development** are shown below; they are categorised according to age.

- Infancy (0–2 years)
- Early childhood (3–8 years)
- Adolescence (9–18 years)
- Early adulthood (19–45 years)
- Middle adulthood (46–65 years)
- Later adulthood (65+ years)

A.2 Key aspects of human growth and development at each life stage

All human beings start from the moment of conception – when a sperm meets and fertilises an egg – but not all human beings develop in the same way. Many factors influence the rate and type of **growth** and development. These are factors not just from our genetic make-up, but also from external influences around us. There is a pattern to human growth and development, but we do not all follow the same pattern at the same rate.

Growth is not the same as development. Some people grow but do not develop.

All of the above stages have key aspects of development, which can be divided into four separate areas: physical, intellectual, emotional and social.

Infancy 0–2 years

A normal pregnancy is around 40 to 42 weeks long. Our development can depend very much on internal and external factors. Pregnancy is the first important stage, when many factors can affect the growth of a baby.

Physical development

Studied ☐

Babies are born with a set of primitive **reflexes**, which are sometimes called survival reflexes. Some of these automatic responses stay with us for life and some disappear as the natural bodily responses take over. This set of reflexes indicates that the newborn's central nervous system is in good working order.

Reflexes include:

- Rooting reflex – this causes babies to turn their cheek in the direction of touch and helps them to direct their mouth towards their mother's breast.
- Sucking reflex – this causes babies to suck any object that touches their lips or enters their mouth and enables them to feed from birth.
- Moro reflex – this causes babies to fling their arms outwards, arch their back then bring their arms together as if they were holding something and occurs in response to a loud noise.
- Grasping reflex – this causes babies to curl their fingers tightly around any object placed in their palm.
- Tonic neck reflex – this causes babies to turn their head, arms and legs to one side when laid on their back; they flex the limbs on the opposite side.

- Stepping reflex – this causes babies to lift their legs as if about to walk when held upright.
- Babinski reflex – this causes babies to fan then curl their toes when the bottom of their foot is stroked.

At this developmental stage, physical development is rapid. The physical increase from newborn to two years old is tremendous. Physical development can be split into two categories:

- gross motor skills – large movements: kicking, hopping, skipping, jumping, running, walking
- fine motor skills – small movements: threading, picking up small things, holding objects.

Gross motor skills

When babies are born, they have little control over their head if an adult does not support it. By six months they usually have complete head control. By nine months they are generally able to pull themselves up to a sitting position, and then to stand alone by 12 months. By around 15 months most babies can walk alone and at two years old most can walk up and down stairs with two feet on one step.

Do remember, some babies and children may develop crawling and walking skills earlier or later than others. These developmental stages are just average guidelines for parents and professionals – it is perfectly normal for babies to develop at different rates.

Fine motor skills

Newborn babies keep their hands closed most of the time. They have an automatic grasp reflex, which usually disappears by about three months old. By six months a child will generally voluntarily grasp an object or toy and hold it. The movements in the hands become more refined by nine months and most children can use finger and thumb to hold objects. By 12 months they can usually hold a crayon using the 'palmar grasp'. At 15 months they can usually take a spoon to their mouth and by two years old they may begin to dress themselves.

Intellectual development

Studied ☐

This area of development is rapid and includes development of language. Think of newborns and how they attract people's attention, then think of a two-year-old and how they attract people's attention. They have gone from crying to talking, often in full sentences.

Intellectual development also includes using the senses. Newborn babies use their senses to explore their surroundings. They are aware of bright colours and sounds. By six months old they are beginning to tell the difference between familiar sights and tastes. Have you noticed that babies always put objects straight in their mouths? Why do you think this might be?

From six months onwards babies repeat actions, like dropping a toy from a pram, but they have only a short attention span. From 12 months onwards they are beginning to understand the world around them and have increased curiosity. By the age of two they can usually point to familiar parts of the body and do simple jigsaws.

Emotional development

Studied ☐

Emotional development is encouraged and supported if the baby has a constant caregiver. This provides babies with a firm feeling of stability and attachment. This sense of attachment is called bonding. Newborn infants may cry if they are left alone too long or not held firmly, because they do not feel a sense of security.

John Bowlby was a well-known theorist in this area and he considered that all infants needed one main caregiver to ensure that attachment and bonding was established. If this attachment from the main carer was removed, his research showed that the infant would suffer emotionally. Further work in this area has been done by Mary Ainsworth and Michael Rutter, which contradicts Bowlby's research. Their work states that so long as relationships are secure, a range of caregivers in an infant's life will not have a detrimental effect.

As they reach three months old, babies can wriggle with pleasure and show happiness. At six months old they may show anxiety towards strangers and at 12 months old they can show emotions like anger, for example if a toy is taken away from them. At two years old they may start to have tantrums – you have probably heard of the 'terrible twos'. However, at this age they are trying to become more independent.

Social development

Studied ☐

Between the ages of birth and three months, babies will start to smile at familiar faces. By the age of six months they may well get upset when their mother leaves the room and may not be confident with others. At 12 months they enjoy being with familiar people and they usually enjoy mealtimes. At two years they often enjoy helping others and they may show concern for other children who may be upset.

Topic A.2

Childhood 3–8 years

Physical development

Studied ☐

In this life stage, children's physical development is showing strength, agility and dexterity. The rate of growth is now steady.

By three years old, most children can climb the stairs properly. By the age of four, gross motor skills have usually improved and they will be able to stand, run, and walk on tiptoe. Their ball skills will have improved and they should be able to catch, throw, bounce and kick. By the age of six or seven they will be able to ride a bicycle and their stamina will be increasing. They will have more ability to climb, manoeuvre and run fast during team games.

By the age of four, fine motor skills are also rapidly improving. Children should have mastered pencil control and be able to thread a string of small beads. Hand–eye coordination improves and children begin to show the ability to manipulate small objects.

Intellectual development

Studied ☐

By the age of three, children will generally start to understand the concepts of 'over', 'under' and 'behind' and they enjoy listening to stories. At the age of four, when a child's concentration span is much longer, children in the UK usually begin their full-time compulsory education. By the age of five they may start to draw quite detailed pictures and even enjoy solving problems. Moving towards the age of ten, children will start thinking in a more complex way and be able to perform simple tasks while listening to instructions.

Language development is also an important aspect: four-year-olds start to talk in full sentences. By the age of four, children will ask many questions, using 'why', 'when' and 'how' and understand the answers. They may be able to tell long stories and enjoy simple jokes. They start to recognise some word patterns, for example the past tense. For example, they may say 'I walked', which is correct, but as they don't yet know the exceptions to the rule they may say 'I runned' and 'I goed' instead of 'I ran' and 'I went'.

By the age of five, children's speech is mostly grammatically correct. By the age of eight or nine, most can use and understand complex sentences and speak expressively. By the age of ten, most children will be fluent talkers and show an understanding of others' points of view.

Another important part of intellectual development is moral development. This means that, as children grow up, they start to develop an understanding of the differences between right and wrong. Parents and carers are the main influence on children's moral development.

Emotional development

Studied ▢

Emotional development is about developing the ability to understand and control one's emotions. As children grow up, they start to understand more about their feelings and the feelings of others. This is a gradual process throughout childhood – and it carries on for most of our lives!

By three years of age children may copy the moods or behaviour of adults around them, so having positive role models is very important.

From the age of five, children start to become more confident and want to do well at school and in games. A six-year-old may show signs of frustration when failing at something. In this life stage children's behaviour may be difficult to handle at times because they are developing control over their emotions. By the age of eight, they are becoming more emotionally stable. There are also other important factors that can affect children's behaviour – see Figure 1.01.

Figure 1.01 Factors affecting a child's behaviour

Social development

Studied ▢

By three years old children will probably begin to take turns when playing with other children and they are becoming more independent.

At the age of four, children still depend on their parents and carers to provide social activities for them and to help them with the new social skills they are learning. For example, they still need help with dressing, eating with a knife and fork and going to the toilet. They will start to learn norms of behaviour (the acceptable values, beliefs and patterns of behaviour); for example, manners, appropriate dress and method of speech. As they grow, most five- and six-year-olds like to choose their own friends and decide on play activities. By the age of ten they will generally develop much fuller awareness of social skills and also be aware of rules and the need to cooperate with others.

Adolescence 9–18 years

This life stage is the change from childhood to adulthood.

Physical development

Physically during this life stage girls and boys start puberty. During puberty, physical changes prepare the body for sexual reproduction. See Table 1.01 for information about the physical changes that take place.

Table 1.01 Physical changes that take place during puberty

Female changes	Male changes
Breasts develop	Facial hair grows
Public hair grows	Public hair grows
Weight gain	Growth spurt
Growth spurt	Growth of penis and testes
Periods start	Voice deepens

These physical changes are due to the growth and maturity of the reproductive organs. The reproductive organs produce hormones, which initiate secondary sex characteristics. The changes have a great effect on the other developmental areas of the adolescent.

Intellectual development

During this life stage, adolescents study for formal examinations at school and may choose to study further subjects at the age of 16. Vocabulary increases and as young people start to develop a sense of values and beliefs, they may question the world around them. Adolescence can be a very impressionable age – young people often make lifestyle choices that have positive or negative effects on their future.

The theorist Piaget believed that problem solving becomes a skill during adolescence. It may not be as refined a skill as in adulthood, but young people have the ability to think deeply and make judgements. They are often aware of the need to find out enough about an issue to allow them to make good decisions.

Emotional development

This stage of development for adolescents can be described as an 'emotional rollercoaster'. They are coping with major physical changes to their bodies. Socially, they strive to be accepted by their peer groups. Emotionally and physically, they may be attracted to the same or the opposite sex and they are also faced with issues of self-esteem and self-concept.

They may be studying for important exams, leaving home, forming important emotional relationships, becoming independent and moving from education to the world of work. Think about your own adolescence. Would you agree that it is an exhausting time?

Social development

Studied

This is a crucial stage for making relationships and fitting in with peer groups. It is a time to establish identity and explore sexuality. Young people may experience conflict with their parents as they begin to form their own ideas about the world and how to be independent. They may be entering the world of professional employment, as well as establishing relationships in other areas.

It is at this stage that young people become less dependent on their families and are influenced by teachers, peers and the media.

Early adulthood 19–45 years

It is difficult to say what marks adulthood as it can vary in different cultures. In the UK, we can vote at the age of 18 and also legally buy alcohol. However, you can legally marry at 16 with your parent's consent and join the Armed Forces. You can also finish compulsory education and go into employment at 16.

Has anyone ever said to you: 'Let's talk about this like adults?' or 'Grow up, stop acting like a child!' When or what makes you an adult?

Physical development

Studied ☐

Early adulthood is often a time of high physical fitness in men and women. Women are most fertile at this time and many have their children in their twenties and thirties. High-risk pregnancies increase with the age of the mother.

Intellectual development

Studied ☐

In early adulthood, students complete their full-time education and may go on to study for other qualifications, or complete specialist studies, at college or university. They usually have a good memory and long concentration span.

Emotional development

Studied ☐

During adulthood, most people's self-esteem and confidence increase, providing that emotional factors in their lives are positive and their personal relationships are stable.

Most adults will have experienced both positive and negative emotions during their lives, and many are able to deal with emotions well and show empathy towards others.

Social development

Studied ☐

New social relationships are made through the world of work. Many young adults meet their life partner through work. Later in adulthood, social relationships may be put under pressure, as marriage and parenting play their part. It is possible that the family income may reduce when one parent cuts down their working hours or leaves work to bring up the children. Family life can be quite tiring or stressful when work and family responsibilities are high.

Middle adulthood 46–65 years

Physical development

Between the ages of 45 and 55, women reach the menopause. A reduction in hormones causes women's periods to stop. This, in turn, can cause a reduction in calcium production and so bones may eventually become brittle – a condition called osteoporosis.

As middle adulthood approaches, some people notice a decline in their sensory abilities. For example, they may need to wear glasses or may not be able to hear certain sounds or noise pitches. Hair loss in men is common. Adults at this life stage may be less active, so may gain weight. This is not an inevitable part of ageing, it happens when people eat the same amount of food but have lower activity levels. In late adulthood there is an increased risk of health problems associated with age.

Intellectual development

By late adulthood, we have acquired many complex intellectual and social skills, as well as plenty of life experience and wisdom to pass on to others. Further learning in specific areas allows intellect to develop, particularly around employment and hobbies.

Emotional development

During late adulthood self-image and self-esteem are defined by those around you. Friends and family will give you reasons for having a positive or negative self-image. These can depend on stable relationships and positive experiences during work and social life.

Social development

Later on, in middle adulthood, as children grow up, responsibilities usually lessen. Some adults feel at a loss as their children leave home – sometimes known as the 'empty nest syndrome'. This is most common in autumn, when vast numbers of teenagers have just left home for college or university.

It can also happen when a child gets married, because matrimony is a clear signal that parents are no longer needed in the same way.

Older people may lose some social relationships on retirement, or if their partner dies. However, for many people social activities increase as they have the extra time and money to enjoy their retirement.

Later adulthood 65+

Around the age of 65 many people retire from full-time work, or reduce their employment commitments. However, owing to the fact that the population is living longer, people are now working longer and retirement age is increasing. Also, because of healthier lifestyles and medical progress, a lot of older people can maintain good health. Therefore some 65-year-old people may not see themselves as 'old'. It can be a time of life to begin new challenges, rather than for slowing down and taking life easy.

Physical development

Studied ☐

During the ageing process, cell and tissue repair is slower and major body systems begin to slow down or suffer malfunctions; these are more likely to occur during the ageing process.

Physical changes that may occur include:

- greater susceptibility to illness
- slower recovery times
- slowing down of physical responses.

Physical health can vary from person to person and is dependent on many risk factors. Older people should always be encouraged to be as physically active as they can to avoid deterioration of body systems, such as the cardiovascular, musculo-skeletal and nervous systems.

Intellectual development

Studied ☐

Although it may take longer to learn new skills, there is no reason to stop learning. Older people who keep their minds active and continue to learn may become able to advise younger members of society with wise decisions and a deep store of knowledge. As we age our short-term memory is affected and older people may find the recall of events from the day before difficult but long-term memory appears to be much easier to recall.

Emotional development

Studied ☐

This can be affected by life events and can lead to the loss of self-esteem or self-confidence.

These include:

- isolation from peers, family, and community
- loss of independence
- progressive deterioration of health
- loss of significant other
- loss of friends
- being ignored despite having wisdom and experience.

On the other hand, many older people gain strength from their experiences and are involved positively in their lives.

Social development

Some older people may suffer isolation because they have suffered bereavement, or they may not be able to get out as much due to illness or physical limitations. This may affect their confidence and desire to join in with social activities. However, some older people may be very proactive in maintaining a social role in the community or family, which enables them to keep in touch with others.

Check your understanding

Human development can be divided into four different areas:

1. Physical
2. Intellectual
3. Emotional
4. Social

A list of explanations for each developmental area is given below. Can you match the correct explanation to the developmental area listed above?

a. problem solving, language development, reading and writing skills, memory, concentration and creativity
b. getting on with others, how to behave in different situations, becoming part of a group and making friends
c. development of the body structure and its systems, how the body works, how each part of the body relates to other parts
d. developing feelings towards each other, making sense of your own feelings, becoming aware of your identity and self-image

Key learning points

Life stages

These are the different points that individuals pass through during the process of normal development. Each stage has significant key developmental stages within it, which can identify it as part of the life stage; for example, puberty is within adolescence.

Physical development

This area of development is concerned with growth, which can be seen visually in height and weight changes; it is also concerned with the development of physical skills, for example walking; and physical maturity of organs, for example bladder control.

Intellectual development

This area of development can also be named cognitive. It is the progression of thinking and learning skills, one of the main areas being that of language.

Emotional development

Emotional development is about learning to deal with, recognise and express our emotions appropriately. Temper tantrums are acceptable in a 2-year-old but not a 22-year-old.

Social development

Social development is concerned with the formation of relationships and acquiring the ability to be part of a social group.

Assessment activity

Study the pictures. Put an age to each child and suggest which gross motor skills are being displayed.

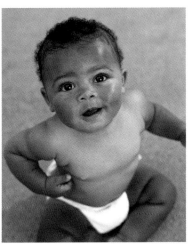

Assessment activity

Study the pictures and put an age to each child. Suggest which fine motor skill is displayed.

Learning Aim B

B.1 Physical factors that affect human growth and development

Genetic inheritance

There are a range of physical factors that can affect growth and development. Some of these factors are built into our make-up so cannot be avoided; others are purely the result of our choice of lifestyle.

Individuals can inherit conditions from their biological parents. Examples of genetic conditions include cystic fibrosis, sickle-cell anaemia and Down's syndrome.

Lifestyle choices

Diet

A diet is the food that a person eats.

A healthy diet is one that is balanced. It should contain foods from all five food groups. The more balanced and nutritious a diet is, the healthier a person will be.

The five main food groups are as follows:

- Fruit and vegetables – these contain a variety of nutrients such as fibre, vitamins and minerals.
- Bread, cereal and potatoes – these provide energy as they contain carbohydrates and fibre.
- Dairy and milk products, including yoghurt and cheese.
- Meat, fish and alternatives – these provide protein, which is essential for growth and repair.
- Fats and foods containing sugars – these should be eaten in small amounts.

Eating too much or too little of a particular food group can have consequences for health. Eating too many fatty foods may lead to obesity. This can lead to an increased risk of heart attacks or heart disease. Eating too much sugar can lead to tooth decay. A lack of certain vitamins and minerals can also lead to health problems; some examples are shown in Table 1.02.

> **Key term**
>
> **Genes:** These are our individual patterns in DNA, which make up our different characteristics, development and appearance.

Studied ☐

Table 1.02 Effects of lack of vitamins and minerals

Vitamin/Mineral	Foods	Deficiencies
Vitamin A	Liver, cheese, eggs, oily fish	A weakened immune system; too much can lead to weakened bones
Vitamin B12	Meat, cheese, eggs	Anaemia, where not enough oxygen is carried in the blood. Can cause tiredness, fainting and breathlessness
Vitamin C	Orange, broccoli	Scurvy
Calcium	Milk, cheese, broccoli, cabbage	Deficiency can lead to bone and tooth decay
Iron	Meat, beans, whole grains, watercress and curly kale	Deficiency can lead to anaemia

The Department of Health also recommends that everyone in the UK should eat at least five portions of fruit and vegetables per day.

There are many benefits of eating a healthy diet. It can help to improve concentration and increase energy and it can also prevent diseases such as 'a third of all cancers, diabetes, osteoporosis (thinning bones), heart disease, strokes and tooth decay, as well as many other diet-related conditions'.

(*Source:* www.nhsdirect.nhs.uk/articles/article.aspx?articleId=474&sectionId=34)

Exercise

Studied ☐

Exercise is beneficial to the body for a number of reasons.

Evidence shows that regular exercise can:

- reduce the risk of getting Type 2 diabetes
- reduce the risk of developing coronary heart disease
- reduce high blood pressure
- promote bone density to protect against osteoporosis
- reduce the risk of cancer and prevent bowel cancer
- help to maintain a healthy weight (when in combination with a balanced diet)
- reduce the risk of death or poor health if you are already overweight or obese
- treat depression
- help you to feel better about yourself and reduce stress
- improve sleep.

(*Source:* http://hcd2.bupa.co.uk/fact_sheets/html/exercise.html)

Therefore, a lack of exercise can have a negative impact upon an individual. For more information, go to 'Keeping Your Heart Healthy' and 'Staying Active' on the British Heart Foundation's website at www.bhf.org.uk.

Topic B.1

17

Alcohol

Alcohol abuse can impact upon a person's growth and development. As different types of drinks have different amounts of alcohol, we use a system of units to compare the amount of alcohol within them. For example, a small glass of wine is about one unit, whereas a pint of standard-strength beer is about two units. The current Department of Health guidelines state that women should drink no more than two to three units of alcohol per day and men should drink no more than four to five units per day.

Over-consumption of alcohol can have serious implications for a person's health. Statistics from the National Health Service (NHS) show that around half of pedestrians (aged 16 to 60) killed in road accidents have more alcohol in their system than the legal drink–drive limit. Statistics also show that around 1,000 children under the age of 15 are admitted to hospital each year needing emergency treatment due to alcohol poisoning.

In the short term, drinking too much alcohol can lead to blurred eyesight, slurred speech, loss of balance, nausea and vomiting – this is what is meant by 'being drunk'. Alcohol can also affect your reactions and your judgement, causing heightened emotions or loss of inhibitions. Due to the high sugar content and alcohol being a diuretic (it increases the rate of urination), alcohol causes dehydration and headaches.

If someone continues to consume an excessive amount of alcohol, there can be many long-term consequences. Alcohol itself is a depressant drug and can affect people in different ways: some may just 'feel down' but others may suffer severe depression. **Binge drinking**, in particular, leads to serious health problems. The Department of Health links 25,000 deaths each year to alcohol. Long-term alcohol abuse can lead to liver disease (cirrhosis), heart failure, brain damage, high blood pressure, as well as various types of cancer. For more information, go to the Alcohol Concern website at www.alcoholconcern.org.uk.

> **Key term**
> **Binge drinking:** This term relates to drinking an excessive amount of alcohol in a short amount of time, leading to serious health and social consequences.

Smoking

Around one in four British adults smokes. According to Cancer Research UK, men are still more likely to smoke than women – 27 per cent of men and 25 per cent of women smoke.

Smoking causes fingers and teeth to become stained, hair, breath and clothes to smell and can cause your skin to dry out. This can impact upon someone's appearance. If someone continues to smoke, there are many serious effects on the body. The habit can cause cancers, especially of the lung, mouth or throat. It can lead to chronic bronchitis or emphysema and can affect breathing and circulation.

The most common conditions caused by smoking are coronary heart disease, lung cancer, bronchitis, emphysema and pneumonia (source: NHS).

Drugs

There is a wide range of drugs – some are legal and some are illegal. We can all think of legal drugs; for example, paracetamol and ibuprofen can be bought in a shop or pharmacy. Used in small quantities, they should not cause harm. However, using illegal drugs can have serious implications; not only can they impact on an individual's growth and development, but their use can lead to prosecution.

Drugs can be divided into different categories: stimulants and depressants. Stimulants increase activity in the brain. Some examples of stimulants are tobacco or ecstasy. Depressants, meanwhile, decrease activity in the brain. Alcohol is in this category.

Drugs may also be hallucinogens – these alter the way a person sees or hears things. Hallucinogenic drugs include cannabis, magic mushrooms and LSD. Drugs that have a painkilling effect are known as analgesics – such as heroin. Some drugs, such as cocaine, may have a stimulant effect at first, then cause depression later. For some people, alcohol also has this effect. As you can see, people respond to drugs in different ways.

Follow this web link to find out further information about drug misuse: www.talktofrank.com

Illness and disease

Children are prone to specific diseases. They are young and their immune systems are not as strong as those of adults. Children may develop rashes all over their body as a result of a viral infection. In some instances, childhood diseases can be potentially life-threatening. Measles, mumps and chickenpox are contagious diseases, which can now be vaccinated against so long-term development can be avoided.

Having an illness or disease can affect all areas of life including work, relationships and social activities. Illness and disease can cause anxiety and depression, as it can make you feel out of control of your body.

During the illness or disease, treatment processes and drugs may cause side effects, some of which can directly affect body systems; for example, thyroid problems can cause depression and anxiety.

Illness can also be classed as chronic which can develop in childhood and remain for many years, for example diabetes and asthma. An acute illness is a short illness but can be very serious, for example meningitis or bronchitis. It can last for several days or weeks.

> **Key terms**
> **Chronic illness:**
> Long-term illness.
>
> **Acute illness:**
> Short-term illness.

Check your understanding

Match the correct statements

A	Foods that are high in sugar cause	1	Stress
B	Exercise can reduce	2	Bad breath and yellow staining on skin
C	Excessive alcohol can cause	3	Tooth decay
D	Smoking can cause	4	Delayed growth and development
E	Illegal drugs can cause	5	Dehydration and headaches

B.2 Social, cultural and emotional factors that affect human growth and development

External factors in our environment can affect growth and development; this can be due to our culture (the way we live our lives) or social and emotional factors, which are more closely related to how we have been brought up or socialised by our families and our peers.

Influence of play

Children learn the skills of socialising with one another in social play. By playing with one another, children learn social rules such as waiting, taking turns, cooperation and sharing things. Children go through stages of play as they grow. These stages highlight their social development.

Types of play include:

- Solitary play – the child will play alone.
- Parallel play – two or more children play near each other but not with each other.
- Associative play – two or more children play the same thing together but do not share or work together.
- Cooperative play – two or more children play with the same activity, talking and working together to create something.

Figure 1.09 Solitary play

Figure 1.10 Parallel play

Figure 1.11 Associative play

Figure 1.12 Cooperative play

Culture

Culture may influence the way an individual acts and behaves. It can also have an impact on the needs of an individual. Because of cultural or religious beliefs, an individual may require special diets or particular care needs. Religious festivals or beliefs may determine someone's diet; for example, being vegetarian or adhering to faiths that include fasting. Some religions also have particular hygiene routines.

Gender

Particular diseases are more prevalent in men – for example, heart disease and bowel cancer. Also, some diseases are said to be genetically inherited and sex linked – for example, Duchenne muscular dystrophy and haemophilia are conditions that only males have.

Information taken from the Office of National Statistics says healthy life expectancy (HLE) increased by more than two years in the period 2008–2010 compared with 2005–2007. Women now live to an average age of 82 years and men to the age of 78 years.

Women now have equal rights in employment and education. However, statistics show that women still have a large proportion of the lower-paid jobs and are the main carers in the family, taking time off work to care for children or older relatives. Traditional roles are changing though and it is now not unusual to see men having paternity leave and women in powerful jobs.

Influence of role models

The behaviour and attitudes of role models are portrayed in the media with positive and negative images; for example, role models who play sport and have healthy lifestyles can be seen by others as positive. However, some role models can portray a negative image such as the use of a 'size zero diet', taking drugs or drinking excessive amounts of alcohol; these images, if seen as glamorous, can be made attractive to teenagers, in particular those who are making their own decisions about lifestyles.

The media makes billions of pounds through advertising sales. We are constantly exposed to and influenced by advertising. We buy what we see on television, in newspapers or magazines – especially products that are endorsed by celebrities that we like. The constant exposure to violent and sexual images, to advertisements for junk food and the influence of the fashion industry to be thin and follow extreme diets can all have negative influences on lifestyle choices, so our emotional and social development can be affected.

Influence of social isolation

Most human beings need social interaction to thrive so the effect of social isolation can be long lasting depending on when a person is exposed to it. A young child who is socially isolated may not develop normally. Social interaction with others will allow language, play and social skills to develop. Teenagers may be socially isolated because they are 'different' in some way and may not feel accepted within a group or by their peers. Such individuals will then remove themselves from the group and can become depressed, anxious and suffer illnesses like eating disorders.

As carers we need to ensure that our service users are offered social activities to help them engage with others, so avoiding social isolation.

B.3 Economic factors that affect human growth and development

Income and wealth

A low income can cause poor dietary choices and result in ill health and lower life expectancy. Housing choices may be limited and may be in polluted areas where there are high crime rates, overcrowding and a stressful environment.

People who are more likely to be on a low income are lone parents, the sick or disabled, unemployed or older people.

Occupation

Occupation or what you do for a living will determine your social class. Occupations can be broken down into the following categories.

1. Higher managerial and professional occupations
2. Lower managerial and professional occupations
3. Intermediate occupations (clerical, sales, service)
4. Small employers and own account workers
5. Lower supervisory and technical occupations
6. Semi-routine occupations
7. Routine occupations
8. Never worked and long-term unemployed

(*Source:* Taken from National Statistics Socio-economic Classification.)

Research shows that those from a lower occupation status may suffer illness and disease and live in poor housing, whereas those in a higher social class, for example people in a professional occupation, may enjoy a better lifestyle. Those in higher-ranked occupations receive higher salaries so have more lifestyle choices, while those who are unemployed or are low-paid workers have fewer choices, which affects their lifestyle.

Employment and unemployment

Employment can have an impact upon the growth and development of individuals.

On the positive side, employment provides a source of income, which impacts upon a person's ability to purchase goods. Employment can also give individuals a sense of value and self-worth, which can increase their self-esteem and well-being. On the negative side, employment can make individuals feel stressed, which can negatively impact upon their growth and development. Employment could also be in an unsafe environment or in poor conditions, so injury or harm may be more likely. Employment that does not value, or undermines, a person can negatively impact on that person's self-esteem. Access to employment can vary according to area.

People with impairments or disabilities may suffer from discrimination regarding employment so could be poorly paid, in unsatisfactory jobs or be unemployed and live on state benefits.

Unemployment affects family units as well as the individual. Those who are unemployed are more likely to suffer with illnesses such as depression and anxiety and have low self-esteem.

B.4 Physical environment factors that affect human growth and development

Housing conditions

Living conditions can affect growth and development depending on where in the world you live.

People who live in underdeveloped countries or countries that have severe weather extremes, political unrest or war zones may suffer serious illness and disease because of a lack of medical care or access to medical help and education.

Living conditions in a western society may affect health if the housing is damp or poorly heated. Cramped or overcrowded conditions will also result in the spread of illnesses.

Poor living conditions may cause stress, depression or low self-esteem.

Pollution

There are many areas of pollution that can impact on our growth and development.

Pollution may be in the form of air, light, water or noise pollution. These kinds of pollution can have a number of effects on the health and needs of service users. For example, air pollution has been linked to breathing and allergy problems, which may cause or make asthma worse. Noise pollution can impact upon people socially and can be so extreme that it may affect sleep patterns and cause anxiety and depression.

B.5 Psychological factors that affect human growth and development

Relationships with family members

Our family can have a positive influence on our growth and development. Our family is responsible for our early socialisation, which can be positive or negative depending on our role models.

Families that live in stressful situations – for example, marriage breakdown, divorce or abuse – will suffer many disadvantages and it may affect educational opportunities, confidence and self-esteem.

Friendship patterns and relationship with partner/s

Peer pressure means the influence that people similar to us, such as friends or co-workers, have on our behaviour. For example, we could be influenced to study, work hard and achieve, or we could be influenced to make choices like smoking or taking illegal drugs. Both these choices can dramatically change our growth, development and health.

Self-concept is affected by our relationships with our family, friends and the outside world. Positive comments will lead to self-confidence and a positive self-image and we will also learn to be positive to others. When we receive negative comments, or constant criticism about aspects of our lives, we may develop low self-esteem.

Growing up in care

A young person growing up in care may have problems if they are not given individual support and care throughout this period. Young people in care need to make their own decisions about their values and morals and will be encouraged to do so. If there is a stable environment and a responsible consistent adult around to assist young people with those decisions, their growth and development can be normal. However, in an unstable environment adolescent girls may become pregnant, and both girls and boys may be more likely to take drugs and abuse alcohol.

Children and teenagers who move places frequently are more vulnerable; as their environment changes so do the role models. New friends have to be made and new schools attended; this is unsettling and social and emotional problems can occur.

Care homes have a duty to provide basic needs such as food, clothing and bedding, so some young people may be better off materially but other factors cannot be assured. Care may be a safer place than 'home', as they may have suffered abuse, harm and neglect.

Check your understanding

Look at the diagram below and imagine yourself in the middle.

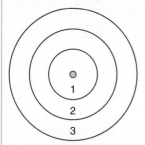

Figure 1.13

1. = Factors about self: age, gender, culture, appearance, health status.
2. = Factors in our immediate environment: family, peers, relationships, socialisation, and income.
3. = Factors in our wider environment: media, education, housing.

Consider all the factors that can influence your growth and development:

- Do these factors have a positive influence on your growth and development?
- Do these factors have a negative influence on your growth and development?
- Have these factors affected your self-esteem?
- Have these factors affected your self-image?

B.6 The expected life events that can affect human growth and development and the positive and negative effects of the events on growth and development

During our lifetime many changes may occur which we all have to deal with and many of these events will influence who we are.

Some of those events are 'predictable', which means they are more than likely to happen or they may have been chosen by ourselves.

Table 1.03 gives details about some expected life events and how they may influence our lives.

Table 1.03 Positive and negative effects of expected life events

Expected life event	Positive effect	Negative effect
Starting, being in and leaving education	• Learning to make new friends • Taking part in new learning experiences • Gaining qualifications	• Leaving home and loss of support • Can be a time when bullying can begin as personal differences appear • Feeling of loss and lack of security
Moving house/location	• New friends and social activities • Fresh start • In control of situations	• Loss of established friends and neighbours • Overwhelmed by amount of work it takes
Entering and being in employment	• Reaching a career goal • Having regular finance • Learning, training, possible promotion	• Long hours, stress • Demands on time and energy • Travelling or using public transport may be an issue
Living with a partner/ marriage/civil ceremony	• Making permanent emotional attachments • Constant person • Sharing of familiar things	• Loss of independence • Sharing problems • Partner may have power over other
Parenthood	• Bonding experience • Shared experience for both parents • Expression of fertility	• Tiredness • Loss of finances • Expensive equipment
Retirement	• Time to enjoy personal activities • Spend time with friends and family • Spend saved money • Away from set routine of working day	• Loss of routine • Loss of role at work • Reduced social activities • Loss of money

B.7 The unexpected life events that can affect human growth and development and the effects of the events on personal growth and development and that of others

'Unpredictable' events may occur which are not expected and can make us feel unstable, shocked or unable to manage. The positive and negative effects of some unexpected life events are set out in Table 1.04 below.

Table I.04 Positive and negative effects of unexpected life events

Unexpected life event	Positive effect	Negative effect
Death of a partner, relative or friend	• Change of lifestyle • Sense of release if illness was giving person poor quality of life • Partner may champion a charity	• Unable to adapt to new lifestyle • Loneliness • Depression
Accidents and injury, ill health	• Change of lifestyle • Injury may change working environment • Money compensation may help adaptations	• Unable to adapt to changed lifestyle • Anger at situation • Reduced money/sick pay
Exclusion, dropping out of education	• Try to develop sense of identity and make own pathway in career • May look at other learning environments which suit needs	• No qualifications for future • Stereotyped for having no qualifications
Imprisonment	• Learn a trade in prison • Safety in community • Time to consider different lifestyle	• May turn to further crime • May be led into drugs in prison • Unable to get employment after prison because of criminal record
Promotion	• Change in lifestyle because of increased salary • Security • Improved lifestyle	• Stress, long hours • Unable to cope with new role • Increased responsibilities
Redundancy/unemployment	• New start in life and career • Time to consider options	• Low self-esteem • Change of lifestyle due to reduced income • Stress and anxiety

Types of support

Depending on the event, we may require support to help us to adjust and deal with particular changes.

This support can be formal or informal. It includes organised professional support, support offered by people – family, partners and friends – by community groups and voluntary and faith-based organisations.

Formal

Studied ◻

This type of support is organised professional support which may deal with **physical** problems; for example, professional care services at home or in a day service. It includes the support provided by district nurses who may provide help with wound dressing, medication, hygiene routines and dietary needs.

Emotional support may be offered by social workers or counsellors, who can visit at home to provide support with coping strategies, referral to agencies for financial support and specific counselling like bereavement.

Informal

Studied ◻

This type of support is usually offered by family and friends who can provide support; it is not usually organised by an agency nor paid for. Friends and family may be called upon to assist with **physical** help such as cooking, cleaning or shopping duties, as well as listening and talking to those who are close to them.

Emotional support can also be offered by local faith groups and organisations that provide voluntary services to those who require it, for example Age UK.

Managing expectations

Life events that are predictable can usually be managed effectively with informal support and sometimes short-term formal support. However, unpredictable life events may occur which we find difficult to deal with so we may require long-term formal support. For example, the death of a child will require intense and specific support, as it is not expected that children will die before their parents.

Check your understanding

1.   Match the correct endings with the sentences:

1. Moving home can give you	A a bonding experience
2. Parenthood can be	B a time when bullying may begin
3. Starting education can be	C reduced social status
4. Bereavement can cause	D a fresh start

2.   Match the correct endings with the sentences:

1. During imprisonment	A compensation for adaptations
2. Exclusion can lead to	B lonliness and depression
3. Death of a partner can lead to	C a trade can be learned
4. Accidents can lead to	D no qualifications for the future

3.   State the type of support offered in each of these situations:

a   A district nurse dressing a wound
b   A neighbour helping with the shopping
c   Volunteers from a local church visiting for a chat
d   A chemist delivering medications
e   A social worker helping to complete benefit forms

Key learning points

Genetic
Revised ☐

During fertilization 23 chromosomes from the sperm and 23 chromosomes from the egg join and provide the genetic make-up for a new human being. Genes give us our features and identity.

Culture
Revised ☐

Culture is the way we live our life and the patterns that we follow. It may be due to religion or tradition.

Pollution
Revised ☐

This is contamination in our environment, which can affect all areas of our growth and development, for example air pollution and noise pollution.

Stress
Revised ☐

This is a negative feeling usually caused by events which lead us to feel that we are under pressure.

Expected life event
Revised ☐

This is a predictable event in our lives which we assume will happen or we choose to make happen; for example, starting school or employment.

Unexpected life event
Revised ☐

This is an unpredictable event which is unforeseen and can cause stress; for example, injury, redundancy and divorce.

Sample assessment material

The learner is given 60 minutes to complete this paper and it is worth a total of 50 marks.

1   The following information is about the Barrow family, who live at number 22 Kingsley Heath Avenue. Read the information and answer the questions below.

Ann and Mark have been married for 12 years; they have two children, Kurt who is 11 years old and about to start secondary school and Megan who is 18 months old. Ann and Mark both work full time and they are 30 years old.

a   Match the following two people to their current life stages (2 marks)

Names	Life stages
Kurt	● Infancy
Ann	● Early childhood
	● Adolescence
	● Early adulthood
	● Middle adulthood
	● Late adulthood

Megan is still very attached to her parents and becomes distressed if she is left with a person she is not familiar with.

Figure 1.14

b   What type of development does this show? Put a cross against one of the boxes below. (1 mark)

A Physical development ☐

B Intellectual development ☐

C Emotional development ☐

D Social development ☐

Mary has just started part time at nursery as her mum, Ann, has returned to work.

c   Give two examples of how this will affect Mary's intellectual development? (2 marks)

Kurt has just started secondary school and is developing secondary sex characteristics.

d   Define what secondary sex characteristics are. (1 mark)

e   Give two examples of male secondary sex characteristics. (2 marks)

Mary is 18 months old. Physically she is developing rapidly – in both her fine motor and gross motor skills.

f   Give an example of her fine motor skills. (1 mark)

g   What activity could you give to Mary to promote this area? (1 mark)

h   Give an example of her gross motor skills. (1 mark)

i   What activity could you give to Mary to promote this area? (1 mark)

Ann and Mark have to move from Kingsley Heath as Mark's business has been relocated.

j   How will this affect the family's social development? (2 marks)

This relocation will bring a higher income to the Barrow family.

k   Explain two positive and two negative factors that may occur because of this. (8 marks)

Total for question 1 = 22 marks

2   The following information is about Bert, who lives at Number 24 Kingsley Heath Avenue. Read the information and answer the questions below.

Living at Number 24 Kingsley Heath Avenue is 77-year-old Bert, who is retired; he has been recently widowed and now lives by himself. Bert has chronic bronchitis. His two sons are Stephen, age 37, who lives over 200 miles away and Simon, age 22, who is in prison serving a sentence for robbery.

a   Identify two expected life events that Bert has experienced. (2 marks)

b   Identify two unexpected life events that Bert has experienced. (2 marks)

c.   Give two economic factors that may affect Bert's life. (2 marks)

Bert's younger son, Simon, has spent time in prison for robbery. He has a young family, but his marriage has broken down because of his offences.

d   How has this affected Simon's development? Give two reasons. (2 marks)

The marriage breakdown has affected the whole family.

e   Why may the marriage breakdown have affected his ex-wife? Explain giving two reasons. (4 marks)

Bert's eldest son, Stephen, has just developed testicular cancer and needs hospital treatment. Stephen is worried about his wife and young family.

f   Suggest two formal and two informal types of support that may be available to help Stephen and his family. (4 marks)

g   How might this illness affect Stephen's own development? Give two reasons. (4 marks)

Stephen would like to return to the Kingsley Heath area to be close to his father, as he feels it would help him to recover. His wife and family are well established in their surroundings and are very anxious about the move.

h   What impact will this move have on the children's development and the family relationship? (8 marks)

Total for question 2 = 28 marks

Unit 2

Health and Social Care Values

This chapter gives an overview of the values that underpin good care. It explores how we can put these values into practice and the impact this has in empowering people who use care services.

Learning aims

In this unit you will:

✓ explore the care values that underpin current practice in health and social care.

✓ investigate ways of empowering individuals who use health and social care services.

Assessment criteria

Level 2 Pass	Level 2 Merit	Level 2 Distinction
Learning aim A: Explore the care values that underpin current practice in health and social care		
2A.P1 Describe how care values support users of services, using relevant examples.	**2A.M1** Discuss the importance of the values that underpin current practice in health and social care, with reference to selected examples.	**2A.D1** Assess the potential impact on the individual of effective and ineffective application of the care values in health and social care practice, with reference to selected examples.
2A.P2 Demonstrate the use of care values in selected health and social care contexts.		
Learning aim B: Investigate ways of empowering individuals who use health and social care services		
2B.P3 Describe ways in which care workers can empower individuals, using relevant examples from health and social care.	**2B.M2** Discuss the extent to which individual circumstances can be taken into account when planning care that will empower them, using relevant examples from health and social care.	**2B.D2** Assess the potential difficulties in taking individual circumstances into account when planning care that will empower an individual, making suggestions for improvement.
2B.P4 Explain why it is important to take individual circumstances into account when planning care that will empower an individual, using relevant examples from health and social care.		

Learning Aim A

A.1 Defining and demonstrating care values

Values underpin what we do and how we do it. Values in care include:

- confidentiality – keeping information private
- dignity – treating people as they would like to be treated
- respect – not judging people but instead helping them to be included
- safeguarding and duty of care – making sure people are emotionally and physically safe
- a person-centred approach – listening to the individual, finding out their needs.

We apply these values in care settings to provide good care. In the following section you will see the impact these values have when applied effectively, or successfully. You will also see what happens if they are ineffectively applied.

Figure 2.01 Care values help us to provide good care

Confidentiality

When dealing with any information about a person who is receiving services, it is important to know the rules of confidentiality: how to store records, who is allowed to have information, who needs to know and whose permission is needed in order to share that information with those allowed to know.

Maintaining confidentiality

Vijay is on work experience at Poppydene Care Home. He is helping to give out tea in the morning when the postman arrives with the mail. As Vijay takes the mail, the postman asks about Mrs Clark, his old neighbour, who is now a resident in the home. He has heard that she is very poorly. Vijay knows he is not supposed to give out information about the residents, so he says 'Wait a minute and I will get Sue the manager for you'. This is an effective way of keeping confidentiality. The impact of keeping confidentiality is that Mrs Clark's privacy is maintained.

Unfortunately, Annie, one of the trained carers, is not so aware of confidentiality. While the postman is waiting for the manager, Annie has a chat and tells him that Mrs Clark is very poorly and not likely to survive the day. This is breaking confidentiality. The postman is upset and while on his rounds he tells all of Mrs Clark's old neighbours the news about her health. Mrs Clark's daughter hears the neighbours saying that her mother is dying. She rushes down to the care home.

The impact of breaking communication is that Mrs Clark has no privacy; relatives and others may hear the wrong information and may even sue the care home. In fact, the carer had mixed up Mrs Clark and Mrs Young. Mrs Young was critically ill and her relatives were at her bedside. Just imagine what could have happened if Annie had told the postman about other confidential matters.

Annie breached confidentiality with verbal information. The care plan has written information about the patient and treatment. How might you feel if hospital visitors saw your medical records at the end of the bed and read them? What if the GP's receptionist left your medical notes out on the desk for all to read? This is poor practice and may have a major impact. Clients may be pointed at in the street because they have a medical condition such as AIDS.

Dignity

Preserving a person's dignity through appropriate actions is a care value.

Here is an example of how to do so.

Preserving a person's dignity

Vijay is again at Poppydene Care Home for work experience. Mr Zaid, a resident, has dementia. He gets confused and one day he started taking his clothes off in the sitting room. Vijay did not know what to do and so told Brenda, a senior carer. Brenda talked to Mr Zaid and tried to help him put his clothes back on, but Mr Zaid became aggressive. Brenda asked Vijay to bring a wheelchair and she took Mr Zaid back to his own room, where he could take his clothes off but not have other residents laughing at him.

This is an effective way of treating Mr Zaid with dignity and the impact is that others will continue to treat him politely.

It would have been ineffective to keep trying to make Mr Zaid put his clothes on, as he was confused. He would have become even more aggressive and perhaps hurt someone. If we do not treat people with dignity, the impact is that they may either become aggressive or, on the other hand, may lose self-esteem and become vulnerable to being bullied.

Respect for the individual

Respect for the individual is shown through the following:

- a **non-discriminatory** and **non-judgemental** approach to practice

Showing respect for individual choice

At Poppydene Care Home some residents are vegetarian so there is always a choice of vegetarian food on offer. This is effectively showing respect for individual choices and the impact of this is that all residents feel they are given equal choices.

In contrast, if respect is not effectively shown, people feel isolated and excluded. At Poppydene, staff used to serve tea at 4 p.m., but the residents who went to a local day centre at the Sikh temple did not get back until 5 p.m., so missed tea. The impact was that they felt as though they did not matter. Sue, the manager, looked at what was happening and decided to make the tea time flexible between 4.00 and 5.30 p.m. As a result of this change, everyone felt happier because they felt valued and included.

- the carer's responsibility for the care and well-being of individuals
- using appropriate terms when addressing individuals; complying with an individual's cultural and religious requirements; not using terms that are offensive to individuals and groups
  An effective way to do this is to ask the person how they would like to be addressed. Some people prefer to be addressed by their first name, while others prefer a more formal approach. The impact of respecting individual wishes in this way is that people feel valued
- using inclusive language to promote positive relationships shows respect, for example demonstrating interest in others and demonstrating respect for difference.

Respecting individual views

Mrs Khan uses the term 'toilet' and hates it when carers say 'Do you want the lavvie?'. She always tried to keep a nice home and taught her children to speak properly. Now that she is in a care home, she does not want to start using slang. All the carers except Annie respect Mrs Khan's wishes, but Annie still uses 'lavvie'. The impact is that Mrs Khan feels Annie does not respect her views. She becomes irritated and upset whenever Annie is on duty.

Figure 2.02 Showing respect for individuals will improve their care

Safeguarding and duty of care

An example of how to ensure the physical and emotional safety of individuals, and avoid negligence is given below.

> **Key term**
>
> **Safeguarding:** This means keeping people safe.
>
> **Duty of care:** This refers to what carers must do.

Ensuring the physical and emotional safety of individuals

Mr Zaid has dementia and can become aggressive. At times he does not know who people are and thinks the other residents are intruders in his home. When this causes him to become agitated, the carers take him to a small sitting room away from other residents. They are safeguarding the other residents and also protecting Mr Zaid by removing the trigger that starts his agitation.

The impact of this action is that Mr Zaid settles down, and others are kept safe. If carers had left Mr Zaid in the big room with others and tried to reason with him, this would not have been effective, because he could not understand the situation. The impact might have been that he hurt someone, a resident or carer, and he might have hurt himself.

Current and relevant codes of practice

Studied ▪

The code of practice for social care workers says they must follow 'practice and procedures designed to keep you and other people safe from violent and abusive behaviour at work'.

(*Source:* http://www.gscc.org.uk/page/91/Get+copies+of+our+codes.html)

Nurses have to follow a professional code of conduct too. The following case study shows the impact when duty of care fails.

Case study

A young man was admitted to hospital for an operation. Part of his medical condition following a brain tumour was that he had to drink water. The staff did not give him vital medication to help maintain his fluid levels and refused to give him water, ignoring his requests. He even telephoned the police to ask for help as he was being denied water. He died from dehydration. Later the hospital admitted civil liability. This shows the fatal impact in this case of not following the code and ignoring the duty of care owed to the patient.

Professional practice

Studied

Professional practice means treating people equally whether you like them or not, whether you approve of their lifestyle or not. A professional relationship has clear boundaries that protect service users and professionals alike. Professionals cannot have favourites.

Person-centred approach to care delivery

A 'person-centred approach to care delivery' means placing the individual at the centre of the plan, asking about their needs and preferences and involving the individual in decisions about their care.

In the case of the young man denied water, the person's needs were ignored and this led to his death. Sometimes the impact is not so severe, but can be harmful emotionally. If individuals are not listened to and their needs are ignored they become 'de-personalised', feeling as though they are of no value. The impact can be that they withdraw into themselves, feeling worthless, or alternatively they feel no one cares about them so they hit back and become aggressive.

On a more positive note, when a person-centred approach to care delivery is used, the impact is empowering and enabling for clients, and helps them to live a better quality of life. Look out for examples of person-centred care in the next section.

Check your understanding

Match the key words given below to their meanings:

Key words

1. Values
2. Care settings
3. Effective
4. Confidentiality
5. Respect
6. Safeguarding
7. Duty of care
8. Person-centred approach
9. Needs
10. Wants
11. Preference
12. Empowerment

Meanings

a. to give power and choice to someone

b. does what it is supposed to do

c. the legal responsibility carers have for those they care for

d. essential requirements

e. treating with consideration

f. putting the person at the heart of the plan

g. nice to have but not essential

h. protecting

i. choice

j. the standards we live by that guide how we behave

k. privacy

l. care home, day centre, hospital, health centre.

Key learning points

Care settings

Revised

Care settings include residential care and nursing homes, day centres, hospitals, health centres and sometimes a person's own home.

Care values

Revised

Care values underpin what we do and how we do it. These include:

- confidentiality
- dignity
- respect
- safeguarding and duty of care
- a person-centred approach.

Effective use of care values empowers people who use the service. Ineffective use of care values can harm people.

Confidentiality

Revised

Confidentiality applies to all information however it is held or exchanged.

Information can only be shared with those who have a need to know and a right to know, after seeking permission.

Dignity and respect

Revised

Dignity and respect show the individual is valued. Carers can do this by including everyone in activities, by addressing people as they would like to be addressed, and by treating them as they would like to be treated.

Safeguarding

Revised

Carers have a legal duty of care and must safeguard the people in their care. Codes of practice tell carers how to care.

Person-centred approach

Revised

A person-centred approach involves individuals in planning their own care. It considers what individuals need as well as what they want.

Assessment activity

Pass

Describe how care values support users of services, using relevant examples. Use the boxes to make notes. An example is included to start you off.

Care values	In hospital	In a day centre	In a health centre
Confidentiality	Notes are kept in a trolley at the nurses' station, where only authorised people can read them.		
Dignity			
Respect			
Safeguarding and duty of care			
A person-centred approach			

Merit

Use examples and discuss the importance of the values that underpin current practice in health and social care. Debate this with a partner and consider each value in turn.

Distinction

Assess the potential impact on the individual of effective and ineffective application of the care values in health and social care practice, with reference to selected examples. Use the table below to make notes. An example is included to start you off. Read the news online – you may find real examples to help you with this.

Care values	In hospital or day centre or health centre	
	Impact of effective use	**Potential impact of poor practice**
Confidentiality		
Dignity		
Respect		
Safeguarding and duty of care		
A person-centred approach	A man is admitted for a routine operation. He requires an empty stomach for the operation so is not given any food or water. He tells the nurse in charge that he needs fluids because of a medical condition. She informs the doctor, who sets up an intravenous infusion of fluid. The impact is that the person has the fluid they need and the operation goes ahead.	A man is admitted for a routine operation. He requires an empty stomach for the operation so is not given any food or water. He tells the nurse in charge that he needs fluids because of a medical condition. She informs him that everyone must have an empty stomach before surgery and ignores his requests for fluid. The potential impact is that he becomes delirious and dies.

Assessment activity

Role play in preparation for placement

Pass

Tested

Choose a setting such as a health centre, day centre, nursery, or hospital ward. Demonstrate the care values in at least two health and social care contexts for different service user groups.

You may wish to make up your own scenarios, but here are a few suggestions, based on real life.

- A person walks into a health centre and demands to see the GP, even though he is not a patient there. Other people are waiting to see the GP. The man becomes verbally abusive towards the staff and towards the waiting patients. You are the practice nurse. Demonstrate how to handle the situation effectively while showing confidentiality, dignity, respect, safeguarding and duty of care, and a person-centred approach.

- In a care home you are on work experience when a resident, who is confused, starts taking their clothes off and distresses other residents. Show how you would handle the situation using care values.

- On a hospital ward a man arrives drunk and demands to see his wife. You know that she is afraid of him, because of his violent behaviour, and has requested that he is not allowed to visit. You are the senior nurse in charge on the ward.

Learning Aim B

B.1 Empowering individuals

In this outcome we apply the values we met earlier to empower people in care settings such as care homes, hospitals, day centres and health centres. This can be done through:

- adapting activities and environments
- taking account of an individual's rights, preferences, needs, likes and dislikes and understanding the importance of taking individual circumstances into account when planning care, and the difficulties in doing so
- being willing to work with others in partnership, including professionals, other workers and families
- promoting choice and recognising the right of an individual to make choices
- using preferred methods of communication
- understanding the reasons for supporting individuals, for example promoting independence, promoting individuality and promoting overall well-being
- promoting autonomy, building trust, encouraging feedback and the right to advocacy
- using positive working practices.

Adapting activities and environments

Activities and environments may be adapted to meet the physical, social, emotional, and intellectual needs of individuals so that they may participate fully in activities. An example is given below.

Meeting individual needs

At Poppydene, Sarah the activities coordinator is planning a trip to a local garden centre. Mr Jones uses a wheelchair as he is paralysed from the waist down. He also has dementia and forgets the names of people and things. He used to be a keen gardener. Sarah checks that the transport can take wheelchairs and that the garden centre is accessible by wheelchair. This means that Mr Jones can join his friends on the trip.

This meets Mr Jones's physical needs for access to the garden centre, but also meets social needs because Mr Jones can be with his friends. Emotional needs are met too, as Mr Jones feels included and that he is valued. Intellectual needs are met as he revisits his old interests. He may not remember the names of plants, but his friends can remind him of these as they go round the garden centre looking at plants. By asking what people like to do and carefully planning the trip, Sarah is empowering all the residents and including Mr Jones in the activity.

Taking account of the individual's rights, preferences, needs and likes

We have already looked at how we take account of an individual's preferences and likes and dislikes when we met Mrs Khan earlier in the chapter. Remember how she hated the word 'lavvie'?

Mrs Khan is very particular and prefers having a shower to a bath. She likes to get up early, have a shower and then have breakfast. These are her preferences. When planning care, Sue the manager tries to include these preferences in the care plan but there are difficulties in doing so.

Staff may encounter difficulties by taking individual circumstances into account when planning care that will empower an individual, as shown in the following example.

Difficulties in taking individual circumstances into account

Mrs Khan likes to have her shower at 7 a.m. when she wakes, but this is just the time that the night staff wake everyone else and there is no one free to help Mrs Khan.

Resources are not available at 7 a.m. If a member of the night staff stayed with Mrs Khan, other residents would suffer as they would not have anyone to help them get up. Mrs Khan would like to be independent, but she has dizzy spells and has previously fallen in the shower because of her physical limitations.

Promoting choice and recognising the right of an individual to make choices

The following example illustrates how to promote choice in a care setting.

Choice

Sue explains the situation to Mrs Khan: either she can have her shower a little earlier than 7 a.m. before staff get busy, or have it when day staff come on duty. Giving this choice empowers Mrs Khan and recognises her right to make her own decisions, while keeping her safe from accidents.

By giving Mrs Khan a choice, the manager is promoting independence and individuality, which in turn promotes Mrs Khan's overall well-being.

Willingness to work with others in partnership

Here is an example of care staff working in partnership with a family.

Working in partnership

Mrs Khan's family live nearby and like to take her home when they can. Sue, the manager, works out a plan with Mrs Khan's daughter so that Mrs Khan can still go out but does not miss her medication, as she is diabetic. Mrs Khan's daughter is very concerned that her mum gets the right food and has changed to a healthier way of preparing meals when mum comes to visit.

This shows that Sue, the care manager, is willing to work in partnership with families. This is positive working practice – valuing the diversity in families and in cultures. Sue assesses the risks of Mrs Khan going home with the family for a visit, and makes sure that Mrs Khan and her daughter understand the risks and how to reduce the risks by having medication at the right time and eating regular meals and the right food.

Using preferred methods of communication

The following is an example of using a preferred means of communication.

> ## Individual's preference to communicate in a chosen language
>
> Mrs Khan's first language is Urdu, but she understands English very well. In fact, her preferred method of communication with carers is English. She likes to speak Urdu with her family when they visit. When Vijay started placement he assumed that Mrs Khan would like to speak Urdu with him, but she soon corrected him.

Vijay finds it strange that Mrs Khan prefers to speak English with him, but he respects her wishes and uses only English with her.

Understanding the reasons for supporting individuals

It is important to understand the reasons for supporting individuals; for example, to promote their independence, individuality and overall well-being.

Sue promotes a good standard of care at Poppydene. She trains the staff and makes sure they know the reasons why people are given choice and respected. She knows that people who are as independent as possible and who are treated as individuals feel better about themselves and are happier and healthier.

Promoting autonomy, building trust, encouraging feedback and the right to advocacy

Sue is a good manager. A week or so later she checks back with Mrs Khan on how the situation is working. By encouraging feedback, she shows that Mrs Khan's views are important. In turn, Mrs Khan knows she can trust Sue if she has a problem in the future. Mrs Khan feels very happy at Poppydene because the staff always listen to her and try to meet her needs.

Positive work practices

Sue put Mrs Khan at the centre of the care plan and looked at her needs: her physical need for the right diet to control her diabetes; and her social and emotional need to keep in touch with her family. She incorporated the risk of Mrs Khan being diabetic and having dizzy spells into the care plan, and made sure that Mrs Khan's family knew what to do in case of emergency, if this happened on a visit home. Sue assessed Mrs Khan's needs, a needs-led assessment, and recognised Mrs Khan's right to decide if she wanted to stay in Poppydene, or go out on a visit. This shows positive working practices.

On the other hand, Sue sometimes has to assess the needs of those unable to fully express their own views, as illustrated below.

Assessing needs when individuals are unable to fully express their own views

Mr Zaid has dementia and gets confused. The family are very pleased with the care at Poppydene, but at times Sue finds it difficult to keep a safe environment for staff and residents, as Mr Zaid can become violent. She asks the social worker to review Mr Zaid, and asks the GP to attend. Mr Zaid's son goes to the meeting to represent his father's views. Mr Zaid attends but does not really understand what is happening, so his son acts as an advocate for him.

Sue explains the difficulty the staff have with Mr Zaid's violent behaviour. Mr Zaid's son says his father is very well cared for and a move to another home would confuse him even more. The social worker understands the problems, but there are no vacancies in other homes at present. The GP looks at the medication Mr Zaid is currently taking and suggests that a change of medication may help. Sue and Mr Zaid's son think this is a good idea. Mr Zaid's son explains the situation to his father and he appears to understand. They agree to try the new medication and review the situation in a month. Sue finds a course about specialist dementia care and arranges to update her skills in this area too.

This is another example of a willingness to work with others in partnership, including professionals, other workers within a setting and families. Sue is again using positive working practices, using a needs-led assessment. She is valuing diversity, recognising the rights of the individual, and incorporating risk assessment in the care plan. She promotes Mr Zaid's right to advocacy.

In all of these examples positive working practices have been employed to support individuals by promoting independence, autonomy and individuality, building trust and encouraging feedback.

Check your understanding

Effective use of care values empowers people who use the service.
Ineffective use of care values can harm people.

Choose one answer (either a or b) for each of the following five statements.

1. Empowerment means
   a Giving everything the person asks for.
   b Giving realistic choices and explaining the reasons why some choices are not available.

2. Needs include physical, social, intellectual and emotional needs.
   a True
   b False

3. A person who is in a wheelchair cannot go on outings.
   a True
   b False

4. A carer works in partnership with other professionals such as the district nurse and the doctor, and with other carers.
   a True
   b False

5. Involving people in their care builds trust and increases their well-being.
   a True
   b False

Real life connections

Podiatrists or chiropodists diagnose and treat abnormalities of the lower limb. They advise people of all ages on how to prevent foot problems and on foot care. In hospital they see many patients at high risk of amputation, for example those who suffer from arthritis or diabetes.

They assess, diagnose and treat foot problems in many settings including hospitals, clinics, health centres and GP surgeries. They do home visits for housebound people and visit patients in care homes. Podiatrists may treat children who have problems walking, people with diabetes or circulatory problems, people with sports injuries and dancers with injuries. Podiatrists may also carry out minor nail surgery or laser treatment.

Key learning points

Adapt activities and environments

Revised ☐

Activities and environments should be adapted to meet the specific needs of individuals and include everyone – Sarah adapted the trip to the garden centre to include people with wheelchairs.

Take account of the individual's rights and preferences

Revised ☐

Take account of an individual's rights, preferences, needs, likes and dislikes. Be aware also of the difficulties in taking individual circumstances into account when planning care – Sue was aware of the difficulties in providing support for Mrs Khan for a 7 a.m. shower.

Work with others in partnership

Revised ☐

Work with others in partnership, including professionals, other workers, and families – Sue worked with Mrs Khan's family to plan home visits.

Promote individual choice and the right to make choices

Revised ☐

Promote individual choice and rights including the right to advocacy – Sue promoted Mrs Khan's right to choose home visits.

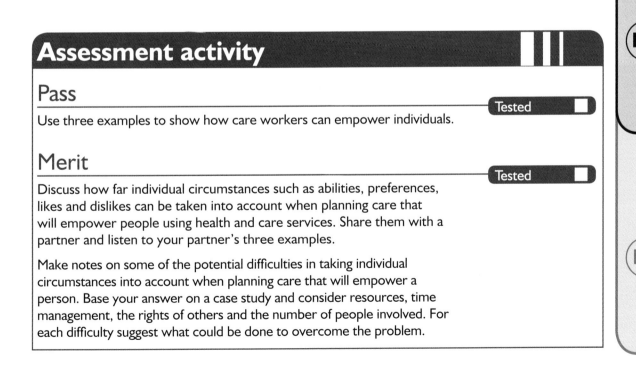

Key learning points

Use the individual's preferred methods of communication

Revised

Use methods of communication that are preferred by the individual – Vijay respected Mrs Khan's wish to use English.

Understand reasons for supporting individuals

Revised

Support individuals to promote their independence, individuality and overall well-being – Sue promoted a good standard of care and trained staff to make sure they knew the reasons why people are given choice and respect.

Promote autonomy, encourage feedback and the right to advocacy

Revised

Encourage feedback – Sue encouraged feedback on changes made to Mrs Khan's care plan. By encouraging feedback, she gained Mrs Khan's trust.

Use positive working practices

Revised

Use positive working practice to assess risks and enable people to develop – Sue enabled Mrs Khan to develop by assessing the risks. Sarah did this too when assessing risks for Mr Jones.

P3

P4

Assessment activity

Pass

Tested

Use three examples to show how care workers can empower individuals.

Merit

Tested

Discuss how far individual circumstances such as abilities, preferences, likes and dislikes can be taken into account when planning care that will empower people using health and care services. Share them with a partner and listen to your partner's three examples.

Make notes on some of the potential difficulties in taking individual circumstances into account when planning care that will empower a person. Base your answer on a case study and consider resources, time management, the rights of others and the number of people involved. For each difficulty suggest what could be done to overcome the problem.

M2

D2

Model assignment

This assignment will assess the following learning aims:

A explore the care values that underpin current practice in health and social care

B investigate ways of empowering individuals who use health and social care services.

Scenario

As a student in a residential care home you have been asked to produce an information booklet for new members of staff about how care values are used to support service users.

Section 1

- A description of how care values support service users using relevant examples.
- Discuss the importance of the values that underpin care with reference to the examples you gave in the previous section.
- An assessment of the potential impact on the individual of:
  a effective application of care values in health and social care practice
  b ineffective application of care values in health and social care practice.
  Use examples to support your assessment in each case.

Section 2

Obtain a witness testimony to show you can demonstrate the use of all the care values in two health and social care settings.
(You may have to do this through simulation if work placement is not arranged.)

Section 3

Describe ways in which care workers can empower individuals using
relevant examples from health and social care.
Include a section discussing the extent to which individual circumstances
can be taken into account when planning care that will empower them,
using relevant examples from health and social care.
Assess the potential difficulties in taking individual circumstances
into account when planning care that empowers individuals. Make
suggestions for improvements to overcome the difficulties.

Section 4

Use a case study to describe how an individual's circumstances can
be used to create a care plan that empowers them. Explain *why* it
is important to take individual circumstances into account when
planning such care. Include examples from a range of health and social
care settings.

Unit 3

Effective Communication in Health and Social Care

This unit focuses on communication. Clear communication is essential in health and social care in one-to-one situations and also in group situations. In emergencies, it can save lives. In less urgent situations it helps people understand their care and helps teams of care workers to give better care.

This unit will look at different forms of communication and how they are used in health and social care. It will also consider the barriers to communication that different individuals will face and how these can be overcome, and the best ways of communicating with individuals and groups of people.

Learning aims

In this unit you will:

✓ investigate different forms of communication.

✓ investigate barriers to communication in health and social care.

✓ communicate effectively in health and social care.

Assessment criteria

Level 2 Pass	Level 2 Merit	Level 2 Distinction
Learning aim A: Investigate different forms of communication		
2A.P1 Describe different forms of verbal and non-verbal communication. **2A.P2** Describe different forms of alternative communication for different needs, using examples from health and social care.	**2A.M1** Explain the advantages and disadvantages of different forms of communication used, with reference to a one-to-one and a group interaction.	**2A.D1** Assess the effectiveness of different forms of communication for service users with different needs.
Learning aim B: Investigate barriers to communication in health and social care		
2B.P3 Describe the barriers to communication in health and social care and their effects on service users. **2B.P4** Using examples, explain ways in which barriers to communication may be overcome and the benefits to service users of overcoming these barriers.	**2B.M2** Explain how measures have been implemented to overcome barriers to communication, with reference to a selected case.	**2B.D2** Evaluate the effectiveness of measures taken to remove barriers to communication, with reference to a selected case.
Learning aim C: Communicate effectively in health and social care		
2C.P5 Demonstrate communication skills through interactions in health and social care, describing their effects.	**2C.M3** Select and demonstrate communication skills through interactions in health and social care, explaining their effectiveness.	**2C.D3** Select and demonstrate communication skills through one-to-one and group interactions in health and social care, evaluating their effectiveness and making recommendations for improvement.

Learning Aim A
A.1 Effective communication

Communication is a two-way process, and the key elements needed are as follows:

- sender – the person starting the communication
- message – what the sender wishes to communicate
- medium – the method of communication: verbal, written, signed, electronic, telephone, etc.
- receiver – the person who receives the message and interprets it
- understanding – the message has to be correctly interpreted by the receiver
- feedback – the receiver needs to show the sender that he or she has received and understood the message.

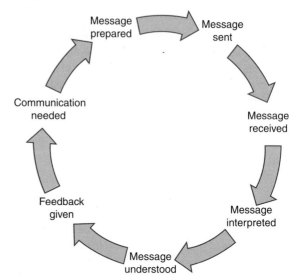

Figure 3.01 The communication cycle

We sometimes describe the steps that need to be taken for communication to be effective as the *communication cycle*.

Verbal communication

This is the main form of communication between people; it uses the spoken word.

Clear speech

Studied ☐

Speaking clearly is essential, particularly when working with service users who may have difficulties when receiving or giving messages. Speaking clearly allows instructions to be absorbed and understood and if hearing or learning difficulties are involved then some service users can lip-read or use body language to gain further understanding.

Selection of appropriate language

Studied ☐

Language can be classed as formal and informal and is used in various ways with different people. For example, making a complaint, having an interview or speaking to a teacher would require formal language, which contains the correct terminology. You may speak to someone by calling them Mr or Mrs. On the other hand, when arranging a night out with friends or chatting with your immediate family you may use shortened words, slang and relaxed terminology; for example, 'what you up to love?'

Age-appropriate language

Studied

This means using language that can be understood by the person you are communicating with. Talking to a group of reception children about how and why they should clean their teeth would not be valuable if medical terminology and long sentences were used; they would understand the concept better if shorter words and pictures were used.

Non-discriminatory use of language

Studied

Conversation topics such as jokes can be a source of misunderstanding and tension. Humour differs between people and between cultures, and what might be funny to one person might not necessarily be funny to someone else. Jokes about religion, for example, might not be unusual but can be offensive to a person with strong religious beliefs.

Pace, tone and pitch

Studied

To communicate effectively, you also need to pay careful attention to the way you speak. Tone of voice can convey different feelings. It is possible to say the same words in a different tone or pitch of voice, perhaps with a slight emphasis on some words rather than others, and yet convey a different meaning. Also don't rush, as information can be lost if you speak too quickly, especially if the person is hard of hearing, or has a language other than English as a first language, or if you are speaking to a child. In most cases, you will speak more slowly to ensure these people can understand you – they all have different barriers to communication.

Active listening skills

Studied

Active listening is about being involved, really listening and asking questions. If someone is leaning away from the other person, gazing around or looking bored, he or she is not listening. Active listeners check out what they have heard. They may ask a question to clarify a point or may nod to give encouragement to the speaker.

Key terms
Active listening skills: Showing that you are listening and using words to encourage the conversation.

Non-verbal communication

Posture

Studied

Posture is a part of body language and gives an indication of whether the person with you is interested, ill or cannot hear you. Individuals who are in a slouched position with their head in their hands can give us many signals as to their feelings.

Facial expressions

Studied

Facial expressions tell us what people are thinking even when they do not realise it. Sometimes what we say is contradicted by what our body language is saying; body language does not lie and gives a true reflection of what we are thinking and many people feel this instinctively.

Eye contact

Studied

Eye contact is essential when communicating as it lets the receiver know you are listening, showing an interest and understanding messages. Lack of eye contact could mean the receiver is not hearing you, so you may need to consider technologies to help with this.

Appropriate use of touch and personal space

Studied

Touch or contact can be very comforting, but you must be careful to use touch respectfully and appropriately. For example, a person may be clearly upset and you might feel like giving the individual a comforting hug as you would with a friend or relation. However, you may not know this person well and you may be breaching personal boundaries if you were to do this – in which case, the individual would be embarrassed and possibly offended. Sometimes touch can be misunderstood, especially if someone is from a different culture. In some cultures, men and women do not touch, even to shake hands. Always ask first what service users would like you to do and tell them how you will need to touch them before you do so.

Gestures

Studied

Gestures are signals used with our body to convey messages. Gestures can be seen a lot when heated discussions are taking place and the message is important. Some gestures such as hand signals are universally recognised, for example 'okay' (when the finger and thumb form a circle). Different gestures can be offensive from culture to culture and not all gestures are universally recognised.

> **Key terms**
> **Gestures:** These can include movement of the hands, face and body and can convey feelings of approval, hostility and dejection.

Non-threatening use of body language

Behaviour that is appropriate at home may not be appropriate at work. A family member may benefit from a hug, but a patient may be highly offended. Unwanted or inappropriate contact is unprofessional behaviour for care workers.

Check your understanding

Consider the words below and say which category they belong to in the table.

- Pronouncing words correctly
- Use of jargon
- Use of gestures
- Use of touch and personal space
- Eye contact
- Formal language
- Facial expressions

Verbal communication	Non verbal communication

A.2 Alternative forms of communication

Various forms of alternative communication are used for people with differing needs; for example:

- the visually impaired
- the hearing impaired
- people with learning disabilities.

Table 3.01 Alternative forms of communication

Alternative form of communication	Explanation of uses
Braille and Braille software	Braille is a writing system which enables blind and partially sighted people to read and write through touch. It was invented by Louis Braille (1809–1852), who was blind and became a teacher of the blind. It consists of patterns of raised dots arranged in cells of up to six dots in a 3 x 2 configuration. Each cell represents a letter, numeral or punctuation mark. Some frequently used words and letter combinations also have their own single cell patterns.
British Sign Language	British Sign Language is a method of non-verbal communication that uses movements of the hands, body, face and head, which make up a complete language system. It is the preferred first language of many deaf people and is used by hearing people to communicate with those who are deaf. Other deaf people rely on lip-reading to understand what is being said to them.
Fingerspelling	People who use British Sign Language use fingerspelling. Signers spell out the word with their fingers for words that do not have a sign, for example names and places.
Text messaging	Text messaging is the exchange of short written messages between mobile phones or other devices that may be fixed or portable. SMS means short message service. Some messages now can include pictures and photographs. Text messages can be used to interact with automated systems, for example when ordering products and services from mobile phones or participating in contests.
Interpreter	This is a person who changes the verbal messages into either sign language or another language so that messages can be understood.
Translation	This is changing written messages into a form that can be understood by those with sensory impairments or who use different languages, including Braille.
Objects of reference	Objects of reference are any objects that represent other things. Children may have a teddy bear or comfort blanket that represents home and safety. They will feel more secure if they have their blanket or favourite toy, especially if they are in a strange place, such as hospital. For a child, the smell of these familiar objects is associated with Mum and home.

Communication passport	Communication passports are a way of recording the important things about a child or adult, in a person-centered way, and of supporting an individual's transitions between services. A passport gives a clear focus for ongoing home/school liaison and partnership when working with families.
Bliss symbols	Bliss symbols are a system of meaning-based symbols, which can be used by people with severe difficulties in speaking to communicate without speech. It is useful for people with cerebral palsy and other physical disabilities who may find reading and spelling difficult but who may still require a system of communication.
Makaton	Makaton is a language programme that uses signs and symbols and pictures to help people to communicate. It is designed to support spoken language and the signs and symbols are used with speech, in spoken word order.
Technological aids	There are many aids that can be used to support individuals who have sensory impairments. For example, the Minicom which can be used for individuals who have a hearing disability, or voice typing for those who have a sight problem.
Pictures	Pictures can be used to represent messages. A system called **Picture Exchange Communication System (PECS)** is an alternative form of communication. It is used as an aid in communication for children with autism and other special needs. The system has been used with a variety of ages including pre-school children, adolescents and adults who have a wide array of communication problems.
Advocate	This is a nominated person who will act or speak on behalf of other individuals who may not be able to put forward their opinions. This individual may speak on behalf of someone who has a learning difficulty, sensory difficulty or who may not speak the required language.

Check your understanding

Alternative forms of communication

Use the words in the list below to complete the sentences.

- Minicom
- children
- vulnerable
- advocate
- touch
- Makaton
- Braille
- settle
- symbols
- spoken
- translator

1. _____ is a writing system which enables blind and partially sighted people to read and write through _____.
2. An interpreter is someone who converts _____ language into signs.
3. _____ may have an object of reference like a toy to help them _____ into nursery.
4. Bliss _____ are a system of meaning-based symbols which can be used by people with severe difficulties in speaking.
5. _____ is a language programme using signs and symbols to help people to communicate.
6. A _____ changes the written word into other forms.
7. _____ is a device used for those who have a hearing problem.
8. An _____ is a person who will speak or act on behalf on a_____ person.

Key learning points

Verbal communication

Revised ☐

This is sending messages to others using the spoken word; it can take place face to face or through the telephone or internet.

Non-verbal communication

Revised ☐

This is sending messages to others without speaking, using body language and gestures. It can be used with service users who have sensory or learning difficulties.

Braille

Revised ☐

An alternative form of communication used with individuals who have sight difficulties. It is an arrangement of raised dots on a page, which indicate letters, words and numbers.

British Sign Language

Revised

A nationally recognised set of signs used to communicate with individuals who have learning and hearing difficulties. Hand signals represent words and phrases to convey messages.

Makaton

Revised

An alternative form of communication used mainly with individuals who have learning difficulties; it is a set of signs and symbols to support speech.

Assessment activity

Posters

Pass

Tested

In small groups you are going to formulate three descriptive posters for your classroom. Each poster should include pictures, examples and descriptions relating to communication in healthcare settings.

- Poster 1 – non-verbal communication
- Poster 2 – verbal communication
- Poster 3 – alternative forms of communication

P1

P2

M1

D1

Learning Aim B

B.1 Barriers to communication and how to overcome them

Thinking about the communication cycle, you can see that any interruptions to the cycle will cause difficulties with communication – the message will be lost or incomplete.

Environmental barriers

Environmental factors, such as a noisy location or poor lighting, may hamper communication. For example, a person who has problems hearing but usually lip-reads will find this difficult in a darkened room. If you are trying to communicate with a service user about a sensitive topic, the seating and area need to be appropriate; a large noisy room with little space would not be adequate.

Physical barriers

These refer to the barriers faced by people who have difficulty with vision or hearing. If you cannot see very well, you are likely to miss non-verbal signals, such as a smile or a frown, although you may be more sensitive to tone of voice. The term 'sensory deprivation' refers to a person who has no vision, no hearing, or neither vision nor hearing.

Mental health issues, especially mental illness, can affect communication, particularly if the person you are speaking to is on medication, which may affect his or her ability to understand the implications of what is said.

People with learning difficulties sometimes have difficulty expressing themselves; for example, they may not be able to process information or remember things well. Others may have coordination (motor skills) problems. Dyslexia is one example of a learning difficulty in which sufferers have trouble reading and writing, although their intelligence is normal or above average.

Language barriers

If you do not speak the same language as the person you are communicating with, there can be barriers to communication and you are much more likely to rely on body language. However, as we have seen, there are cultural differences in body language, particularly gestures.

Jargon

Studied ☐

Jargon is specialist language. It can be a barrier to communication if the person receiving the message does not understand the jargon. A person might feel scared if he or she is told they have 'plantar fasciitis'. If the doctor says they have 'heel pain', it sounds a lot less scary.

Slang

Studied ☐

Slang or informal language can be a barrier to communication if the person you are communicating with does not understand the slang. For example, rhyming slang, such as the original East London slang, replaces ordinary words with others that rhyme with them, so that 'mince pies' means 'eyes' and 'dog and bone' means 'telephone'. This is fine if the other person knows the same slang, but it can be utterly confusing if the other person does not recognise the same terms.

Colloquialisms

Studied ☐

Colloquialisms are words that are specific to a local geographical area. For example, in parts of the Midlands region of the UK, people may use 'y'am' to mean 'you are'. Similarly, in some parts of Yorkshire, people use 'tha' to mean 'you'. Someone who comes from the south of England might have difficulty understanding both of these people.

Acronyms

Studied ☐

Acronyms are words formed from the initials of other words. For example, CPR stands for cardiopulmonary resuscitation. Acronyms help communication only if everyone knows what they mean, otherwise they actually prevent communication.

> **Key terms**
> **Acronyms:** These are words formed from the initials of other words and are used in all walks of life, for example BLT (bacon, lettuce and tomato). Can you think of any more?

Social isolation

Anxiety can pose similar problems for communication in that it prevents individuals from making a realistic assessment of what is being said because of the emotions the words stir up. This again means the person has difficulty in decoding the message.

Depression causes feelings of hopelessness and isolation, which can prevent communication. Isolated or depressed people take a negative view of the world and may not value anything that is said to them.

Sometimes messages are misinterpreted. For example, nurses in hospital are not allowed to take a verbal prescription from a doctor over the telephone. The doctor must go to the ward and write the prescription, the dose, the route of administration, how much and how often so that there are no mistakes. It is easy to mishear phone conversations and interpret messages wrongly.

P3 P4 M2 D2

Effects of barriers on individuals

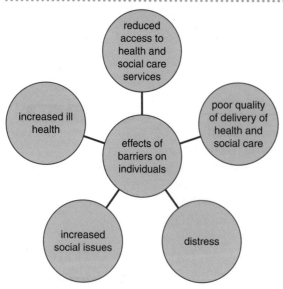

Figure 3.02 Effects of barriers on individuals

Overcoming barriers to communication

There are a number of things you can do to minimise some of the specific communication difficulties discussed above. These suggestions are outlined in Table 3.02. You will, of course, need to make your own judgements about which methods to use with a particular person and in a specific context.

Table 3.02 Overcoming communication difficulties

Communication issue	Suggested actions
Poor sight or blindness	<ul><li>Ask individuals what they are able to see, e.g. light/dark/shapes.</li><li>Make sure they are wearing the correct glasses.</li><li>If they have some sight, make sure there is plenty of light and that you are facing the person.</li><li>Make sure they have any required aids or equipment, e.g. magnifying glass, especially if you need them to read or write anything down.</li><li>If they are blind, speak to them as you approach so they know you are there.</li><li>Use language to describe the surroundings and assist them to explore things using touch – they may wish to touch your face.</li><li>If escorting a blind person, give a running commentary on where you are going and your progress.</li></ul>
Hearing difficulties	<ul><li>As with sight-impaired people, you must first make sure any hearing aids or appliances are being worn and are adjusted to the correct level.</li><li>Make sure you are face to face and at the same level. Try not to have your back to the light as your face will be in shadow.</li><li>Make sure the environment is as quiet as possible.</li><li>Do not shout but speak normally, slowly and clearly, giving time for lip-reading. Use gestures.</li><li>Use pictures or write messages on a pad or chalkboard.</li><li>Learn Makaton or how to sign.</li><li>Use an interpreter who can sign.</li></ul>

Communication issue	Suggested actions
Language issues	• Use pictures and symbols, including programmes such as Makaton, to illustrate your words. • Make sure you use an interpreter, especially for conversations with medical content, but be wary of getting children to interpret for their parents. Parents may not wish their children to have full knowledge of their illness or personal issues. • Be on guard about making assumptions – stereotypical thoughts and phrases often start with 'they all…' • Do not use jargon, acronyms or slang and be careful to speak as clearly as possible in plain English, using short sentences.
Emotions	• Learn to become aware of the signs that show someone is becoming upset or angry. • Learn how to recognise anxiety and depression. • Remain calm and speak kindly and reassuringly, without being patronising. This will help the person to maintain self-control. • Learn about managing challenging behaviour. • Carefully choose the time and place in which to have difficult conversations. • Be careful not to make jokes initially. Once the person is calmer it may be possible to use gentle humour to reduce the tension, depending on the person and the situation. • Remember, you may have to repeat the information again at a later time.
Intellectual difficulties	• Learn about the most common types of intellectual difficulties in your work area, e.g. if you mostly work with older people, you may need more understanding about dementia or about communicating with someone who is confused and disorientated. • Share your knowledge of what works with other staff members. • Be very patient, repeating things if necessary, using straightforward language and re-wording if necessary. • Use symbols and pictures if the person has learning difficulties. • Remember that people with intellectual difficulties may have normal or above-average intelligence in certain areas and they are not stupid. • Encourage people with intellectual difficulties to join support groups.
Adaptations to the physical environment	• Choose the time and place for communication carefully, e.g. do not discuss personal issues loudly in the presence of others; this is disrespectful – think about how you would feel. • Make sure there is plenty of light, preferably natural daylight and that it is fairly quiet so that you can be clearly seen and heard.
Effective non-verbal communication	• Learn about different cultures and their ways, especially gestures and body language. • Always check for understanding (see active listening below). • Be aware of gender differences in different cultures. • Do not make assumptions. • Try different ways to get your message across and encourage the person you are communicating with to do the same. • Be especially clear when speaking on the phone or using electronic communication (texts and email) as the absence of facial and body language can be a barrier to understanding.

Benefits to individuals when barriers are removed

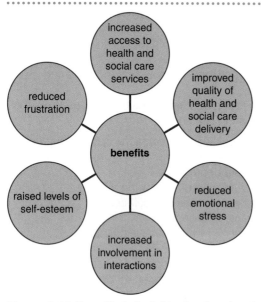

Figure 3.03 Benefits to individuals when barriers are removed

Check your understanding

Case study 1

Christopher is working at a residential home as a care worker. Over the past few months his hearing has deteriorated and he is having trouble hearing what his colleagues and the clients are saying. Because of this, he does not hear important information that his supervisors are passing on to him and this is having a negative impact on his daily duties.

Questions

1. Suggest ways in which Christopher's supervisors could support him so that he can do his job effectively.
2. What could Christopher do to help himself?
3. What problems do you think can happen when Christopher does not hear or misunderstands the information that has been passed on to him?
4. How do you think this affects the clients in the residential home?
5. Can these barriers be overcome? If so, give examples of the strategies that could be put in place.

Case study 2

Yasser is five years old and he has recently moved to the UK with his family. Yasser does not speak or understand any English, while his family can understand basic English words. Yasser, who has just started at a local primary school, does not communicate with other children in his class and his teacher cannot speak Urdu. Yasser is very quiet in class and does not complete the work that is set.

Imagine that you are the teacher. What support needs to be put into place to ensure that Yasser is supported in the classroom and developed in the same way as the other children?

Questions

1. What are the problems that occur because the teacher does not speak Urdu?
2. How do you think Yasser is feeling?
3. What could the teacher do to overcome this communication barrier in the short and long term?
4. What type of aids do you think may be helpful for both the teacher and Yasser?
5. What could the parents do to help with the communication barrier?

Key learning points

Barriers

Revised

Something which hinders the communication message being sent, received or understood.

Environmental barriers

Revised

These are part of our surroundings which stops messages; for example noise, light and temperature.

Physical barriers

Revised

This relates to difficulties in sending and receiving messages because of physical problems; for example, hearing difficulties, sight and learning problems.

Language barriers

Revised

Not understanding a foreign language will cause problems, as will the way in which a part of the language is spoken, for example dialect (which is different in different parts of the country). Technological terms and pace and tone of the speaker may also cause problems.

Adaptions

Revised

This relates to methods put in place to overcome communication barriers; for example, sign language, technology (hearing loops) and change of environment.

Assessment activity

Pass and Merit

Tested

This exercise is rather like the game of Chinese whispers. Sit your group in a circle and all except one person should put either earplugs (the soft rubbery sort you can get for sleeping that fit in your ears) or cotton wool in their ears. The individual who has no earplugs in then takes one person aside and tells that person something – for example, 'The train from Manchester will arrive in Euston at half past two.' Ask the group to pass the message to each person in turn, and then ask the last person to repeat the message. See what they say! What would have helped you to understand the message more easily?

Learning Aim C

C.1 Communicating with groups and individuals

Communication is a skill that requires practice. Effective communication is when the message you send to the other person is received, accurately interpreted and understood and responded to appropriately. **Facial expressions**, the tone of voice you use, the type and level of **eye contact**, the gestures you make, and the way you stand or sit are all part of communicating. Sometimes we are not fully aware of how we appear to other people – for example, the expression we have on our face.

To communicate effectively, we need to be aware of those hidden messages we are giving out unconsciously because our words may not match our actions. For example, if we are communicating with someone who has strong body odour we may not be able to disguise our distaste. Even though we might observe social conventions by pleasantly asking how they are, our noses might unconsciously wrinkle or we might turn our faces away slightly. This is especially true when we are talking about our feelings; it has been suggested that body language provides up to 55 per cent of meaning when discussing feelings and emotions.

It is a useful exercise to observe other people communicating. Be observant when you are in social situations and you will learn a lot about how people communicate. Next time you are on a bus, for example, watch people and make a note of how they are communicating. What methods are they using? Can you guess what they are talking about? You must be careful not to stare or pay too much attention though, in case you are accused of eavesdropping!

There are a number of skills and techniques you can practise to enhance and improve your communication skills. In particular, good listening is a key communication skill. What do we mean by good listening? One way of thinking about it is to consider that, as we have two ears but only one mouth, we should listen twice as much as we speak! In other words, you need to develop the skill of active listening, which is much harder than it seems.

> ### Key terms
> **Facial expressions**: These are important in effective communication as your face tells us what you are really thinking and feeling.
>
> **Eye contact**: This gives the service user a feeling of understanding and confidence if we make good eye contact.

Check your understanding

In a group of three, practise active listening. One person should tell one of the others something, such as what he or she did over the weekend, including their feelings. The third person is to act as observer and practise the active listening techniques as described above. Once you have finished, ask the observer what he or she observed and then swap places. When all have had a turn at each role, discuss your experiences. You may find that active listening is much harder than it seems!

Real life connection

Learning disabilities' nursing

People with learning disabilities often have a wide range of physical and mental health conditions. Learning disability nurses work in partnership with them and family carers to provide specialist health care. Their main aim is to support the well-being and social inclusion of people with a learning disability by improving or maintaining their physical and mental health; by reducing barriers; and supporting the person to pursue a fulfilling life. For example, teaching someone the skills to find work can be significant in helping them to lead a more independent, healthy life where they can relate to others on equal terms.

Learning disabilities' nursing is provided in settings such as adult education, residential and community centres, as well as in patients' homes, workplaces and schools. You could specialise in such areas as education, sensory disability or the management of services. If you work in a residential setting, you may do shifts to provide 24-hour care.

See www.nhscareers.nhs.uk/explore-by-career/nursing/careers-in-nursing/learning-disabilities-nursing/

Key learning points

Active listening

Revised

This means using body language, eye contact and facial expressions to show that you understand the message being sent.

Proximity

Revised

This refers to the acceptable distance between individuals when a conversation is taking place.

Clarifying

Revised

Redirecting a question to the sender to ensure you have the correct message or set of instructions.

Assessment activity

Role play – one-to-one and group activity

Pass

Tested

1 A care assistant is chatting with an older resident, trying to find out what sort of help the individual requires with her everyday needs. One person should play the assistant, the other the older service user. Develop a script to act out a short scenario.

2 As a group identify a health and social care issue you would like to discuss. Try to have some of the class making a case for the subject and some against so the discussion is not one sided. Some examples are listed below:

   ● binge drinking
   ● social media sites
   ● healthy food choices
   ● smoking ban.

Ask your tutor to observe these interactions and comment on how effective your communication skills are.

P5

M3

D3

Model assignment

This assignment will assess the following learning aims::

A investigate different forms of communication
B investigate barriers to communication in health and social care
C communicate effectively in health and social care

Scenario

As a student in a residential care home you have been asked to produce an information booklet for new members of staff about 'Effective Communication'.

Section 1

- A description of different forms of verbal, non-verbal and alternative forms of communication which are used in your care setting.
- An explanation of the advantages and disadvantages of different forms of communication that are used, for example one-to-one and group interactions.
- An assessment of how useful different forms of communication are to the service users in the home, for example those with sight and hearing problems.

Section 2

In the care home some barriers exist at present that are stopping effective communication; for example, for service users whose first language is not English and service users who have dementia.

- A description of the barriers which stop communication and their effects on the service users within the care home.
- Explain how these barriers can be overcome within the care home. Include examples of these barriers.
- An evaluation of how the removal of these barriers may benefit the service users at the care home.

Secondary socialisation

This is the way that a young person learns about the world from others.

Agents of secondary socialisation

Studied

The agents of secondary socialisation are:

- friends and peers – they may shape a person's behaviour
- the media – for example, advertising, social networking, television, celebrity culture, music, newspapers and magazines. These may influence what music a person listens to, or who they admire
- other agents, outside the immediate circle, include early years workers at nursery or playgroup; then later on, teachers, youth workers, representatives of religions, work colleagues, social workers. These influence how a young person develops ideas of how to interact with others.

Figure 4.02 An example of secondary socialisation

Check your understanding

Match the key words listed below (1–4) to their explanation (a–d).

Key words

1. Primary socialisation
2. Secondary socialisation
3. Agent of socialisation
4. An effect of socialisation

Explanation

a. A change in behaviour or beliefs
b. The means by which socialisation happens
c. A later way we learn how to interact with others
d. First way we learn how to interact with others

Gender roles

Socialisation shapes gender roles and expectations for male and female behaviour. Traditionally, boys play with cars and girls play with dolls. This negatively affects the well-being of some children, as some girls like to play with cars and some boys like to play with dolls. Many people are challenging this traditional view and bringing their children up to play with all types of toys so they grow up as rounded people, with a positive sense of well-being.

Attitudes

Socialisation shapes attitudes; for example, the development of tolerance or prejudice, attitudes to religion and to authority and what choices people make about how to behave.

Tolerant attitudes

Jamie's parents, Paul and Marie, have lots of friends from different countries. They think it is great to meet different people. It is likely that Jamie will grow up with this tolerant attitude, but it was not always like this. Marie was brought up to be less tolerant. In fact, her parents were very prejudiced against immigrants, as was Marie until she went to school and met people from other cultures. Secondary socialisation changed Marie, so that when she met Paul, the fact that he was Polish did not matter to her.

Development of social norms and use of language

Socialisation affects the development of social norms and values; for example, views of right and wrong, manners and behaviour. At times secondary socialisation changes what we learn through primary socialisation.

Influence of secondary socialisation

Chelsea was brought up by her parents to know right from wrong (primary socialisation) but at school she got in with the wrong crowd (secondary socialisation). After school they would go into town and look at the shops. One day they dared Chelsea to steal a lipstick. She did so and got caught. Now she has a caution on her criminal record.

Socialisation also influences how we use language. Text language is one way that some people are socialised into using a different language. Can you think of examples where language changes as we are exposed to wider influences?

Influence on lifestyle choices

Socialisation influences lifestyle choices, such as getting a job or being unemployed.

Effects of lifestyle choice

After training, Chelsea got a job as a mentor but some of the friends who led her into stealing got into further trouble. Two got involved with drugs and dropped out of education, limiting any career choices they might have had and negatively affecting their well-being.

Socialisation influences marriage and long-term relationships. Chelsea's mum and dad have been together a long time. Chelsea is more likely to be able to sustain a long-term relationship because she has seen how her parents work through the bad times, and don't give up on the relationship. This has a positive effect on her well-being.

Chelsea's grandmother is a heavy smoker and so is her mother. Socialisation would suggest that Chelsea will also copy them and start smoking, thus having a negative impact on her health. No one in the family drinks alcohol and Chelsea has not yet started, but when she is exposed to wider influences, through secondary socialisation, she may start drinking to fit in with friends and this may damage her health, especially if she binge drinks.

Alternative lifestyles, religion, use and choice of medical care and treatment, and participation in sport or exercise are all influenced by socialisation. The government is spending a lot of money trying to involve more people in sport and exercise. Through secondary socialisation using television, the press, the Olympic legacy and role models such as David Beckham, it is trying to change people's behaviour so that we become healthier.

Check your understanding

Match the beginnings and endings correctly.

1. An example of socialisation shaping gender roles: _____
2. An example of socialisation shaping attitudes: _____
3. Socialisation affects the development of social norms and values: _____
4. Socialisation influences how we use language: _____
5. Socialisation influences lifestyle choices: _____

Endings

a. Children are taught to say 'please' and 'thank you'.
b. Girls being given dolls and boys being given cars.
c. Learning to respect others.
d. Mary's mum got pregnant at sixteen and had a large family. Mary also got pregnant at sixteen and had three children by the time she was twenty.
e. Young people may use slang with friends but are unlikely to use it in an essay.

Figure 4.03 Healthy behaviour

Key learning points

Primary socialisation

This is the first way we learn to interact with others. Jamie's parents smile at him and he learns to smile too.

Secondary socialisation

This is the second or later way we learn how to interact with others in the world. Through secondary socialisation Chelsea learned to steal but later learned how to contribute to society by becoming a mentor.

Agents of primary socialisation

These include parents, siblings, carers and close family. Jamie's parents are agents of primary socialisation.

Agents of secondary socialisation

These include friends and peers, the media, advertising, social networking, television, celebrity culture, music, newspapers and magazines. Other agents include early years workers at nursery or playgroup, teachers, youth workers, representatives of religions, work colleagues and social workers.

Shaping of gender roles

Socialisation affects the shaping of gender roles – Nicola Adams and Katie Taylor won gold medals in Olympic boxing, challenging stereotypes about gender.

Shaping of attitudes

Socialisation affects the shaping of attitudes – Nicola and Katie are changing people's attitudes about what women can do.

Development of social norms and values

Socialisation affects the development of social norms and values – Chelsea's first socialisation taught her right from wrong.

Lifestyle choices

Socialisation affects lifestyle choices – the Olympic legacy aims to use media to change lifestyles and make people healthier by being active.

Effects of socialisation can be positive or negative

The effects of socialisation on our well-being and health can be positive or they can be negative.

Assessment activity

Pass

Ask someone with a baby what sounds the baby can make already. If the baby is a year old, this may be words not just sounds. Compare your findings with that of a partner in class. Do you know of any baby that is learning a different language?

Pass/Merit

1   Think of your own secondary socialisation. Which agents have had a lot of influence on you? Which agents have not influenced you? How have you been influenced by secondary socialisation?

2   Use the following checklist and conduct a class survey of socialisation:

Agents of socialisation	Influenced you? 10 = maximum influence 1 = no influence	Influence on health and well-being? Positive = P Negative = N
Primary socialisation		
Parents		
Siblings		
Others, e.g., grandparents, carers		

Secondary socialisation		
Friends		
Peers (people of similar age but not friends)		
Advertising		
Social networking, e.g. Facebook, Twitter,		
Television		
Celebrity culture		
Music		
Newspapers/magazines		
Other, e.g. early years workers at nursery/ playgroup, teachers, youth workers, representatives of religions, work colleagues, social workers		
Any other		

Distinction

- Which agent of secondary socialisation has most influenced your class?
- Which agent of secondary socialisation has least influenced your class?

Learning Aim B

B.1 Influence of relationships on individuals

The relationships individuals have can influence their health and well-being. When these relationships change, this can also affect their health and well-being. In this section we look at how this happens.

Chelsea eventually found a good group of friends at school. This gave her confidence, and positively affected her sense of well-being. When she left school she lost touch with most of them. Changes in the relationship with friends affected her – she was sad and lonely until she built new friendships.

Types of relationships

Different types of relationships include:

- family, for example, extended, nuclear, reconstituted, single parent
- working, for example, teacher/student, colleagues, line managers
- social, for example, friends, fellow members of religious and secular groups
- intimate and sexual relationships.

Relationships influence an individual's health and well-being, for example, self-esteem, levels of stress and anxiety, and the effects of dysfunction.

Using case studies we can see how this works.

Effects of family relationships

Studied ☐

Following Chelsea and Becky through some of their relationships, we can see how they affect their health and well-being. First we will look at their family relationships.

An extended family relationship

Chelsea has an extended family. She lives with her mum and dad and older brother. She has a grandmother 'Nan', who lives nearby, and her Uncle Pete and Aunty Sarah who live in the next street. They all get on well with each other. Sometimes Chelsea stays over at her grandmother's house and at the weekends she babysits for her aunt and uncle as they have a ten-month-old baby boy.

Having an extended family like this is good for Chelsea. She feels secure and knows there is always someone around if she needs help. The same could be said for her grandmother. Having a supportive extended family is a positive influence on health and well-being. Chelsea is lucky too because her nuclear family of mum, dad and brother are also there for her, even though her brother is a pain at times!

Chelsea's friend Becky has a different family type.

Reconstituted and single parent families

Part of the time Becky lives with her mum and stepdad and her stepsisters as part of a reconstituted family. Part of the time Becky lives with her dad as part of a single parent family. Her mum and dad divorced after lots of arguments, and then her mum went to live with her new boyfriend, leaving Becky with her dad.

The divorce negatively affected Becky's health and well-being. She stopped eating, and felt guilty, as though she ought to be able to make her parents stop quarrelling. Even after the divorce she still wished her mum and dad could get back together so she could be part of her own family.

Chelsea had stable and secure family relationships and this gave her confidence to tackle what problems life sent her way. Becky, on the other hand, lost the stability of a settled family and this change affected her negatively. She lost confidence, became unhappy and took her anger out on others by becoming a bully.

Influence of relationships on health and well-being

Relationships influence health and well-being. They influence:

- Self-esteem – secure and happy relationships boost self-esteem; unhappy and destructive relationships destroy self-esteem
- Levels of stress and anxiety – too much stress can make people ill, too little can make them bored. The ideal stress level is just enough to keep someone motivated and busy.
- Effects of dysfunction – dysfunctional relationships are ones where there is conflict, anger and sometimes violence. Children in a dysfunctional family may be abused or just neglected. The effects on children are that they become wary, not knowing if they will be hurt by those whom they should rely on. Adults in dysfunctional relationships may be unhappy and either become bullies or victims.

At school Becky got a reputation for being rude and badly behaved. She kept getting into trouble for not doing her homework. The teacher thought she was making excuses. This made her feel worse about herself – negatively affecting her well-being. Her health suffered and she became anorexic.

A positive sense of well-being

Chelsea had a much better time once she became a mentor helping others. Her line manager and trainer praised her and her colleagues were always glad to see her. This positively affected Chelsea's sense of well-being – she felt valued by others.

Social relationships were much easier for Chelsea. Because she already felt good about herself she found it easy to smile and talk to people. She made friends easily at the local youth club, where she helped out.

Influence of dysfunctional family relationships

Becky, however, did not have such an easy time socially. Becky found it hard to make friends. Other students were either frightened of her, or avoided her. It seemed her mum did not want her, and her dad often forgot when it was his weekend to have her. The negative impact of other relationships coloured even this part of her life. When she went to the youth club where Chelsea helped out, she stood around feeling awkward.

Chelsea had lots of friends but had one special boyfriend. They got engaged when Chelsea left school. Having a boyfriend, someone special who cared for her positively, influenced Chelsea's health and well-being. Chelsea was healthy, happy and had a positive sense of well-being.

Unfortunately, Becky did not have that sense of well-being to help her form positive social relationships. She had a succession of boyfriends, but none of them stayed long. When she got pregnant, her mum threw her out.

In these two case studies we can see how relationships can influence a person's health and well-being. Chelsea had problems but with relationships positively influencing her sense of well-being, she could cope with the ups and downs of life. Even when her Nan passed away, she was upset, but remembered the good times and thought of how much her Nan had loved her.

Becky on the other hand had relationships that negatively influenced her sense of well-being and health. She had higher levels of stress and anxiety, becoming anorexic. The dysfunctional relationship with her family negatively influenced her sense of well-being. She did not feel that anyone valued her, and so did not value herself.

Becky did eventually get her happy ending. She met someone who accepted her as she was and taught her to value herself, and that changed her life. Slowly she learned to accept that she could not have kept the family together and that her mum and dad's divorce was their business. Being in a secure relationship, feeling loved and learning to love herself has positively influenced her sense of well-being and her health. She is no longer anorexic and has a happy healthy little boy.

Check your understanding

Quiz

Are the following statements true or false? Choose the correct answer.

1.	All relationships affect our health and well-being.	True/False
2.	Relationships can affect our health and well-being positively.	True/False
3.	Relationships can affect our health and well-being negatively.	True/False
4.	Being in a secure relationship can help you tackle problems better.	True/False
5.	Being in an abusive relationship can make you ill.	True/False

Key learning points

Relationships can influence a person's health and well-being

Revised ☐

The relationships a person has can influence his or her health and well-being – Chelsea had positive relationships with family and eventually with friends, and was healthy and happy.

When these relationships change, this can also affect the individual's health and well-being. When Becky's relationship with her parents changed, she became unhappy and developed anorexia.

Family relationships

Revised ☐

These may include extended, nuclear, reconstituted and single-parent relationships. Chelsea has an extended family, with aunts and uncles. Becky was part of a reconstituted family eventually.

Working relationships

Revised ☐

These may include teacher and student, colleagues and line managers. Becky had poor relationships with other students when she started to bully them.

Social relationships

Revised ☐

These include relationships with friends and fellow members of religious and secular groups. Chelsea found a mentor who helped her to turn her life around.

Intimate and sexual relationships

Revised ☐

These can also influence health and well-being. Becky felt worthless and did not value herself. She slept around, seeking love.

Self-esteem

Revised ☐

Relationships influence individuals' health and well-being by affecting their self-esteem. Becky's family problems made her feel worthless with a low self-esteem.

Stress and anxiety

Revised ☐

Relationships can influence levels of stress and anxiety. Chelsea was anxious when she got in with the wrong crowd.

Dysfunctional relationships

Revised

Dysfunctional relationships can harm a person's health and well-being. Becky needed affection and sought it by sleeping around, having dysfunctional relationships; and she became ill.

P3

Assessment activity

Draw your family tree or use one based on a family from a popular TV serial.

Pass

Tested

- Make a note of the types of relationships that can impact on a person's health and well-being. Which relationships positively influenced health and well-being? Which relationships negatively influenced health and well-being?

Merit

Tested

- Use evidence (such as research from media articles, or summaries of scientific/health-related reports) and give reasons to support the point(s) you make.

Distinction

Tested

- Compare the negative and positive influences of relationships, clearly linking each to the subsequent effects on the individual's health and well-being.

M2

D2

Social factors that influence health and well-being

Social factors that influence health and well-being include:

- income
- education
- occupation
- social class
- wealth
- values and behaviours
- family
- peers
- media
- living conditions
- gender
- culture.

When these factors come together negatively, for example low income, poor education and no job, they can reduce a person's sense of well-being and badly affect their health.

'The Atlas of Deprivation 2010', published by the Office for National Statistics, gives a picture of poverty in the UK based on factors such as income, employment, health and disability, education, skills and training, barriers to housing and other services, crime and living environment. According to the Atlas of Deprivation, Liverpool, Middlesborough, Manchester, Knowsley, Hull, Hackney and Tower Hamlets are among the most deprived areas in England. Looking at some of the factors we see how they influence health and well-being.

Social factors can have a positive effect or they can have a negative effect.

Figure 4.04 Living in a deprived area can affect well-being

Gender

Studied ▢

Our gender affects our health and well-being. According to government statistics, women born in the UK between 2008 and 2010 can expect to live, on average, until they are 82, but men can expect to live only until they are 78.

(*Source*: www.statistics.gov.uk)

Income

Studied ▢

Income or how much money comes into a household, dictates whether a person can afford to eat, what food they can buy, and whether they can afford heating.

> ## Living on benefits
>
> Jay is a single parent on benefits and has two children of school age. She finds it hard to give them the things they need for school and provide healthy food. Sometimes she misses meals so the children can eat. Since her divorce, they have not had a holiday. Low income affects her health and well-being. Before her divorce, the family income was high. They never had to worry about money and took the children to Spain every year for their holiday. Jay's health and well-being was better then.

Wealth

Studied ▢

Wealth is the amount of money and possessions a person has, including savings and income. A person who is wealthy can afford to pay for private health care when they need it. The following example shows how wealth can affect health and well-being.

> ## Effect of wealth on health and well-being
>
> John is wealthy and needs a hip replacement so he pays privately and gets the operation when he wants it.
>
> Peter also needs a hip replacement but he is not wealthy, so he has to go on a waiting list for a year and put up with the pain. He can no longer go out but stays at home feeling depressed.

P4

D3

95

Education, occupation and social class

These are often linked together in the way they influence health and well-being. In 2010 more people died from work-related injuries in the construction industry than in any other occupation.

(*Source*: www.hse.gov.uk)

Social class is usually determined by occupation. People working in professional and managerial occupations, such as doctors and lawyers, have a higher social class than those in unskilled occupations such as labourers. Higher social classes earn more, enjoy better health and, according to research from the University of London Institute of Education, their children do better at school than those from lower social classes.

(*Source*: www.guardian.co.uk/education/2010/dec/07/social-class-parenting-study)

Values and behaviours

These influence what we do. Some people take responsibility for their own health, eating and drinking in moderation, and taking exercise. They feel good about their health. Other people think the NHS will be able to cure them if they drink too much or become obese. Their values are that it is someone else's responsibility to make them better and this influences behaviour.

Someone who takes care of their body generally feels better and has better health. Unfortunately, those who binge drink, overeat, smoke and do not take exercise find that the NHS cannot cure everything. They realise too late that liver failure from binge drinking and lung cancer from smoking cannot always be cured. By not taking responsibility they face poor health, disability and a shorter life.

Family, culture and living conditions

Family, culture and living conditions work together to influence health and well-being.

Positive influence of extended family culture

Sameera and her husband Akram have a two-month-old baby. They live with Akram's parents as part of an extended family. This is part of their culture, so that old people do not get isolated and younger people have help.

Sameera is very happy with this arrangement. When the baby has been awake all night, her mother-in-law looks after the baby while

Sameera catches up on sleep. Sameera does not have to worry about shopping or cooking, as there is always someone to help.

Akram's parents are happy to spend time with their grandchild. In this extended family, everyone benefits by having reduced stress levels and a sense of well-being. They are fortunate that Akram's parents have a big house, so there is plenty of room for everyone. Sameera and Akram have their own room and a room for the baby too.

Sameerah's family structure, culture and living conditions positively influence her well-being and health. In contrast look at Jay's situation.

Negative influence of divorce and single parenthood

Since the divorce Jay and the children have had to move to a rented one-bedroom flat, as that is all they can afford. As a single parent, Jay does not have anyone to help her. She sleeps on the sofa and gives the children the bedroom. Fortunately, they are both girls so they can share the bed, but the youngest one caught flu and now both children are ill. Jay does not sleep well, worrying about money.

Jay's parents retired to Spain sometime ago and she has no contact with her ex-husband's parents. This is part of Jay's culture. Neither set of grandparents can help with the day-to-day chores, so Jay has to do everything. She is stressed and anxious. She is currently looking for work to fit round school hours, but all the jobs she is offered involve weekends or evenings. The girls are too young to be left and she cannot afford a baby sitter.

In this case study we can see that Jay's family structure, living conditions and culture negatively influence her and her children's well-being and health.

Peers and the media

Studied ☐

Peers and the media influence health and well-being. Look back at Chelsea's story. When she was in with the wrong crowd, she was dared to steal, did so and got caught. This caused her a lot of stress, negatively influencing her well-being. Later when she made new friends and became a mentor, she felt happier and had a better sense of well-being. Earlier in the unit we saw how Becky felt no one cared for her. She became anorexic. When people said she was too thin, Becky did not believe them. The media – television, teen magazines – focus on being attractive. In trying to be liked, Becky was influenced by the media and her health suffered.

Effects of social factors on health choices

Social factors affect choices about:

- diet
- smoking
- living accommodation
- use of recreational drugs
- alcohol consumption
- participation in sport or exercise
- seeking medical care.

Low income restricts health choices. Poverty means Jay cannot afford sports shoes for her children, cannot afford a bigger flat, and cannot afford better food. Some people on low income do not have dental care because they cannot afford it. A good education can lead to a professional job and higher social class, giving better health choices. Families and culture, backed by media and peers, often determine health choices such as whether smoking, drinking alcohol or taking drugs are encouraged.

Effects of social factors on health and well-being

Social factors affect:

- self-esteem
- levels of stress and anxiety
- access to health and social care services
- physical health.

Social factors also have long-term effects. Health is more than being free from physical illness. Physical, intellectual, emotional and social well-being are aspects of health and well-being. Self-esteem, levels of stress and anxiety and access to health and social care services, all contribute to how happy we are: to our sense of well-being. A recent government survey, 'Measuring National Well-being', found that women tend to be happier than men. Having leisure and being in a steady relationship all have positive effects on well-being. Both 16–19 and 65–69 year olds are happier than middle aged people. The highest sense of well-being was among the professional classes, higher earners and those with an occupation.

(*Source*: www.guardian.co.uk/lifeandstyle/2012/jul/24/national-well-being-index-annual-results?newsfeed=true)

This is the first survey on well-being so it is hard to tell whether the social factors contributing to well-being now will have a long-term impact on health and well-being, but previous research has shown a definite link between poor health and shorter life expectancy and poverty.

Real life connection

Working as a counsellor

The NHS employs a range of staff that provides counselling to patients. Examples of counselling roles include the following:

- Primary care counsellor – providing counselling to clients with mild-to-moderate mental health problems
- Care coordinator/counsellor – working with individuals with drug-related problems
- Genetic counsellor – helping individuals understand and deal with genetic disorders
- Counsellor (unplanned pregnancies) – providing counselling support for patients presenting with this condition.

Usually, a counsellor needs to have a recognised counselling qualification, such as those accredited by the British Association of Counselling and Psychotherapy (BACP). Some posts may also require a qualification such as that of a registered nurse, occupational therapist, social worker or other professional. It is an advantage to have another language and to have experience of mental health care.

Check your understanding

Match the words given below (1–4) to their meanings (a–d).

1. Well-being
2. Social factors
3. Health and well-being
4. Health choices

Meanings

a. income, education, occupation, social class, wealth, values and behaviours, family, peers, media, living conditions, gender, culture
b. happiness
c. what decisions we make about our health
d. physical, intellectual, emotional and social well-being

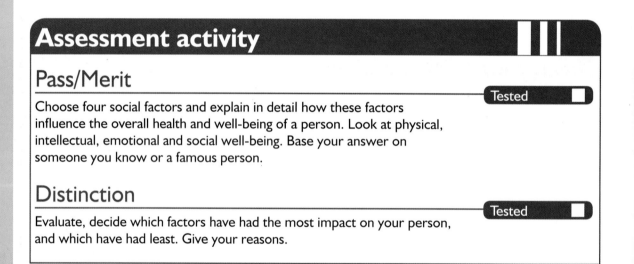

Key learning points

Social factors

Revised

These include income, education, occupation, social class, wealth, values and behaviours, family, peers, media, living conditions, gender and culture.

Social factors affect health choices

Revised

Jay did not have much money and could not afford good food for the children. Her choices were limited.

Social factors affect health and well-being.

Revised

Becky had difficulty making friends and her self-esteem was low.

Assessment activity

Pass/Merit

Tested

Choose four social factors and explain in detail how these factors influence the overall health and well-being of a person. Look at physical, intellectual, emotional and social well-being. Base your answer on someone you know or a famous person.

Distinction

Tested

Evaluate, decide which factors have had the most impact on your person, and which have had least. Give your reasons.

The following framework may be useful:

Brief description of the person and their circumstances			
	How it influenced the person	Grade factors in order 1 = most influence 4 = least influence	Why it was a major factor or not
Social factor is…	Physically: Socially: Emotionally: Intellectually:		
Social factor is…	Physically: Socially: Emotionally: Intellectually:		
Social factor is…	Physically: Socially: Emotionally: Intellectually:		
Social factor is…	Physically: Socially: Emotionally: Intellectually:		

Model assignment

This assignment will assess the following learning aims:

A explore the effects of socialisation on the health and well-being of individuals
B understand the influences that relationships have on the health and well-being of individuals
C investigate the effects of social factors on the health and well-being of individuals.

Scenario

While on placement at your local health centre, you are involved in a health promotion event to raise awareness among parents of the effects of socialisation. You are asked to prepare a series of posters or storyboards to show this, basing your response on a set of fictional characters.

Section 1

Explore the effects of socialisation on the health and well-being of individuals

Devise a poster or storyboard to explain the influence of agents and the effects of primary and secondary socialisation on **three** fictional characters.

Describe the effects of primary and secondary socialisation on the health and well-being of these individuals, with relevant examples.

Section 2

Understand the influences that relationships have on the health and well-being of individuals

Produce a poster or leaflet describing and explaining the influences that different types of relationships have on the health and well-being of individuals.

Compare the potential positive and negative influences of different types of relationships on the health and well-being of individuals.

Section 3

Investigate the effects of social factors on the health and well-being of individuals

Produce a written report to describe and explain how social factors can affect the health and well-being of individuals, using a range of relevant examples.

In your written report, evaluate the link between social factors and their effect on the health and well-being of individuals, using a range of relevant examples.

References

www.guardian.co.uk/education/2010/dec/07/social-class-parenting-study

www.hse.gov.uk/statistics/tables/index.htm#riddor – Injuries in Great Britain by industry and severity of injury

www.statistics.gov.uk/hub/population/deaths/life-expectancies/

www.guardian.co.uk/lifeandstyle/2012/jul/24/national-well-being-index-annual-results?newsfeed=true

Unit 5

Promoting Health and Well-being

This unit explores what health promotion is and why health promotion activities are carried out. It will investigate the benefits for individuals and the nation as a whole. The unit will also assess different methods of health promotion and the roles of those in health and social care, whose job it is to deliver health promotion.

Learning aims

In this chapter you will:

✓ explore the purpose, types and benefits of health promotion.

✓ investigate how health risks can be addressed through health promotion.

Assessment criteria

Level 2 Pass	Level 2 Merit	Level 2 Distinction
Learning aim A: Explore the purpose, types and benefits of health promotion		
2A.P1 Describe health promotion and the purpose and aims of three different health promotion activities.		
2A.P2 Describe how different types of health promotion are used to benefit the health and well-being of individuals and the nation.	**2A.M1** Discuss how different types of health promotion are used to benefit the health and well-being of individuals and the nation, using selected examples.	**2A.D1** Analyse the benefits of different types of health promotion to individuals and the nation, using selected examples.
Learning aim B: Investigate how health risks can be addressed through health promotion		
2B.P3 Describe the chosen health risk and its main effects on individuals, using research findings from different sources.	**2B.M2** Explain how the chosen health risk affects individuals and how these effects can be addressed through health promotion, using research findings from different types of sources.	**2B.D2** Evaluate the strategies used to address the chosen health risk, using research findings.
2B.P4 Produce appropriate materials for a health promotion activity, describing the health risk and health advice.	**2B.M3** Produce materials for a health-promotion activity tailored to a target group, describing the health risk and health advice.	**2B.D3** Make recommendations for how the health promotion materials could be adapted for a different target group.

Learning Aim A
A.1 Health promotion

What is health promotion?

Health promotion is about raising the public's health awareness so that individuals may make informed choices about their health and lifestyles. Individuals, communities and nations are given health information so that they can control areas of their lives which they may not have done before.

Purpose and aims of health promotion

Purpose

Studied ☐

The purpose of health promotion is to give people the personal skills to enable them to change their behaviours and attitudes and be positive about their health and lifestyles. This will allow individuals to choose a healthy lifestyle and understand the reasons for those choices. Health promotion encourages people to take action and communities to come together to improve their health and environments.

Aims

Studied ☐

Health promotion activities do not all have the same focus or take the same approach. Table 5.01 gives some of the aims of health promotion activities and includes examples of activities and campaigns to show how they link.

Table 5.01 Aims of health promotion activities

Aims	Examples
Raising awareness This is about providing information and education about diseases and disorders that occur commonly or are little-known diseases.	In leaflets about signs and symptoms of different cancers; for example, cervical, bowel and breast cancer.
Encourage safety and reduce accidents This type of information can be aimed at all age groups and can also include personal safety.	Food safety, fire safety, road safety, home safety, risks of substance abuse, personal safety.

Aims	Examples
Reduce number of people smoking This aim can be tackled in many ways. For example, explaining the harmful effects of smoking to young people so they do not start smoking. Trying to reduce the number of people smoking will eventually reduce the cost of treating ill heath linked to smoking on the NHS.	Facts on this topic can be given in information leaflets, TV adverts about giving up smoking and how secondary smoke affects children. Information can be seen in chemists, doctor's surgeries and hospitals.
Encourage healthy eating habits Healthy eating campaigns, warning about obesity, tooth decay, diabetes and heart disease, encourage parents and schools to ensure that children eat healthily from an early age. The effects of an unhealthy diet are costing the NHS time and money. So encouraging healthy eating habits is a necessity.	Government supported campaigns like 5-a-day Supermarkets will advertise healthy eating recipes and support weight loss groups, such as Weight Watchers and Slimming World, to encourage healthy eating plans. Dentists' surgeries and school policies encourage healthy eating to avoid tooth decay and obesity.
Reduce alcohol intake This aim can be tackled from different angles. Young people may be taught in schools about the dangers of alcohol; this is a good time as teenagers often experiment with different habits during this stage. A more informative approach may be taken to advise people later in life about alcohol limits and the long-term health effects.	National government campaigns support this aim, as it is also linked with road accidents, street fighting and domestic violence. Rehabilitation programmes and support groups aim to reduce the alcohol intake of people, for example AA (Alcoholics Anonymous). Drink-drive campaigns seek to meet this aim, as do adverts on TV and in magazines about diseases related to alcohol abuse, such as cancer.

Types of health promotion and health promotion activities

Health risk advice

Studied

There are many ways in which health advice can raise awareness. The method used to raise awareness also depends on the individual. We are not all the same and will change in different ways and because of different experiences.

Some people will change their lifestyles because of personal experiences. For example, a smoker may suffer chest pain and a possible heart attack; the fact that the individual's life has been affected and he or she may suffer ill health because of it, is enough to change the individual's behaviour to stop smoking. Other individuals may change their behaviour because of seeing other people's lifestyles and change because of others' experiences.

A range of different types of health-risk advice with examples to explain them is given in Table 5.02.

Key terms

Shock tactics: An example could be when a smoker suffers a heart problem which may affect their life, so a change would benefit them.

Table 5.02 Types of health-risk advice

Types of health risk advice	Examples
Peer advice	This is a very powerful method of health advice and can be used in schools and colleges and can promote important discussion points. Peer-led advice is about learning from someone who is in your own group of friends, or someone your own age, or who has the same interests as you. Take a look at the following web link and its future events about personal social and emotional health. http://loudmouth.co.uk/
Shock tactics	Some individuals will change their behaviour if given shocking facts, figures and information. The campaign about stopping smoking which put graphic photographs on cigarette packets was created for this type of impact. Introducing individuals to people who suffer from the effects of smoking or overeating, for example, can also be a way of using shock tactics. You are then facing the person you could become if you don't change your lifestyle.
Advice from professionals	Health advice based at hospitals, GP surgeries and clinics can be excellent sources of health-risk advice. An educational approach may be taken in presenting the information, but some individuals will change their behaviours if they understand the reasons for change. For example, healthy eating, safe driving and increased exercise. Health professionals may also support emotional issues that lead to unhealthy lifestyles; for example, a counsellor may be required to find out why a person overeats or misuses alcohol or drugs. Social and financial circumstances may prevent change, so it is important to discover the root causes of poor health behaviours.
Advice from police and fire services	As with health professionals, this advice can be educational and informative. The police and fire services can give detailed and sometimes shocking accounts of their day-to-day life, which would be helped by individuals who where more aware of road safety, drink-driving, and cyberbulling.
Testimonies from people personally affected by issues	Personal case studies, conversations and newspaper reports from sufferers of a disease or disorder can be a form of health advice. This direct approach offers a 'wake-up call' to individuals and can be very effective. For example, skin cancer from sunbeds, lung cancer from smoking and obesity from overeating are all valid topics. Follow the following link to see a story about a sufferer who wants to give advice. www.liverpoolecho.co.uk/liverpool-news/local-news/2012/07/09/liverpool-tanaholic-sounds-sunbed-warning-for-nhs-merseyside-s-year-of-action-on-cancer-campaign-100252-31351309/

Health promotion campaigns that are produced by the government can be nationwide or locally led. Nationwide campaigns may be set up in response to health research that is produced and the plans set to improve particular areas of health.

Department of Health national campaigns

The Department of Health runs campaigns to support and promote its work. They aim to target a large audience and are usually about reducing the numbers who may suffer from the diseases as well as spreading awareness. You can find out about the latest campaigns here:

www.dh.gov.uk/health/category/campaigns/

The Department of Health launched new campaigns in 2012. Examples inlcuded:

- **Bowel cancer** – the 'Be Clear on Cancer' bowel cancer campaign incorporated TV and radio advertising as well as face-to-face events around the country. The campaign featured real GPs and encouraged people who have had blood in their stool or looser stools for three weeks or more to see their doctor.
- **Stoptober** – This campaign encouraged smokers across England to take up the challenge to stop smoking for 28 days. Follow the link to find out about the 'Stoptober starts today!' campaign. www.dh.gov.uk/health/2012/10/stoptober-starts-today/
- **Dementia** – The Department of Health launched a campaign, supported by the Alzheimer's Society, to encourage people to talk to loved ones showing signs of dementia. It included television and print advertising. Sir Michael Parkinson, Fiona Phillips and England goalkeeper Gordon Banks shared their personal experiences of dementia in a series of short films. Find out more at www.dh.gov.uk/health/2012/09/dementia-campaign/

Figure 5.02 Be clear on bowel cancer

Figure 5.03 Stoptober

National and local NHS campaigns

The NHS runs many campaigns, some of which are nationwide and some of which are local. If a particular area has had a large increase in meningitis then local campaigns may be rolled out and information published in local newspapers and surgeries to inform the public within that area.

Also the NHS has a series of awareness days/weeks over the year and local events are held because of this. This will raise money and awareness.

Use of different forms of media

Using the media to give information to a large audience is an excellent method. It has many different formats. Advertisements on TV, in newspapers, magazines, billboards and wall-displays can deliver simple thought-provoking health messages with advice lines and websites for further information. These forms of media are discussed in more detail in section B1 of this unit.

Manufacturers of products can give health advice; for example, through the sale of wholemeal bread to promote good digestive habits and sugar-free drinks to prevent tooth decay. Supermarkets now label food with a traffic light system to advise shoppers about the contents of processed and packaged foods.

Figure 5.04 Food labelling

Books, health journals and television documentaries give factual and educational information through the media. Often we see new reports and research findings about health issues in this way.

Health issues can be portrayed as news items through celebrities who may have struggled in an area of their lives and then discussed it through the media to spread health awareness. An example of how Angelina Jolie did just that is given below.

PI

It is important to point out that although the media can reach a large audience, we have no way of knowing how many people it affects; so this type of advice should be backed up with leaflets and support lines to help people to change their health behaviours with the right support.

Medical intervention

Studied

This type of health promotion can be called preventative health advice, as it is usually advisory and gives information about protecting the individual with the help of the medical profession.

It can be issued as a national initiative from the Department of Health, for example bowel cancer screening; or given as a protection for those in a vulnerable target group, for example childhood immunisations.

Childhood immunisations

All children starting the immunisation programme at two months of age will follow the schedule shown in Table 5.03.

Table 5.03 Schedule for immunisation programme

When to immunise	What is given
Two-months-old	Diphtheria, tetanus, pertussis, polio and Haemophilus influenzae
	Pneumococcal
Three-months-old	Diphtheria, tetanus, pertussis, polio and Haemophilus influenzae
	Meningitis C
Four-months-old	Diphtheria, tetanus, pertussis, polio and Haemophilus influenzae type b
	Pneumococcal
	Meningitis C
Between 12- and 13-months-old - within a month of the first birthday	Haemophilus influenzae type b, Meningitis C
	Measles, mumps and rubella (MMR)
	Pneumococcal (PCV)
Three-years-four-months to five- years-old	Diphtheria, tetanus, pertussis and polio
	Measles, mumps and rubella (MMR)
Thirteen to 18-years-of-age	Tetanus, diphtheria and polio

Vaccinations

1. **Human Papilloma Virus (HPV):** The age group that is given the HPV vaccination is usually in Year 8 at schools in England.
   Some types of HPV can cause cervical cancer and the HPV vaccine is also known as the cervical cancer jab.
   The vaccination programme is delivered largely through secondary schools, and consists of three injections that should be given over a period of 12 months.
   Research has shown that the HPV vaccine provides effective protection for at least six years after completion of the three-dose course. It is not known how long protection will last beyond this time.

2. **Influenza:** Anyone can get flu, but it can be more serious for certain people, such as:

   - people aged 65 or over
   - people who have a serious medical condition
   - pregnant women.

   These individuals are invited for vaccination at the local GP surgery.

3. **Pneumonia:** A pneumococcal infection can affect anyone. However, some groups of people need the vaccination because they have a higher risk of an infection developing into a serious health condition. These include:

   - children under the age of two (as part of the childhood immunisation programme)
   - adults aged 65 or over
   - children and adults with certain chronic (long-term) health conditions, such as a serious heart or kidney condition.

> **Key terms**
>
> **Vaccination:** This is a preparation made and given to the public to provide immunity from a particular disease.

Screening programmes

1. **Cervical cancer**: All women between the ages of 25 and 64 are eligible for a free cervical screening test every three to five years. Cervical screening is not a test for cancer. It is a method of preventing cancer by detecting and treating early abnormalities which, if left untreated, could lead to cancer in a woman's cervix (the neck of the womb). This website explains screening programmes and contains a wealth of information about different types of cancer – www.cancerscreening.nhs.uk/

2. **Breast cancer**: Breast screening is a method of detecting breast cancer at a very early stage. The first step involves an x-ray of each breast – a mammogram – which is taken while carefully compressing the breast. Women under 50 are not currently offered routine screening.

3. **Bowel cancer:** About one in 20 people in the UK will develop bowel cancer during their lifetime. It is the third most common cancer in the UK, and the second leading cause of cancer deaths, with over 16,000 people dying from it each year.

   Regular bowel cancer screening has been shown to reduce the risk of dying from bowel cancer by 16 per cent.

   The NHS Bowel Cancer Screening Programme offers screening every two years to all men and women aged 60 to 69.

4. **Diabetes**: The diabetes screening test shows whether there is glucose present in the urine of the person taking the test. The test gives a simple positive or negative answer as to whether glucose is present.

> ## Key terms
> **Screening:** This is a method of looking at the public and identifying how at risk they are of a disease or condition. Physical tests will be involved.

Check your understanding

Discuss with your class if you think the following are areas of health advice or not.

- TV adverts about drink-driving
- Healthy recipes in supermarkets
- Next door neighbour telling you about cervical cancer screening
- A lesson in school/college about cyberbullying
- Immunisation programme for children
- Self-help groups for stopping smoking
- Health and safety course on how to lift properly
- Exercise class at a local church hall for over 60s
- Cycling to school campaign
- Speaker from fire service talking about kitchen safety.

A.2 Benefits of health promotion to the health and well-being of both the individual and the nation

Health promotion is a complex issue and is not a quick fix. Some individuals may blame personal, social and economic circumstances for their ill health, so health promotion aims to empower individuals, improving their self-esteem so that they want to change. Sensitive health promotion can empower individuals and nations.

Benefits to individuals and the nation are shown below.

Benefits to individuals

Increased understanding of health issues

Studied ☐

By informing, educating and making individuals aware of health issues, they will hopefully understand the reasons behind health advice and make sensible changes because they have been empowered with knowledge. Being aware of disease processes provides an understanding of the effects of making healthy or unhealthy choices.

Increased responsibility for own health

Studied ☐

If an individual has knowledge and professional support this can improve self-esteem and so health behaviours. The responsibility becomes a personal issue, not something that we can blame others for.

For example:

- I am really stressed about work so I need a cigarette to help.
- I cannot afford the time or money to go to the gym.

Do these sound familiar?

Decreased risk of disease or injury

Studied ☐

By attending courses about personal safety, home safety and road safety individuals can make changes in their own environments, so decreasing the risk of injury or disease. Good hand-washing practices are simple and safe lives.

Improved quality of life

Studied ☐

If individuals take advice to change their habits and lifestyles then they should notice improvements in their quality of life; for example, changed eating and drinking patterns may avoid obesity and damage to internal organs.

Increased life expectancy

Studied

By changing to healthier practices obviously life expectancy will improve; for example, stopping smoking and avoiding illegal drugs will avoid illness and diseases such as cancer. Some individuals will be told to stop smoking in order to live longer.

Benefits to the nation

Health promotion is very effective for the nation. One person having cervical screening is not going to lower the incidence of cervical cancer in women, so national programmes are most effective. Once advice has been given, it is up to the individual to take up the vaccination or screening programme – this is called an 'informed choice'. Some of the reasons for improvements in the nation's health are listed below.

Reduced level of illness and disease

Studied

By taking part in vaccination and screening programmes the levels of illness and disease can be reduced; for example, some childhood diseases which are vaccinated against have almost been eradicated.

Impact on crime levels

Studied

As communities take responsibility for their own behaviours, and with the help of community support work, levels of crime and use of alcohol in underage individuals can be lessened. Take a look at this news web link, which shows how the community of Peterborough tackles crime and anti-social behaviour.

www.peterborough.gov.uk/safer_peterborough.aspx

Increased uptake in vaccination and screening programmes

Studied

If screening programmes and vaccination programmes are nationally promoted, it is more likely that the uptake will make a difference to the nation's health. Those people who are screened and then need follow-up treatment will more than likely recover, as the disease process has been identified early. These individuals may naturally then promote the screening programme to encourage others.

Address high-profile health and well-being concerns

Studied ☐

High-profile issues may be addressed with the help of health promotion and taking a group approach will have a large impact on health. For example, Channel 4 and Cancer Research UK's 'Stand Up to Cancer' concert raised over 6 million pounds. (see http://su2c.channel4.com/about-su2c/ to find out more).

Reduced financial cost to the NHS and the government

Studied ☐

An overall aim of health promotion is to reduce the financial burden that ill health has on the NHS. Many hospital beds have individuals in them who are suffering with the results of smoking; for example, people who have lung disorders, heart disease and live with circulatory problems. A growing concern is the effect that overeating has on the nation. The NHS now has a special area of medicine that deals with obesity, its causes and treatments; this is called 'bariatrics'.

If health promotion works, this preventative approach will eventually lead to a reduction in cost to the NHS and the nation.

Check your understanding

Please unscramble the words below:

1. agnanwdhihs
2. dgsru
3. ytsbieo
4. tnciavocian
5. tvenrongme
6. rtaetnmte
7. eecirsex
8. onimgks
9. fesltyeli
10. bitsah

Key learning points

Aims of health promotion

Health promotion aims to improve individual and national health. It includes giving people tools, strategies and support so they can change their health behaviours.

Health risk advice

This covers many areas of health, from physical health to mental health and social health. It is based on the belief that health advice can be aimed at individuals and communities to change lives and the nation's health for the better.

Health advice is not a quick fix

Depending on circumstances health advice can take time to make a difference. Do you know anyone who has tried to give up smoking more than once?

Design of campaigns

Campaigns can meet local needs while being seen on a national basis. These programmes are usually designed to meet the findings of research, so areas with a high incidence of lung cancer will have more advice and support injected into that area.

Medical intervention

Medical intervention is called preventative advice. It is given to protect vulnerable or high-risk individuals from ill health and comes in the form of screening and vaccination programmes.

Assessment activity

Pass/Merit

Design an annotated poster entitled 'Health Promotion and its Benefits'.
Include:
- at least three aims of health promotion
- say how these aims can be achieved using different types of health promotion activities
- include what the benefits of this will be. How will it improve the health of individuals and groups?

Learning Aim B
B.1 Targeting selected health risks

Topics for health promotion and their associated effects

To enable learners to be able to select a health risk, research it and produce a suitable campaign the next part of the unit will give advice about the choices and why appropriate methods should be considered, as well as a format to follow.

Having studied sections A1 and A2 you should be aware of a range of health-promotion topics and how they may affect health.

Substance misuse

Studied ☐

Substance misuse can have a wide array of physical effects other than those expected. The excitement of a cocaine high, for instance, is followed by a 'crash': a period of anxiety, fatigue, depression, and an acute desire for more cocaine to alleviate the feelings of the crash. Marijuana and alcohol interfere with movement control and are factors in many road accidents. Users of marijuana and hallucinogenic drugs may experience flashbacks and unwanted recurrences of the drug's effects for weeks or months. Sharing hypodermic needles used to inject some drugs dramatically increases the risk of hepatitis and AIDS. Many drug users engage in criminal activity, such as burglary and prostitution, to raise the money to buy drugs, and some drugs, especially alcohol, are associated with violent behaviour.

Mood changes at home can affect family life, relationships and marriages; they may cause a family to be afraid of the drug abuser, cause financial problems and lead to loss of employment.

Binge drinking

Studied ☐

Binge drinking is the term used when all the weekly alcohol units are consumed in one episode; this can not only cause physical effects internally, but can also lead to violent behaviour, unsafe sexual practices and may lead to abuse of other substances. The two main sites of damage are the liver and the nervous system. The liver may become damaged through a condition called cirrhosis, which may lead to liver failure, liver cancer and death. Damage to the brain can interfere with intellectual workings, and increase the risk of mental health issues. Excessive alcohol intake can lead to damage to small blood vessels and can lead to diabetes, high blood pressure and stroke. Drinking alcohol when pregnant can harm the development of the unborn child.

Safe sex

Studied

Having unprotected sex can not only lead to unwanted pregnancies but also sexually transmitted infections (these are detailed in Unit 10).

Healthy eating

Studied

Unhealthy eating habits can lead to a range of difficulties. These may include bone and muscle problems like arthritis and limited mobility and joint pain; heart and circulatory problems like raised blood pressure and heart attacks may be caused by increased fat and salt in the diet. Excessive amounts of simple carbohydrates and sugars can lead to diabetes.

Obesity can lead to low self-esteem and depression. It is important to treat the underlying causes of eating habits before we try to change behaviours.

Smoking

Studied

Smoking can be linked to many different forms of cancer; for example, tongue, mouth, throat, lung and breast cancer.

Look at this web link for further details about cancer – it states that one in two long-term smokers will die of cancer.

www.cancerresearchuk.org/cancer-info/utilities/atozindex/atoz-smoking

Smoking also damages small vessels in our body so they do not function well, in particular those vessels that feed the heart and the brain. Once these have been damaged, blood clots, narrowing or total blockage can occur which leads to strokes and heart attacks and can be fatal.

Road safety

Studied

Having an awareness of road safety will equip you as a pedestrian and a driver. You may then avoid accidents from speeding and unsafe driving and know how to correctly use crossings and pathways. Use the ROSPA website for detailed information. Teaching children from a young age about traffic and its dangers is a very important piece of health advice.

Hand washing

Studied

Correct hand-washing procedures are very important, particularly in a work setting with vulnerable service users. Failure to use the correct hand-washing procedures can lead to vomiting, diarrhoea and dehydration, all of which are serious in young children and elderly or sick service users. Diseases that can be contracted from not washing your hands range from the common cold and flu to parasitic diseases such as E. coli, giardia and salmonella, so hand washing is essential after handling food, animals, tissues and after using the toilet.

Routine sport and exercise are important if we are to avoid weight gain, improve our cardiovascular system and feel happy. It is said that exercise boost our endorphins and makes us feel good about ourselves.

Lack of exercise can lead to heart problems, stiffness of joints and low energy levels.

Team sports, in particular, can build our confidence as well as improving our social health.

It is important that from a young age children are encouraged to go out and enjoy physical activities. Obesity in young children is increasing and can be avoided.

Research using different sources

Table 5.04 presents a list of topics for health promotion with some suggested websites as research sources.

Table 5.04 Topics for health promotion and suggested websites

Substance misuse	http://www.talktofrank.com/
Binge drinking	http://www.drinkaware.co.uk/
Safe sex	http://www.netdoctor.co.uk/sex_relationships/facts/safesex.htm
Healthy eating	http://www.nhs.uk/livewell/healthy-eating/Pages/Healthyeating.aspx
Smoking	https://www.quitwithhelp.co.uk/
Road safety	http://www.rospa.com/roadsafety/
Hand washing	http://www.livestrong.com/article/132470-hand-washing-safety/
Sport and exercise	http://www.nhs.uk/Change4Life/Pages/why-change-for-life.aspx

Use the following sources for information for your campaign:

- books
- newspapers (up to date)
- leaflets
- journals
- DVDs and documentaries
- Department of Health
- health professionals
- service users.

Gathering data

It is important to gather data from many different areas in order to understand your research topic. It may be useful to consider local and national health campaigns to find out what has been done before and also to gain a better understanding of your topic area.

Health promotion materials

Health promotion materials need to be selected carefully to match the needs of your target audience and to promote your topic in the best way.

Posters

Studied

These can be used to attract initial attention to your topic with a brief message or 'tag line'; for example, 'Ditch the pies and exercise'. In posters you may be bold and use colours and pictures. Your poster could be humorous, if required, but make sure it catches your audience's attention. For example, if the poster is aimed at children you may want to use a cartoon character. Don't put too much on the poster – less is more!

Put your poster somewhere that is very obvious.

Leaflets

Studied

Leaflets can be used to support the message in your poster, giving further details such as contacts and support services.

Leaflets contain more detailed information but again remember your audience and don't bore them. Divide your leaflet up into sections with pictures and diagrams, bullet points and writing.

Make sure your key message is clear and visible.

Games

Studied

Games can send a message in a fun way and may be used to recap information or on their own.

Games are useful for children who will want to interact and learn at the same time. Examples include board games or computer games. The website below will help school children to discover the dangers of smoking and alcohol.

https://www.lookoutzone.co.uk/default.aspx

Presentations

Studied

Presentations will usually be used in training and teaching establishments to show key points of learning. The presentation may be associated with a practical area of learning, for example, first aid, or it may be used to reach a large audience with question sessions held afterwards.

Include pauses in the presentation to allow for discussions, quizzes and recaps.

Wall displays

Studied

Wall displays may include more detailed information than posters, as they will aim to cover a larger area. A wall display may include writing, charts, pictures and diagrams and cover more than one topic area.

Target groups

Your target audience can be any of the following:

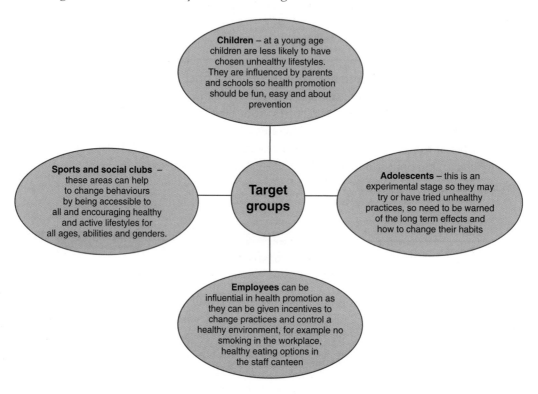

Remember the type of service user is important. For example, have you chosen to target your campaign at those who have not taken drugs so you are going to inform them of the dangers? Or are you targeting those who may have taken drugs and need health promotion advice about how to change behaviours and come off drugs? These are two totally different target groups but the same topic area.

Health promotion materials are appropriate to target group

Your health promotion materials should be appropriate to your target group. Consider the following factors.

Language

Studied

Is the language in your health promotion materials suitable for the age group? Have you considered that someone who cannot read well may want your leaflet, or the needs of someone whose first language is not English?

Images

Studied ☐

Are the images used in the promotion materials appropriate? Remember that you don't want to offend anyone. Are the images correct for the age group? Cartoon characters are great for getting a message across to children.

Activity

Studied ☐

Check that the activity is neither too complex nor too easy for the target group.

Position of display

Studied ☐

Your display should be bold, eye catching and positioned correctly where your audience will see it.

Timings

Studied ☐

If you plan to give a presentation ensure that you give precise information. But check that the duration of your presentation is not too long and break it up with activities and opportunities for the audience to ask questions.

Ethics

Studied ☐

Ethics means you will not harm anyone in the process – so do not use any offensive slogans which may discriminate or single people out. Make sure you don't give information to the wrong audience; for example, a campaign about safe sex to under 10-year-olds would be ethically wrong to do.

Form of media

Studied ☐

We have discussed different forms of media earlier in the unit so your choice should meet your audience's needs.

Adaptations

Studied ☐

If necessary you may have to adapt/change your health promotion campaign to suit another target group.

How could you do this? You could, for example:

- use a different form of media
- use different information – from non-smokers to smokers
- include games
- adapt it to people with learning needs (so language levels will change)
- use more pictures to attract younger audiences
- include more details and educational content to suit older audiences.

P3

P4

M2

M3

Evaluation of strategy

Following your campaign, you need to evaluate it – that means look at its strengths and weaknesses and suggest ways to change and improve your campaign if you have to repeat it.

Ask yourself the following questions:

- Was the setting/environment suitable?
- Did I have sufficient time?
- Did I have enough resources?
- Were my resources suitable?
- Was health and safety adequate?
- Did the service users participate and enjoy the activity?
- Did I meet all service users' needs?
- Did I achieve what I set out to do?
- Would I do this activity again?
- How might I change it?
- Did I enjoy it?

Real life connection

A practice nurse

Practice nurses work in a GP surgery as part of a primary healthcare team, which might include doctors, nurses, pharmacists and dietitians. In larger practices, there may be several practice nurses sharing duties and responsibilities, but in smaller ones you will work on your own, taking on many roles.

You will be involved in almost every aspect of patient care and treatment, undertaking such tasks as:

- treating small injuries
- helping with minor operations done under local anaesthetic
- health screening
- family planning
- running vaccination programmes (for example against flu)
- running programmes to help people to stop smoking.

You must be a qualified and registered nurse and will need to undertake further training and education to enable you to become a member of the primary healthcare team.

Check your understanding

Match the statements.

1. Posters deliver _____
2. Leaflets can be _____
3. Children prefer _____
4. Ethics means _____
5. Evaluate means _____

a. …taken away and read at leisure.
b. …to look at the end product and improve it.
c. …to do no harm to others.
d. …simple messages.
e. …practical activities.

Key learning points

Health promotion materials

These can be used to meet specific needs. For example a poster is effective for displaying a simple message. A presentation will allow interaction so can be used to send more complex messages.

Use appropriate materials for the target group

This is essential if health promotion is to be effective. The theatre in education is effective for teenagers. Use interactive activities for children. An educational and informative approach with presentations or written material is more effective with adults.

Adapt materials according to the service user's needs

Materials need to be adapted according to service users' needs. For example, you would approach someone differently when telling him or her not to smoke than you would when advising someone to stop smoking.

Assessment activity

Pass/Merit

Compile an information leaflet about a chosen health risk (detailed in Section B) and a target group. Include:

- information about the health risk
- the effects of the health risk to the target group
- how health promotion can address these effects

Suggest a range of health promotion materials that would be best suited to tackle your chosen health risk.

Model assignment

This assignment will assess the following learning aims:

A explore the purpose, types and benefits of health promotion
B investigate how health risks can be addressed through health promotion.

> ## Scenario
> As a student you have been asked to make a presentation about a possible health promotion campaign that could be done in your school/college.

Section 1

As an introduction to your campaign:

- Describe the AIM and PURPOSE of three different health promotion activities that would fit in with teenagers in the establishment.

Your next slides should include the following information:

- Describe how different types of health promotion are used to benefit the health and well-being of individuals and the nation.
- Using examples of health promotion activities discuss, analyse how they meet the needs of individuals and the nation.

This should also be part of your presentation:

- You have now been asked to select one health risk as your campaign – before producing your campaign your school/college wishes you to describe its main effects on individuals, stating where you found your evidence. You need to show at least two different sources; for example, Department of Health, NHS website and professional journals.
- Explain in your presentation how the effects can be addressed with the help of health promotion – show evidence of at least two sources of research; for example, internet, books and health professionals.
- To complete your presentation, evaluate the strategies used to address the health risk, for example how did the internet compare with journal and books?

Section 2

- You now need to produce a campaign with resources. You may wish to use a plan like the one shown below.
- Produce the materials and, with information about your health risk and advice and target group, get your class or tutor to review your campaign.
- After feedback from your class and your tutor you should write a reflection about your campaign and include changes/adaptions you would make if you had to aim your campaign at a different target group.

Health promotion campaign: Action plan		
To do	Comments	Date /by when
Topic area/health risk		
What advice am I giving?		
Target group		
Why have I chosen this topic?		
The aim of my campaign is…		
Methods/activity to be used		
What resources do I need?		

Unit 6

The Impact of Nutrition on Health and Well-being

This unit explores the key principles of nutrition and how it is linked with good health. It highlights the dietary needs of individuals and looks at different requirements – for example, life stages, culture, or specific health needs. This unit also considers health problems that are linked to unbalanced diets and how they can be avoided.

This knowledge will help you to give advice to those you may be caring for and understand personal preferences. With this knowledge you will be able to create nutritional plans for individuals with special dietary needs.

Learning aims

In this unit you will:

✓ explore the effects of balanced and unbalanced diets on the health and well-being of individuals.

✓ understand the specific nutritional needs and preferences of individuals.

Assessment criteria

Level 2 Pass	Level 2 Merit	Level 2 Distinction
Learning aim A: Explore the effects of balanced and unbalanced diets on the health and well-being of individuals		
2A.P1 Describe the components of a balanced diet and their functions, sources and effects.	2A.M1 Compare the effects of balanced and unbalanced diets on the health and well-being of two individuals.	2A.D1 Assess the long-term effects of a balanced and unbalanced diet on the health and well-being of individuals.
2A.P2 Describe the effects of an unbalanced diet on the health and well-being of individuals, giving examples of their causes.		
Learning aim B: Understand the specific nutritional needs and preferences of individuals		
2B.P3 Describe the specific dietary needs of two individuals at different life stages.	2B.M2 Explain the factors influencing the dietary choices of two individuals with specific dietary needs at different life stages.	2B.D2 Discuss how factors influence the dietary choices of two individuals with specific dietary needs at different life stages.
2B.P4 Create a nutritional plan for two individuals with different specific nutritional needs.	2B.M3 Compare nutritional plans for two individuals with different nutritional needs.	

Learning Aim A
A.1 Dietary intake and food groups

Essential nutrients

A healthy diet should contain a balance of all the essential nutrients. In this section we look at the sources, functions and effects of each group of nutrients.

A balanced diet contains five main groups of nutrients:

- carbohydrates
- proteins
- fats and oils
- vitamins
- minerals
- water.

Nutrients can be split into two groups: **macro nutrients** and **micro nutrients**.

Carbohydrates

Studied ☐

There are two main types of carbohydrates: simple and complex

1. **Simple** carbohydrates, for example sugar
   - There are many different types of sugar. Sugar contains monosaccharide (simple sugars) and disaccharides (complex or double sugars).
   - Sugar is found in foods like jams, sweets, honey and soft drinks. It is also added to desserts, cakes and biscuits.
2. **Complex** carbohydrates, for example starch
   - Starches are called polysaccharides. 'Polysaccharide' means 'made up of many units of monosaccharide' ('poly' means many).
   - Starches (polysaccharides) are found in foods like bread, potatoes, rice and pasta.
   - Non-starch polysaccharides are more commonly known as cellulose or dietary fibre.
   - Cellulose or dietary fibre (non-starch polysaccharides) is found in foods like vegetables, fruit and cereals (it used to be called roughage).

Key terms

Macro nutrients (macro means large/big): These are needed in our body in large amounts. They are proteins, fats and carbohydrates.

Micro nutrients (micro means small): These are needed in small amounts in our body. Micro nutrients are vitamins and minerals.

UNIT 6 The Impact of Nutrition on Health and Well-being

Functions and effects of carbohydrates

Sugar and starch carbohydrates both provide equal amounts of energy, but starch carbohydrates are the healthier option. Sugar carbohydrates are strongly linked with tooth decay. Carbohydrates are needed in our diet to provide our main source of energy. Experts have estimated that over half the energy in our diets should come from carbohydrates.

Non-starch polysaccharide is fibrous and our bodies cannot digest it, but it has many health benefits. It encourages us to chew our food thoroughly and adds bulk to the diet, so encourages our digestive tract to work effectively. It also helps to avoid constipation and may prevent some bowel disorders and diseases.

Figure 6.01 Sources of complex carbohydrates

Figure 6.02 Sources of protein

Proteins

Studied ☐

Proteins are made up of building blocks called amino acids. Some of these amino acids are called 'essential amino acids'. These have to be supplied by diet. Protein is found in a range of foods, the main sources being red meat, poultry, fish, eggs, milk and yoghurt.

Function and effects

Proteins are essential in our diet and are used in the body for repair and growth of new cells. The immune system, which fights infection, is also made up of protein. Therefore it is really important that groups of people like babies, children, older people and people who are ill, in particular, have a good supply of protein in their diets. Vegetarians and vegans (who do not eat meat or fish) need their supply from other foods, such as nuts, pulses (peas, beans and lentils), soya protein and some vegetables.

Fats and oils

Studied ☐

Fat is an important part of a healthy diet. However, some fats are better for us than others. Saturated fats increase blood cholesterol. Mono-unsaturated and polyunsaturated fats tend to lower blood cholesterol. The different types of fats and oils, their sources and effects on the human body are shown in Table 6.01.

Table 6.01 Fats and oils: their sources and effects on the human body

Fats and oils	Sources	Effects
Saturated fats	Found in foods such as milk, cream, full-fat cheese, lard and butter.	If eaten in excess they can cause heart disease.
Polyunsaturated fats	Found in foods such as soya oil, corn and fish.	
Monounsaturated fats	Found in olive oil. Many unsaturated fats come from plant oils.	They are said to benefit the heart.
Essential fatty acids	<ul><li>Essential fatty acids are polyunsaturated fats that cannot be made by the body so have to be provided by the diet.</li><li>Omega 3 fats can be found in oily fish.</li><li>Omega 6 fats can be found in sunflower oil, corn oil, soya oil, cereal, eggs and poultry.</li></ul>	<ul><li>They help to build cells.</li><li>Omega 3 fats can help prevent heart disease and are helpful in joint diseases.</li><li>Omega 6 fats can help prevent heart disease as they reduce cholesterol levels.</li></ul>

Functions and effects

Fat is required in the diet to help to build cells in the body. It provides energy and helps with the absorption of Vitamins A, D, E and K into the body. Fat also provides taste and texture to food.

Figure 6.03 Oily fish is a source of Omega 3, a type of fatty acid

Figure 6.04 Fresh fruit and vegetables are a good source of vitamin C

Vitamins

Studied ☐

Table 6.02 shows the sources of vitamins, their role and the effects of shortage of vitamins in the human body

Table 6.02 Vitamins: their sources, role in the body and effects of shortage

Vitamin	Sources	Role in the body and effect of shortage
A (Retinol)	<ul><li>Animal foods, milk, cheese, eggs, oily fish, fruit and vegetables.</li><li>In animal products it is known as retinol and in plants as carotenes (which the body converts to retinol).</li></ul>	<ul><li>Essential for vision in dim light.</li><li>It helps keep skin healthy and keeps mucous membranes (such as eyes and throat) free from infection.</li><li>It assists in the growth of bones and teeth and helps fight infection.</li><li>Too much vitamin A can a toxic effect as the liver cannot process it.</li><li>There is also a link between too much vitamin A and birth defects. Pregnant women are advised not to take nutritional substances which contain vitamin A.</li></ul>
D (Cholecalciferol)	<ul><li>Found in fish liver oils, oily fish, eggs, dairy products, and is added to margarine by law.</li><li>It is also found in the UV rays in sunlight.</li><li>Vitamin D is stored in the liver and can be used as required.</li></ul>	<ul><li>Required for bones and teeth</li><li>vitamin D helps the absorption of calcium.</li><li>People are unlikely to be deficient in vitamin D unless they have limited exposure to the sun.</li><li>Lack of vitamin D can cause weak bones and teeth. Bones may then bend, which can cause rickets in children or osteomalacia in adults.</li><li>Too much can lead to deposits of calcium in the joints, which can damage organs.</li></ul>
C (Ascorbic acid)	<ul><li>Fresh fruit and vegetables</li><li>Fruit juices</li></ul>	<ul><li>Aids absorption of iron and helps build bones and teeth</li><li>It aids vitamin E as an antioxidant and is necessary to build and maintain skin and digestive system</li><li>Helps fight infection by protecting immune system</li><li>Shortage can lead to scurvy and poor healing of damaged cells</li></ul>
B1 – Thiamin	<ul><li>Milk, eggs, vegetables, fruit</li></ul>	<ul><li>Helps release energy from carbohydrates</li><li>Shortage causes beri beri (linked with alcoholism), depression, pins and needles</li></ul>
B2 – Riboflavin	<ul><li>Milk and milk products</li></ul>	<ul><li>Helps utilise energy from foods</li><li>Shortage causes sore mouth and tongue</li></ul>
B3 – Niacin	<ul><li>Cheese, meat (especially chicken)</li></ul>	<ul><li>Helps utilise food energy</li><li>Shortage causes skin peeling, diarrhoea, memory loss, insomnia</li></ul>
B6 – Pyridoxine	<ul><li>Meat, fish, eggs</li></ul>	<ul><li>Metabolism of amino acids and helps form haemoglobin</li><li>Shortage causes nerve problems and fatigue</li></ul>

PI

Vitamin	Sources	Role in the body and effect of shortage
B12 – Cyanocobalamin	• Meat (especially liver), milk, eggs, cheese • Does not occur in vegetables	• Needed by cells that divide rapidly. One example is bone marrow, which helps make red blood cells • Shortage causes pernicious anaemia and degeneration of nerve cells
Folate (Folic acid)	• Leafy green vegetables, potatoes and oranges	• Helps vitamin B12 with rapidly dividing cells. Important in pregnancy • Shortage may cause anaemia
E (Tocopherol)	• Vegetable oils, nuts and egg yolk	• Major role as an antioxidant. Stored in the body to protect body cells from free radicals (unstable compounds that damage healthy body cells) • It also maintains a healthy reproductive system, nerves and muscles • Shortage causes muscle and cell dysfunction
K	• Widespread in many foods including leafy vegetables such as spinach, cauliflower • It can be produced in the body by bacteria	• Essential for blood clotting • Babies tend to be given an injection of vitamin K at birth • Shortage is rare, and is usually in babies, called Vitamin K deficiency bleeding

Minerals

Studied ☐

Minerals are split into essential minerals and trace minerals. Table 6.03 shows the sources and roles and effects of shortages of the essential minerals in the body.

Figure 6.05 Nuts are a source of iron

Table 6.03 Minerals: sources, roles and effects of shortages in the human body

Mineral	Sources	Role in the body and effect of shortage
Calcium	Milk, cheese, eggs, bones of canned fish and is added to white flour by law.	• Calcium combined with phosphorous gives strength to teeth and bones; it helps with blood clotting and nerve functioning. • Shortage causes poor teeth development, rickets in children and osteomalacia in adults. Tetany may result if muscles and nerves do not function properly.
Iron	Red meat, offal, fish, dark leafy green vegetables, pulses, cereal, nuts, dried herbs and spices	• Iron carries oxygen in the blood to all cells. Vitamin C helps the body absorb more iron. • Shortage causes anaemia, particularly in infants 6–12 months, teenage girls who are menstruating and older people.
Sodium	Found in many additives, snacks and preservatives, naturally found in eggs, meat and vegetables	• Helps to maintain fluid balance with potassium and sodium chloride. Important for nerve and muscle impulses. • Shortage causes muscle cramps; excessive amounts can lead to high blood pressure

Water

Studied ☐

Adults are recommended to drink approximately 2 litres of water a day, but this can be found in various drinks in addition to foods such as celery, lettuce, cucumber, jelly and soups.

Figure 6.06 Water has many important functions

Functions and effects

Water has several important functions in the body and we cannot survive without it. It makes up about 70 per cent of our body weight and is required for:

- regulating body temperature
- transporting nutrients
- enabling chemical reactions to take place
- maintaining bowel function.

It is very important to encourage vulnerable service users to drink, as they may not recognise thirst. This could very quickly lead to dehydration.

Recommended daily intakes (RDIs)

Studied ☐

For food groups this will depend on age and the health of the individual. The following charts are guidelines for a balanced diet.

	Boys 9–13	Boys 14–18	Girls 9–13	Girls 14–18
Calories	1,800-2,200	2,200-2,400	1,600-2,000	2,000
Protein (g)	34	52	34	46
Fat (g)	62-85	61-95	62-85	55-78
Saturated fat (g)	20-24	20	18-22	20
Cholesterol (mg)	<300	<300	<300	<300
Salt (g)	5	6	5	6
Sodium (mg)	1,500-1,900	1,500-2,300	1,500-2,200	2,300
Iron (mg)	8	11	8	15
Calcium (mg)	1,300	1,300	1,300	1,300
Fibre (g)	25-31	31-34	23-28	23
Vitamin A (ug)	500	600-700	500	600-700
Vitamin C (mg)	30	35-40	30	35-40
Folate (ug)	150-200	200	150-200	200

	Adults 19-50	Adults 50 and over	Boys and Girls 4-8
Calories	2,000-2,800	2,200-2,500	1,400-1,600
Protein (g)	55	53	19
Fat (g)	55-95	55-78	39-62
Saturated fat (g)	24-27	24-27	16-18
Cholesterol (mg)	<300	<300	<300
Salt (g)	6	6	3
Sodium (mg)	1,500-2,300	1,500-2,300	1,200-1,900
Iron (mg)	14.8	9	10
Calcium (mg)	1,300	1,300	800
Fibre (g)	31-34	31-34	19-23
Vitamin A (ug)	600-700	600-700	400
Vitamin C (mg)	35-40	35-40	30
Folate (ug)	200	200	100

(*Source:* Food Standards Agency Nutrient and Food Based Guidelines for UK October 2007.)

Check your understanding

Quiz

Are the following statements true or false?

1. Water makes up over 70 per cent of our body.
2. Calcium is found in soya milk.
3. Potatoes are a rich source of vitamin C.
4. Vitamin D can be gained from sunlight.
5. High content of water can be found in soup.
6. Olive oil is high in salt.
7. Calcium is required for development of bones and teeth.
8. Polyunsaturated fats are low in calories.
9. Vegetarian food is a healthier option.
10. Fruit juices can be harmful to our teeth.
11. Red meat is higher in fat than poultry.
12. Micro nutrients are needed in large amounts.
13. Lemon-flavoured sweets are a good source of vitamin C.
14. Baked beans are a rich source of protein.
15. Frozen vegetables have good vitamin content.
16. Dark chocolate is a good source of iron.
17. High protein food is required for the immune system.

Effects of a balanced diet

The effects of a balanced diet are:

- raised immunity to infection
- greater levels of energy and concentration
- faster healing of skin tissues and mucus membranes.

Raised immunity to infections

Studied ☐

Where possible, breast milk is the best form of infant feeding, as it contains substances which promote the development of the immune system of the baby; this in turn will prevent infection so enhancing development of the child.

As you grow and develop your diet can be linked to how well your immune system works.

A diet rich in vitamin C-rich foods will help to improve immunity. Vitamin C contains substances that prevent permanent damage to our cells. It can also combat foreign invaders that cause illness.

Adequate protein intake promotes white blood cell production to support the immune system and helps prevent infection.

Zinc is a trace mineral that is only needed in small amounts, but it helps the immune system to function. Having inadequate zinc in the diet increases the risk of infections. Foods that are high in zinc are dark poultry, meat, beef, pork and oysters.

Fibre in the diet will improve immunity. Fibre is not broken down, but it helps to improve digestion, which allows the body to fully absorb important immune-boosting nutrients, such as vitamin C and zinc.

Good web link for further reading: www.webmd.com/cold-and-flu/ss/slideshow-immune-foods

Greater energy levels and increased concentration

Studied ☐

Tiredness and inability to concentrate can be a common problem. Often this can be improved with lifestyle changes (such as additional sleep) and dietary changes. Certain foods and nutrients can often improve these factors.

- Drinking sufficient water has been said to improve functioning of the body and mind, but there are also some food products that have a similar effect. It is important to drink plenty of water throughout the day for good brain function, as the brain does not have any way to store water.

- Vitamin B6 is a vital supplement that the body cannot produce. It helps the body to produce brain chemicals and can support concentration abilities and energy levels.
- Omega-3 fatty acids, which the body cannot produce, are known to support heart health, reduce bodily inflammation and balance mood. Omega-3 fatty acids can be found in rich amounts in the brain and also contribute to brain development, mental sharpness and memory skills.
- Whole grains provide nutrients such as B vitamins, iron and magnesium which are rich in glucose, which is the body's primary energy source that supports physical and mental function.
- Many women lack energy because they lack iron in their diet. During their reproductive years iron is lost in blood each month through the menstruation cycle. Unless it is replaced in the diet iron-deficiency anemia and chronic fatigue may occur.
- Good web link for further reading: www.webmd.com/add-adhd/ slideshow-brain-foods-that-help-you-concentrate

> **Key term**
> **Dehydration:** Babies may be dehydrated if they have a sunken soft spot (fontanelle) on their head, few or no tears when they cry, dry mouth, fewer wet nappies, drowsiness and fast breathing.

Faster healing of skin, tissues and mucus membranes

Studied ☐

Diet has an important role in healing. In addition to a balanced diet, specific nutrients speed up the healing process.

- Protein makes up a part of every cell, tissue and organ in the body. Additional protein is required when the body needs to make cells and tissue to promote the healing process. Inadequate consumption of protein delays healing.
- Calories should be increased during periods of healing, as the body needs a good number of calories to allow repair of the damaged tissue. Without adequate intakes of carbohydrates, the body begins to use its own muscle and protein as a source of fuel, which can hinder wound healing.
- Zinc is needed for protein production, and demands for zinc increase during periods of healing.
- Vitamin A maintains healthy skin and immune health and promotes the formation of healthy scar tissue.
- Food sources of vitamin C play an important role in healing.

Effects of an unbalanced diet

The effects of an unbalanced diet include:

- malnutrition
- vitamin deficiency
- mineral deficiency
- nutrient excess.

Malnutrition

Unbalanced diets have a detrimental effect on our health. They can cause **malnutrition**, which means unbalanced or disordered eating.

> **Key term**
>
> **Malnutrition:** This can occur as a result of under- or over-eating over a long period of time, which can lead to illness or disease. This condition can often be undetected and so go untreated, which can cost the NHS millions of pounds.

Over-nutrition

This is more likely to happen in developed countries where there is over-consumption of fatty foods. **Over-nutrition** can result in the following conditions.

Coronary heart disease

Coronary heart disease describes what happens when someone's heart's blood supply is blocked, or interrupted, by a build-up of fatty substances in the coronary arteries. Over time, the walls of your arteries can become furred up with fatty deposits. This process is known as atherosclerosis and the fatty deposits are called atheroma. If the coronary arteries become narrow, due to a build-up of atheroma, the blood supply to the heart will be restricted. This can cause angina (chest pains).

> **Key term**
>
> **Coronary heart disease:** This is one of the UK's biggest killers and has caused over 94,000 deaths (nhs.co.uk) – just think how many deaths could be avoided by having a balanced diet, avoiding smoking and excessive drinking and including healthy choices like exercise.

Obesity

This means more than just a few extra pounds gained in weight. **Obesity** is the heavy accumulation of fat in the body, to such a degree that it greatly increases your risk of various diseases. It can damage your health and cause death from conditions such as heart disease and diabetes.

> **Key term**
>
> **Obesity:** Excess body fat that calculates to a BMI of over 30; this will then cause major health problems.

For medical purposes, the **body mass index** (BMI) is used to determine whether your weight is in the healthy range. Go to www.eatwell.gov. uk/healthissues/obesity/ to discover information about BMI and how to calculate it using a special formula and web calculator.

Type 2 diabetes

This occurs mainly in people who have had a poor diet over a long period of time. This poor diet includes excessive amounts of high sugar foods and drinks, processed foods and high fat foods. The pancreas is responsible for producing a hormone called insulin, which controls blood sugar, but over time this can become impaired because of this sort of diet and so stop working, or not work properly. When this happens a large amount of glucose will remain in the blood stream and will eventually damage blood vessels, nerves and organs.

Stroke

Fatty deposits can build up in arteries over time and sometimes a piece of this 'plaque' can break off and block a small artery in the brain; this blockage stops blood getting to that part of the brain and causes a stroke. Depending on where the blockage is will determine the severity of the stroke. This build-up of fatty deposits can be caused by a high fat diet (particularly cholesterol); a high salt diet, which raises the blood pressure; and high sugar intake, which can cause obesity. Other factors that may contribute to stroke include lack of exercise, smoking and high alcohol intake.

Under nutrition

This occurs mainly in underdeveloped countries. It results from too little dietary energy and proteins.

Low concentration span

There is some evidence that sugar, food additives and colourants affect children's concentration. Packaged foods and junk foods, which contain tartrazine and monosodium glutamate, may make children restless and unfocussed.

Importance of varied diet for vegetarians and vegans

Vegetarians do not eat meat, poultry, fish, shellfish or foods containing meat products. Vegans will not eat dairy products, eggs or any other food derived from animals. For good health, vegetarians and vegans should consider certain factors such as, for example, including good sources of protein, iron, and vitamin B12 in their diet.

Calcium from plant foods isn't so well absorbed. For vegans, calcium-fortified foods such as fortified soya milk may be useful.

Vitamin and mineral deficiency

Studied ☐

For information about vitamin deficiency see Table 6.02. For information about mineral deficiency see Table 6.03.

Nutrient excess

Studied ☐

Bacteria and food particles in the mouth build to form a sticky substance called 'plaque' if you do not brush your teeth. Over time, the acid in plaque begins to break down the surface of the tooth. Left untreated, the plaque can completely destroy the outside of the tooth and expose the nerves inside. Tooth decay is one of the most widespread health problems in this country.

Check your understanding

Select the correct answer for each question to complete the following five statements.

1. _____ is when insufficient insulin is produced by the pancreas.
   a Diabetes
   b Stroke
   c Heart attack
   d Angina

2. Concentration span can be improved by increased _____ in the diet.
   a Sugar
   b Fruit
   c Water
   d Milk

3. Lack of vitamin C can cause _____.
   a Anaemia
   b Scurvy
   c Rickets
   d Night blindness

4. Excessive saturated fats taken in the diet may lead to _____.
   a Coronary heart disease
   b Liver failure
   c Constipation
   d Nausea

5. Over-consumption of high energy foods and excessive weight gain according to BMI readings can cause _____.
   a Obesity
   b Tooth decay
   c Indigestion
   d High blood pressure

Key learning points

P2

Nutrients
Revised

These are beneficial chemicals which naturally occur in our diet and can be grouped in specific categories.

Balanced diet
Revised

A diet which contains a range of nutrients, which meets the needs of an individual in the correct proportions.

Recommended daily intakes
Revised

A set of guidelines produced by the government which suggests specific intakes which are required for good health.

Malnutrition
Revised

This is a diet which is poor and not balanced; it can be under-nutrition or over-nutrition, both will cause ill health.

Deficiency
Revised

This is a lack or shortage of a specific nutrient in the diet, which can in the long term cause health problems, for example, a diet short in iron may eventually cause anaemia.

M1

Assessment activity

Pass/Merit
Tested

Prepare a wall display for your classroom. Split into three groups:
Group 1 should prepare a poster that identifies using pictures and diagrams what makes up a healthy balanced diet.
Group 2 should prepare a poster that explains with pictures and diagrams the long-term effects of a balanced diet.
Group 3 should prepare a poster which explains with pictures and diagrams the long-term effects of an unbalanced diet.

D1

Learning Aim B

B.1 Factors influencing the diet of individuals and their associated dietary needs

Religion and culture

Culture and religion play a large part in food choices. Also, certain foods may be accepted by one member of the family and not by another, even if they share the same background, culture and religion.

The diets associated with different religions or cultures are shown in Table 6.04

Table 6.04 Diets associated with different religions or cultures

Religion or culture	Diet
Hindu	Diet should not include meat or fish. In some cases Hindus do not eat eggs. Cows are considered sacred, therefore Hindus do not eat beef. Also consumption of alcohol is forbidden.
Judaism	Jews should eat kosher food. So a devout Jew can only eat certain types of meat and fish. Meat must be prepared in a ritually acceptable manner. Meat and dairy products must not be eaten in the same meal and pork is forbidden.
Muslim/Islam	Meat that is eaten should be 'halal', which means that the animal's throat is cut and the blood is drained out, and then a prayer is offered to Allah. Animals that have died from natural causes should not be eaten. No alcohol.
Buddhist	Many Buddhists are vegetarian but it is not mandatory. They should not drink alcohol and avoid strong foods such as onions and garlic.

Moral reasons for diet

A vegan eats a mainly plant-based diet; so they will avoid foods like meat, milk, eggs and honey. Being a vegan will also mean avoiding other animal products in their lifestyle; for example, silk, wool and leather. A vegetarian will avoid meat products.

Environment

The environment relates to the country where you live. A developed country will have a wide variety of food and can import wider choices. A poor country may suffer from extremes of weather, so crops may be destroyed, or food may be of low quality or limited supply. Environment may relate to how close you live to shops or supermarkets. If you live in a rural area your choice of shopping may be limited, but you may also have a plentiful supply of fresh produce. If you live in an urban area your choice of food may be much wider. Environment is also to do with access and transport. Large supermarkets are usually on out-of-town sites and transport is needed to access them. Sometimes older or disabled people may be unable to get to them.

Socio-economic factors

This is a major factor that affects our dietary choices. Groups of people who have a very limited budget may have less choice in their diet. There is some evidence that different social classes may make different dietary choices. People from higher social classes may eat a healthier diet because they have been well educated and can afford better food, whereas people from a lower social class with less money may have a poorer diet.

People around you may influence your dietary choices. Children and young people are particularly influenced by their peers. Information in the media such as television adverts, magazine articles, leaflets, posters, soap operas on television, published research articles and news events all have an influence on our food choices, although we sometimes don't realise it. The position in the family may determine your dietary choices. The person who does the shopping is likely to make food choices.

Personal preferences

This is not just about taste and likes and dislikes but can also be linked to habits. For example, you may habitually not have breakfast. It may be difficult to change long-term habits.

Illness

Ill people often have a poor appetite or feel sick due to treatments and eat less than usual. If this reduced food intake is prolonged, it can cause weight loss, malnutrition and death. They should therefore be encouraged to adopt good eating habits, including high-protein and high-energy foods in the diet in order to gain weight and an improved nutritional status.

Underlying health conditions

An underlying health condition may mean that an individual has specific nutritional needs. See Table 6.05 in B3 for examples.

Check your understanding

Select the correct answer from the list to complete the following statements.

1. Vegans do not eat any _____
2. Crohn's disease may be made worse with _____
3. A Muslim diet should contain _____
4. Lactose intolerance means avoiding _____
5. Judaism says you cannot mix _____
6. To avoid tooth decay children should not have _____

a. Halal meat
b. meat and dairy
c. spices foods
d. sweets and fizzy drinks
e. animal products
f. dairy products

B.2 Nutritional variations during life stage development

An individual's needs for nutrition will change over their lifespan for many reasons. Increased nutrients are required during growth periods in particular; as growth slows down so does the need for certain nutrients.

Infancy 0–2

Newborn babies

Newborn babies are unique in that they can rely on a single food, milk, in order to meet all their nutritional needs. Breast milk is ideal for many reasons:

- It contains all nutrients in the correct amounts.
- It contains antibodies that protect the newborn baby against diseases in the first few months of life.
- It is clean.
- It is in correct proportions and readily available.
- It does not cause allergies.

6–12 months

When the baby is introduced to solid foods the process is called **weaning**. This can be started at around 6 months of age so that damage to the young kidney, as well as obesity and allergies, is avoided. Research has proved that babies only require breast or formula milk up until this time.

Figure 6.07 Weaning

> **Key term**
>
> **Weaning:** The Department of Health recommends weaning from 6 months, but as each baby is different some babies may need weaning earlier than others. However, weaning should not take place before 17 weeks.

12–18 months

At 12–18 months toddlers can be given cow's milk (full-fat milk) and they should be eating quite a varied diet. They will be drinking less milk, as they start to eat more solid foods with the rest of the family. Skimmed milk should be given only after the age of five. Up to the age of three the diet should include iron-rich foods. Children who are weaning are also starting to move around and use more energy, so their diet should contain enough carbohydrates, which provide a good source of energy for crawling and toddling youngsters.

Early childhood 3–8 years

At this age children are actively exploring and also beginning their education, so their diet should reflect their growing needs. Their energy requirements will be high, but only in relation to their body size. This is a very important time for children's nutrition. By encouraging healthy meals, snacks and drinks we can help children to establish good eating habits for the future. Sweets, fizzy drinks and fatty and sugary foods should generally be avoided, as they can cause a range of health problems including obesity, but they can be given occasionally as treats.

Adolescence 9–18 years

Adolescents grow rapidly in weight and height, and many physical changes are taking place, both internally and externally. These changes all require energy so an adolescent's appetite can be large, but their diet should still be well balanced.

Early to middle adulthood 19–65 years

Adults need to maintain a healthy, well-balanced diet. Adults' nutritional requirements reduce with age as they become less physically active. They should still be advised to take regular physical exercise. Adults should also be advised about the safe intake of alcohol per week (14 units for women, 21 units for men).

Pregnancy and breastfeeding

Studied ☐

In teenage pregnancy, girls are more likely to suffer with nutrient deficiencies as their bodies are still growing and developing, so they should eat extra nutrients to help the foetus grow and provide breast milk. During adult pregnancy and breastfeeding a woman's nutritional needs increase slightly, for the development of the foetus and the placenta and the production of breast milk. The saying 'eating for two' is well known, but is not entirely accurate. Rather than eating a lot more food, women should ensure that their diet is nutritious and well balanced. When planning to get pregnant and during early pregnancy, women are advised to take extra folic acid in the diet or in tablet form. Folic acid has been proven to lower the risk of spina bifida in the foetus. Generally, if the mother and family have good dietary habits they will be able to pass them on to their growing children.

Later adulthood 65+years

As we age we become less mobile, so our energy requirements decrease slightly. Although they do not need a lot of food, older people still need good sources of protein, vitamins and minerals. Gentle exercise should also be promoted to help with their physical, mental and social well-being.

Check your understanding

Complete each of the following statements by selecting one of the items (a-g) listed below.

1. Pregnant women should supplement their diet with _____ to prevent spina bifida.
2. The recommended alcohol intake per week for men is _____.
3. The recommended intake of salt per day should not exceed _____.
4. Older people are more at risk of _____.
5. Children should be encouraged to drink water and not sugary drinks to avoid _____.
6. The process when a baby is moved from a liquid diet to a more solid diet is called _____.
7. Pregnant women should avoid _____ in their diet as it may harm the unborn child.

a. malnutrition
b. unpasteurised dairy products
c. 21 units
d. folic acid
e. tooth decay
f. 6 grams
g. weaning

B.3 Considerations for nutritional planning

With the information discussed in Section B.1 and given in Tables 6.05 and 6.06 it is possible to appreciate how important specific dietary needs are, along with life stage variations; all these factors should be considered when planning for individual dietary requirements.

Table 6.05 Specific diets required for underlying health conditions

Underlying health condition	Diet required
Food allergies An allergy is a reaction of the body to an allergen. These can include insect bites, drugs and some foods, such as nuts, fruits, dairy products and wheat.	Avoid the known allergen. Always check labels on packaging.
Lactose intolerance Lactose is a sugar that is present in dairy products. Intolerance means some people are unable to accept this sugar in their diet. It causes stomach cramps and diarrhoea.	Dairy products should be replaced with soya-based foods, e.g. soya milk.
Gluten/wheat allergy (coeliac disease) Gluten is present in wheat, barley and oats. An allergy to gluten affects the digestive system and correct absorption of nutrients does not take place.	Foods that contain wheat, barley and oats should be replaced with gluten-free products.
Type 2 diabetes Constant high sugar levels cause the production of insulin to be affected.	Low glucose intake. The diet should contain carbohydrate foods that are low-glycaemic, which means glucose is realised from the foods gradually to maintain a constant energy level.
Irritable Bowel Syndrome Can be caused by overactivity in the gut, which causes constipation and diarrhoea. Situations of stress can make this condition worse.	Eat regular meals. Don't skip meals or eat late at night. Don't eat too quickly, take your time. Sit down to eat and chew your food well. Take regular exercise. Make time to relax. Some research recommends a high-fibre diet, which maintains regular bowel movements.
Crohn's Disease No known cause for this disorder but it may be genetic and made worse by smoking, long-term antibiotics, and previous infections of the gut.	Certain foods, such as dairy products, fatty foods and spicy foods can worsen symptoms in some people. Therefore, eliminating them from the diet may help.

Table 6.06 Dietary suggestions for individuals at various life stages

Life stage	Dietary suggestions
Preconception and pregnancy	• Before pregnancy, the couple should both be in the best health possible, considering their diet and alcohol intake. High levels of alcohol can affect sperm production and in pregnancy can affect the child intellectually and physically. • The woman should include folic acid in her balanced diet, which will help with the development of the spinal cord in the baby. • During pregnancy, protein is essential for new growth. Foods that may contain bacteria should be avoided, for example unpasteurised milk and cheese and uncooked eggs.
Baby	• Up until around 6 months old the baby should be totally breastfed or given formula feed, depending on the choice of the parents. • Weaning onto solid foods is not recommended until after six months. The food should have a variety of tastes and be introduced in a smooth consistency, gradually getting lumpier so the baby can learn to chew.
Child	• At this stage, the diet should be high in protein as the child is growing rapidly. • Carbohydrates are required for energy, as the child is becoming more mobile and learning new skills. • Calcium and vitamin D are required for bone and tooth development.
Adolescent	• Girls reaching puberty need a diet high in iron. All adolescents require enough protein in their diets as growth spurts are common at this life stage. • Peer pressure may lead to eating 'junk' foods, which can lead to obesity and tooth decay. Education is required about the benefits of a balanced diet and the dangers of excessive alcohol intake.
Adult	• Adults should have good knowledge about a balanced diet. • Later in adulthood the metabolism slows down so portion sizes should be adjusted. Diets should contain enough iron.
Older person	• In this life stage, activity often slows down so the diet should be lower in fats and contain more protein to help with repair of cells particularly in times of illness. The diet should contain calcium to help maintain bone density. • Portion sizes should also be reduced as the person is less active.

Key learning points

Religion

P3
P4

Revised

A particular faith which is followed by a set of individuals and can mean that strict rules are applied to areas of diet, for example some foods are not allowed. Festivals are celebrated which may include 'fasting periods' in which individuals cannot eat at certain times.

Culture

Revised

This means that certain ways of life and traditions give individuals a shared identity. This can mean food preparation and cooking are done in particular ways, for example being a vegan.

Environment

Revised

Environment relates to your living surroundings, either immediate or globally. So the fact you have to travel to a supermarket may affect your food choices as do extremely dry climates which may ruin crops.

Socioeconomic

Revised

This relates to financial and social circumstances which can affect your diet, for example income and job status can affect dietary choices.

Assessment activity

M2
M3
D2

Pass /Merit

Tested

In a care home you have to care for various individual nutritional needs. These need to be documented for the service user's relatives. Using the two examples of service users below, create a brief case study for each of the service users.

1   A Muslim man
2   A woman who is lactose intolerant.

For each case study give details of the two individuals' specific dietary needs with a recommended daily menu.

Merit

Tested

Consider each of the above menus and compare them. Say what differences there are in the specific needs and also state what similarities there are in each diet plan.

Model assignment

This assignment will assess the following learning aims:

A explore the effects of balanced and unbalanced diets on the health and wellbeing of individuals

B understand the specific nutritional needs and preferences of individuals.

Scenario

As a health and social care student one of your work experience settings is in a health centre.

The manager has asked you to produce an information booklet about 'nutritional needs'. It should contain pictures, diagrams and descriptions which will give guidance to all service users who visit the centre.

- The information should describe the components of a balanced diet; this will include all the essential nutrients, giving their source, function and effects. (See Topic A1 for help.)
- Include information which describes the effect of an unbalanced diet on the health and well-being of individuals. For example, excessive amounts of high-fat foods may cause coronary heart disease; a lack of vitamin D from not eating sufficient dairy products may cause rickets or brittle bones. (See Topic A.2 for help.)
- Choose two individuals who may visit the centre frequently (children, the elderly) and compare the effects of balanced and unbalanced diets. (Compare means to look at the similarities and differences between the effects of the two diets.)
- As a conclusion to your booklet, assess the long-term effects of a balanced and unbalanced diet on the health and well-being of individuals in general. For example, a balanced diet will aid with faster healing properties and an unbalanced diet over a long time may cause anaemia, tooth decay or diabetes.

Case studies

Read the following case studies. Choose two individuals who you would like to continue writing about.

Case study 1

Ronnie is 78 years old and has just returned home after recovering from a stroke, which has left him with a weakness down the right side of his body. He lives alone in a bungalow, which is close to local amenities and some close relatives. He prefers eating small meals, as his appetite is not what it used to be.

Case study 2

Adam is 18 years old and is just about to start university, living away from home for the first time. He has been diabetic since the age of 10. He is studying a sport science degree and has secured a part-time job in a local gym. Adam is very partial to the menu from his local takeaway pizza outlet.

Case study 3

Rosie is 4 years old and has just started in reception at the local primary school. Her parents have chosen that she takes packed lunches with her, as she has lactose intolerance and they would like to be sure of her dietary intake.

Case study 4

Salem runs his own business; he is 35 years old and has an extremely active and busy lifestyle, where his mealtimes can occasionally be very erratic. He is a Muslim and follows religious festivals and a strict Muslim (Islamic) diet.

(Use Topic B1 and B2 for help.)

Section 1

Using two of these case studies as a starting point:
- Describe the specific dietary needs of the two individuals.
- Explain the factors which influence their dietary choices. For example, it could be religion, health condition, environment, which affects their choices.
- Discuss (give more details) why these factors affect diet choices for these two individuals.

(Use topic B3 for help.)

Section 2

You need to prepare a nutritional plan for each individual. The plan should include the following:

- breakfast and a drink
- mid-morning snack and a drink
- midday meal and a drink
- mid-afternoon snack and a drink
- evening meal and a drink.

When planning your menu, remember your client's personal needs and preferences, his or her life stage, and ability to follow the plan. Make sure that your menu is appropriate.

Following the two plans, include a piece of writing that compares the plans for your two chosen individuals. Consider their life stages and specific needs.

Unit 7

Equality and Diversity in Health and Social Care

This unit gives an overview of how we deliver care in a way that is fair and equal to all. It looks at why non-discriminatory practice is important and how we can adapt the service to meet the needs of individuals. It explores how we practice health and social care in order to meet the different health and social care needs of individuals in our very varied society.

Learning Aims

By the end of this unit you will:

✓ understand the importance of non-discriminatory practice in health and social care.

✓ explore how health and social care practices can promote equality and diversity.

Assessment criteria

Level 2 Pass	Level 2 Merit	Level 2 Distinction
Learning aim A understand the importance of non-discriminatory practice in health and social care		
2A.P1 Describe non-discriminatory and discriminatory practice in health and social care, using examples. **2A.P2** Describe how codes of practice and legislation promote non-discriminatory practice in health and social care.	**2A.M1** Explain the importance of legislation and codes of practice in promoting non-discriminatory practice in health and social care, using examples.	**2A.D1** Assess the impact of discriminatory practice for health and social care workers, with reference to selected examples.
Learning aim B: explore how health and social care practices can promote equality and diversity		
2B.P3 Describe the different needs of service users in health and social care, with reference to examples.		
2B.P4 Describe how health and social care provision can be adapted to meet the diverse needs of different individuals, with reference to examples.	**2B.M2** Explain the benefits of adapting health and social care provision to meet the diverse needs of different individuals, with reference to two selected examples.	**2B.D2** Assess the effectiveness of health and social care provision for different individuals with diverse needs, with reference to two selected examples.

Non-discriminatory practice

In this section we look at what it means to have non-discriminatory practice. Some of the words used in this unit can be complicated. Let's try to unpack some of the jargon.

Non-discriminatory practice means:

● not treating individuals or groups less fairly than others
● valuing diversity
● adapting care to meet diverse needs.

Treating people fairly, using non-discriminatory practice is especially important in health and social care. Most people would like to think that they are being treated equally when it comes to care.

Valuing diversity, appreciating differences, is one way we have non-discriminatory practice. Health advice should be available for all, whatever gender or culture a person is.

Adapting care to meet diverse needs is another way we have non-discriminatory practice. A dietician should be able to help a diabetic person plan a diet whether they are vegetarian, or meat eater. The person should not have to change their beliefs to get health care.

Examples of discrimination in health and social care

The following examples of discrimination in health and social care show what NOT to do. They include:

● Prejudice or 'prejudging' someone: an 80-year-old lady wishes to donate a kidney but her donation is refused because she is too old. She is pre-judged, discriminated against because of her age.
● Stereotyping: this is having a fixed generalised belief about a group of people. Often this is a negative view; for example, a belief that only teenagers sleep around so health campaigns about sexually transmitted infections are aimed only at them.
● Labelling, or seeing just one aspect and putting someone in a category, happens in health care. Smokers are seen as a problem and offered ways to stop smoking. People with partial sight are labelled as visually impaired and may be offered the same care as someone with no sight.

- Refusing medical treatment is discrimination but it happens. Older people may face this discrimination. A 78-year-old man diagnosed with bladder cancer was told that nothing could be done as he was too old. His family paid for a second opinion; he was treated and now is cured. See www.dailymail.co.uk/health/article-2126379/Sentenced-death-old-The-NHS-denies-life-saving-treatment-elderly-mans-chilling-story-reveals.html
- Offering inappropriate treatment or care is discriminatory practice. People with dementia require specialist care, yet often they are placed in a residential care home where workers do not understand how to care for them.
- Giving less time when caring for an individual than needed discriminates against them. Often cuts are made to staffing on elderly care wards. One nurse wrote that on a 32-bed ward with patients who wet the beds, there was only one nurse and one care assistant, so they could not give each person the time needed to care for them properly. See www.guardian.co.uk/commentisfree/2012/jan/09/nhs-reforms-nurses-time-care.

Those examples of poor practice, unfortunately, do happen. Let's look now at how care should be done using non-discriminatory practice.

Examples of non-discriminatory practice in health and social care

Examples of non-discriminatory practice in health and social care are easy to find. They include:

- providing appropriate health and social care to meet the needs of individuals
- adapting care to meet the diverse needs of different individuals
- providing equality of access to health and social care services.

These are met by the personalisation of care, especially in the area of learning disabilities. Personalisation of social care puts the individual at the centre of the assessment process, so they can say what they need and make their own choices. This is done through:

- person-centred planning
- supporting people towards independent living
- direct payments to the individual, so they can employ their own personal assistant. In 2010 the Care Quality Commission reported that 115,000 people used direct payments.

Figure 7.01 Personalisation helps to meet the needs of a diverse group of individuals

Personalisation in residential care is moving towards meeting the diverse needs of individuals. Anchor Homes have introduced a system whereby residents decide what they want to eat just before they eat, instead of a day ahead. Chefs gather feedback from residents on what they would like on the menu.

User groups such as the Essex Coalition of Disabled People (www.ecdp. org.uk) provide information about what services are available and work to influence developments so that people with disabilities have equal access to services.

(*Source*: www.scie.org.uk/publications/reports/report20.pdf)

Personalisation is being implemented in social care, mental health and the area of learning disabilities, and to a certain extent in children's nursing; however, in adult health care progress is slower.

Check your understanding

Complete the following text by selecting the correct words from the list below.

Discrimination is selective and means one thing or person is preferred above another. In health and social care we use _____ practice. This means we treat people equally according to their needs. The other sort of practice is called _____. This is where prejudice and labelling happen.

An example of _____ practice is adapting care to meet the needs of individuals, for example, providing a ramp so that wheelchair users can get into a building.

An example of _____ practice is not providing the right medicine because it is expensive.

discriminatory   non-discriminatory

non-discriminatory   discrimination

A.2 Impact of discriminatory and non-discriminatory practice in health and social care

Effects of discrimination on service users

The effects of discrimination on service users include:

- loss of self-esteem
- stress
- reluctance to seek support and treatment
- longer waiting times for some groups.

A 70-year-old person who is told they are too old to be treated will experience stress and a loss of self-esteem. A person who is obese will be reluctant to seek medical help for other problems because she knows the first thing she will be told is to lose weight. As a result of cuts to healthcare funding, waiting times for operations have lengthened. According to a report by the Patient's Association, knee and hip surgery waiting times have increased across the country.

(*Source*: www.patients-association.com)

Simon, a 50-year-old sports teacher, is waiting for a hip replacement. Because of the pain, he has to have a lot of time off work, and is at risk of losing his job. The waiting list in his area is more than 18 weeks and the thought of spending so much time in pain is stressful. He is depressed at the thought of becoming unemployed.

Most people needing this type of surgery are middle aged or elderly. The impact on waiting times for different groups is great. It implies that their health is less important.

Effects of non-discriminatory practice for individuals

Non-discriminatory practice that meets the diverse needs of individuals is enabling. Care that is tailored to the needs of an individual will help them stay healthy and active.

James has cerebral palsy and uses a wheelchair. He employs a personal assistant to help him dress and shower in the morning so that he can get to his part-time job as a receptionist at a local hotel. His care package, planned by him with support from the social worker, enables him to be an active member of society.

UNIT 7 Equality and Diversity in Health and Social Care

159

Legal and workplace requirements

Legal and workplace requirements are important. Laws such as the Equality Act 2010 bring together previous laws on equality and tell us what we can and cannot do. The Equality Act 2010 protects people from discrimination, harassment and victimisation on the grounds of:

- age
- disability
- gender reassignment
- marriage and civil partnership
- pregnancy and maternity
- race
- religion or belief
- sex
- sexual orientation.

Employers cannot discriminate against people on these grounds when employing people such as care workers. It also places a duty on employers to make reasonable adjustments to help the person do the job. The law is meant to increase equality of opportunity for those in protected characteristics. If an employer breaks this law they can be called before a tribunal, or in some cases taken to court.

Workplace and national codes of practice on non-discriminatory practice

The following codes of conduct further support equality.

- The General Social Care Council publishes a code of conduct for employers of social care workers and one for social care workers too.
- The Nursing and Midwifery Council (NMC) has a code of conduct for professionals. Each code promotes equal opportunities.

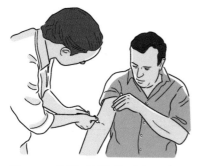

Figures 7.02–7.03 Social workers and nurses work to a code of conduct

The Social Care code promotes equal opportunities for service users and for workers. The employer's code says they must provide equal opportunity policies and procedures for service users and for staff. A social care worker who ignores this may be reported to the council, a social worker may be removed from the register, and an employer ignoring the code may face sanctions.

The NMC disciplinary process is similar, with a regulatory body that holds conduct hearings. A nurse or midwife who is shown to be discriminatory may lose their registration.

Supporting non-discriminatory practice

Legislation and codes of practice protect both carer and service user by making it a duty to be non-discriminatory. The legal framework:

- protects carers and service users
- enforces non-discriminatory practices
- enforces employer and employee responsibilities and ensures that people who break the law face losing their registration
- ensures safeguarding.

Policies and procedures in the workplace also help workers to be non-discriminatory. If a care worker does discriminate, there is a complaints process and the care worker can be reported to their professional body. Employers and employees each have a responsibility in this area – the employer must provide guidance and the employee must follow it and their professional code. Social workers, nurses and doctors can be reported to their regulatory body. If a conduct hearing finds them guilty, they may be de-registered, which means they can no longer work in that profession.

Check your understanding

Match the key words to their explanation:

Key words

1. Non-discrimination
2. Valuing diversity
3. Stereotyping
4. Personalisation of social care
5. The effects of discrimination
6. The Equality Act 2010
7. Protected characteristics are
8. Codes of conduct

Explanation

a. Puts the individual at the centre of the assessment process so they can say what they need and make their own choices

b. Having a fixed generalised belief about a group of people

c. Being fair

d. Age, disability, gender reassignment, Marriage and civil partnership, pregnancy and maternity, race, religion or belief, sex, sexual orientation

e. Appreciating differences

f. Loss of self-esteem, stress, and reluctance to seek support and treatment

g. Are issued by professional regulating bodies

h. Protects people from discrimination, harassment and victimisation

Non-discriminatory practice

Revised ☐

This means being fair.

Valuing diversity

Revised ☐

This means appreciating differences.

Discrimination in health and social care

Revised ☐

This may involve prejudice, stereotyping and labelling, refusal of treatment or inappropriate treatment.

The effects of discrimination

Revised ☐

The effects of discrimination include loss of self-esteem, stress, and reluctance to seek support and treatment.

Personalisation

Revised ☐

This may include person-centred planning, independent living and direct payments.

The Equality Act 2010

Revised ☐

The Equality Act 2010 makes it illegal to discriminate against protected groups.

Codes of practice and conduct

Revised ☐

Codes of practice and conduct help professionals to avoid discrimination.

Assessment activity

Pass

Tested

Make a booklet for service users, in which you describe discriminatory practices. Give examples of discriminatory practice in treating individuals or groups less fairly than others, not valuing diversity, and not adapting care to meet diverse needs.

Use the planner shown below to help you. For each example, say what should be done to make practice non-discriminatory.

Discriminatory practice	E.g. treating individuals or groups less fairly than others	E.g. not valuing diversity	E.g. not adapting care to meet diverse needs
	Offering one person in a care home more drinks than the others get		
What should be done (non-discriminatory practice)			

In your booklet, describe at least two codes of practice and one law that promote non-discriminatory practice in health and social care.

Merit

Tested

Explain the importance of non-discriminatory practice to health and social care workers, with reference to at least two relevant examples.

Distinction

Tested

Use two examples to provide an assessment of the impact of discriminatory practice for health and social care workers.

Learning Aim B

B.1 Factors that may affect the care needs of individuals

Meeting the different care needs of individuals

In this section we look at what may influence the care needs of individuals and how we can adapt services to meet their different needs.

The following factors may affect care needs.

Gender

Studied ☐

A person's gender may affect their care needs. They may prefer a same sex ward. For example, Mrs X is admitted to a medical ward and is put in a room with three male patients. Mixed sex wards can cause stress for patients.

Sexual orientation

Studied ☐

An individual's sexual orientation may affect their care needs. John Smith and his partner Jason have been in a relationship for many years. When John has a heart attack, only next of kin are allowed to visit, but as the hospital policy is to respect sexual orientation Jason is allowed to visit. This helps John to relax and he makes a speedier recovery.

Gender reassignment

Studied ☐

Toni has decided after counselling to change gender and become female. The nurse admitting Toni asks how she would like to be addressed. Using the correct form of address and respecting Toni's gender will positively influence care and recovery.

Age

Studied ☐

Age is a factor that affects care. Evelina Children's Hospital was designed with the input of children. It is bright and colourful with play areas and lots of things for children to do. Even the window cleaners are dressed as superheroes! This helps children to be less stressed. Older patients in hospital may prefer a more formal approach to care, being addressed as Mr or Mrs, but it is important to ask the individual what they prefer. Age affects care needs.

Figure 7.04 Helping children in hospital to be less stressed

Disability

Studied ☐

Disability may affect care needs. A person with learning disabilities may not clearly understand and may need their care to be explained in a simpler way. Someone with visual impairment may have difficulty finding out what services are available at their medical centre. Equality of access to services may be affected by disability.

Marriage and civil partnership

Studied ☐

Marriage and civil partnership can affect care needs. We already saw that John Smith was shown respect for his wishes by having his partner visit and this improved his chances of recovery. Sometimes people do not want the involvement of partners or family in their care. Their wishes must be respected.

Pregnancy and maternity

Studied ☐

During pregnancy women are given a choice of birthing plan, including the type of delivery they would like, whether a home birth or hospital birth. They can choose who will be their birthing partner. During antenatal care they are offered advice about breastfeeding. These factors affect how a woman copes with pregnancy and giving birth.

Race

Studied ☐

Race is a factor which should not affect access to services. Regardless of ethnic or national origins, people should be cared for according to their needs. According to a parliamentary report, research shows that black and minority ethnic groups generally have worse health than other ethnic groups, despite several attempts to change this.

(*Source*: www.parliament.uk/documents/post/postpn276.pdf)

P3

P4

M2

D2

Religion and belief may affect the care needs of individuals.

Religious groups

Jehovah's Witnesses do not accept blood transfusions, and this will affect the care they receive if they need surgery, as the surgeon may not be able to do the operation without a transfusion. This can be an issue when Jehovah's Witnesses refuse a transfusion for their children.

Festivals and holy days are often decided by the lunar calendar. Both the dates of the Christian festival of Easter and the Muslim festival of Eid are decided that way. The Jewish Passover requires special food, which is eaten in a specific order and symbolises different things. Relatives may ask if they can bring in food for the person so they can share the festival ceremony. In some care settings this may not be a problem, but if a person is in hospital prepared for theatre this may be a problem.

Muslims fast during the month of Ramadan. This means they do not eat or drink anything between sunrise and sunset. This may affect the care they need especially if they are diabetic, as they will need to adjust their insulin and eating times to after sunset. Neither Jews nor Muslims eat pork, and both require that any meat should be killed in a special way. Jews call this Kosher and Muslims call this Halal. If meat killed in this way is not available, both Jews and Muslims will require vegetarian food. Hinduism is closely linked with Jainism, Buddhism and Sikhism. Most Hindus are vegetarian and even those who eat meat will not eat beef. Some Buddhists and some Sikhs are vegetarian too.

Forms of worship vary. In many religions, praying together brings a community together, but people do not have to attend a place of worship in order to pray.

Strict Muslims pray five times a day facing Mecca. Jews pray three times a day. Many Hindus have a small shrine at home where they pray and offer a flower to the deity. Buddhists may use meditation, and many secular people who do not have a religion use meditation to help them cope with illness. Usually, care needs are met in hospital by providing a quiet room where people of all religions or no religion can find peace.

Many religions require a modest form of dress that does not expose the body. This should be remembered, for example, when people are undergoing a procedure and required to wear a hospital gown that opens down the back. Even people who hold secular or non-religious beliefs feel uncomfortable if they are unduly exposed. It is better to offer everyone a larger robe that wraps around and covers them decently.

Symbols such as a cross or crescent or Star of David may help religious people cope with illness. A patient in hospital, or a resident in a care home, may like to keep a copy of the Bible with them if they are Christian, or a copy of the Koran if they are Muslim. Each religion has its own religious texts that bring peace of mind to its believers. It is important to respect the care needs of individuals in this and not to impose other religious beliefs on people. The end of life is a time when people often turn to religion. Christians, Muslims, Jews, Hindus and Buddhists are taught that there is life after death, and this may bring comfort when they are at the end of life. They may wish to visit their place of worship or have a person visit them. Many Catholics would like to make a confession before they die. It is very important to find out what the person wants and not make assumptions. Just because a person is Catholic, it does not mean they wish to talk to a priest.

Secular groups

Secular beliefs must be respected. An atheist who does not believe in God, or a humanist who aims to make the best of life whether there is a God or not, may wish to talk to a religious person such as a priest when facing the end of life. The important thing is to ask the person you are caring for what their religious needs are, and not make assumptions.

Social class

`Studied`

Social class affects whether people access health care. A professional person is more likely to have better housing, a better diet and therefore better health. They also know how to get services. People in social classes associated with manual labour, or those unemployed, are more likely to suffer from cancer, heart disease and breathing problems, often linked to poor diet and housing. They are also more likely to suffer from violence and their children are more likely to have accidents than those of the professional classes.

The homeless have least access to health care because you need an address to register with a GP. Most homeless people do not get health care until they attend a hospital emergency department. Primary care is developing to try to make sure more people can get health care through walk-in centres.

Family structure

`Studied`

Family structure impacts on access to care. A single parent may have little money so cannot afford to have dental treatment or eye tests for themselves, as these are not free. Health needs are greater for children and the elderly, especially those living alone, but they do not necessarily access services. Sure Start centres have been effective in improving access to health and care services for children and families, especially in disadvantaged areas where there are more unskilled and unemployed people.

Geographical location

Geographical location, or where you live, impacts on access to health and social care services. In rural areas, people may travel many miles to a hospital but those living in a city may have several nearby. In the city, people have a wider choice of doctors, dentists and other services.

Check your understanding

Select the missing words from the list below to fill in the blanks in the following statements.

1. A 23-year-old male has to share a hospital room with three young women. They are all embarrassed. This is an example of how _____ affects care needs.

2. Mrs J. is a resident in Poppydene Care Home. She likes to go out with her daughter once a week for lunch. This is an example of how_____ affects care needs.

3. Mrs X lives in a small village 20 miles from the nearest hospital. She has a sick baby and it takes the ambulance half an hour to get the baby to hospital. Her sister lives in a city where there is a children's hospital. It takes an ambulance 10 minutes to get her sick child to hospital. This is an example of how _____ affects access to care.

Missing words

a. geographical location

b. gender

c. family structure

B.2 How adapting services to meet the diverse needs of service users promotes equality and diversity in health and social care

Adapting services to meet needs of service users

In this section we shall look at adapting services to meet individual needs, linking them to the factors given in B1, which are:

- Gender
- Sexual orientation
- Gender reassignment
- Age
- Disability
- Marriage and civil partnerships
- Pregnancy and maternity
- Race
- Religion and belief
- Social class
- Family structure
- Geographical location.

Adapting services to meet diverse needs

Studied ▢

We have already seen some ways that services are adapted to meet the differing needs of service users; for example in making Evelina Children's Hospital a place where children can have fun. Here are a few more examples of how we adapt services to meet differing needs and promote equality in care.

Sonali Gardens Day Centre offers person-centred care for Bangladeshi and other communities in Tower Hamlets and is a model of good practice. The staff speak English and Bengali. There are purpose-built prayer rooms and a door-to-door minibus service brings people in to the centre to have chiropody and exercise classes. It also takes them on a weekly shopping trip.

Figure 7.05 Sonali Gardens Day Centre

http://sthildas.org.uk/projects/sonali-gardens-day-centre/

Here we see access to services, provision of support, provision of dietary requirements, provision of personal care, provision of prayer facilities, access to washing and toilet facilities, observing religious rituals, and a person-centred approach.

Many care providers now offer person-centred care. Sunrise Senior Living provides a range of care based on individual needs. Couples can move into care together, or friends can share rooms. Residents can have pets and bring some of their own furniture. Anchor Housing provides a range of support from care in the person's own home to full 24-hour dementia care. Retirement villages offer differing levels of support according to need, from restaurants and hairdressing to help with personal care.

Benefits to service users

Studied

The benefits to service users of personalised care are immense. Many older people living in retirement villages remain active and are part of a social community. Maintaining their dignity and privacy and feeling safe, results in an improved quality of care and a better quality of life for older people, enabling them to contribute to society.

Check your understanding

Match the start with the correct sentence ending:

1. Adapting services to meet the diverse needs of service users _____
2. Factors that may affect the care needs of individuals include: _____
3. The effect of adapting services is _____
4. Sonali Gardens Day Centre _____
5. Evelina Children's Hospital _____
6. Sure Start _____

Sentence endings

a. gender, sexual orientation, gender reassignment, age, disability, marriage and civil partnership, pregnancy and maternity, race, religion and belief, social class, family structure and geographical location.

b. better quality of life for people.

c. promotes equality and diversity in health and social care.

d. is an example of effectively promoting equality and diversity in health care for children of different ages and races.

e. is an example of effectively promoting equality and diversity in social care for people of different races, religions and beliefs.

f. is an example of effectively promoting equality and diversity for families from less advantaged social classes.

Real life connection

NHS clerk

Clerks work in a variety of places such as hospital wards or departments, health centres and clinics, trust headquarters and even central stores.

They perform a range of duties, including booking patients in for appointments, keeping patients records, filing, dealing with telephone calls and helping to cover a reception desk/area.

In some posts typing and word processing skills may be a significant part of the job role. Other clerical staff may work as admissions clerk/clerical officer, ward clerk/clerical officer or as a clerk/clerical officer in a specific section, such as a health records department.

The skills you will need include using computer programmes, using the telephone, and being happy to deal with people.

Most employing authorities require a good all-round education and administration experience. Clerk/typist posts will usually require a typing or word processing qualification.

Key learning points

Equality and diversity

Revised

Health and social care practices can promote equality and diversity.

Factors affecting individual care needs

Revised

An individual's care needs may be affected by their gender, sexual orientation, age, ability, marital status, race, religion and belief, social class, family structure and geographical location.

Adapting services to meet individual needs

Revised

Adapting services to meet individual needs promotes equality and diversity in health and social care.

Adapting services benefits service users through improved quality of personalised care.

Assessment activity

Role play

Scenario: two individuals with differing needs such as disability or religious beliefs are thinking of coming to stay at Poppydene Care Home, where you are the deputy manager.

Pass

Tested

Prepare a leaflet showing how care will be adapted to meet their needs.

Merit

Tested

During each interview, you will talk through the content of the leaflet with the prospective resident and answer any questions they may have. (Observation records of this may provide evidence for the unit.)

Distinction

Tested

Make notes in which you assess the effectiveness of health and social provision for individuals with the diverse needs listed in key learning points. Make a judgement as to whether it was appropriate and sufficient overall.

References

www.guardian.co.uk/commentisfree/2012/jan/09/nhs-reforms-nurses-time-care

www.guysandstthomas.nhs.uk/our-services/childrens/childrens-services.aspx

Model assignment

This assignment will assess the following learning aims:

A   understand the importance of non-discriminatory practice in health and social care
B   explore how health and social care practices can promote equality and diversity.

Scenario

You have been asked to produce a booklet for new staff at Poppydene Care Home to help them understand the importance of non-discriminatory practice and how codes of practice and legislation improve health and social care practice.

Section one

The importance of non-discriminatory practice in health and social care

Give examples of non-discriminatory and discriminatory practice in health and social care.

Describe how codes of practice and legislation promote non-discriminatory practice in health and social care.

Use examples to explain the importance of legislation and codes of practice in promoting non-discriminatory practice in health and social care.

Use examples and assess the impact of discriminatory practice for care workers.

Section two

Explore how health and social care practices can promote equality and diversity

Use three short case studies and describe the different needs of service users in health and social care.

Use these same case studies and describe how health and social care provision can be adapted to meet the diverse needs of individuals

Explain the benefits of adapting health and social care provision to meet the diverse needs of two individuals, and assess the effectiveness of this provision for them.

Unit 8

Individual Rights in Health and Social Care

This chapter looks at the rights of individuals when using health and social care services and the responsibilities of employers and employees to uphold these rights. It also considers how these responsibilities impact on the rights of individual users.

Learning aims

In this unit you will:

✓ investigate the rights of individuals using health and social care services.

✓ examine the responsibilities of employers and employees in upholding service users' rights in health and social care.

Assessment criteria

Level 2 Pass	Level 2 Merit	Level 2 Distinction
Learning aim A: Investigate the rights of individuals using health and social care services		
2A.P1 Summarise the individual rights of service users in health and social care.	**2A.M1** Explain ways in which service users' individual rights can be upheld in health and social care, using selected examples.	**2A.D1** Assess the benefits and potential difficulties of upholding service users' rights in health and social care, using selected examples.
2A.P2 Describe how current and relevant legislation protects the rights of service users, using examples.		
Learning aim B: Examine the responsibilities of employers and employees in upholding service users' rights in health and social care		
2B.P3 Describe how an employee can plan to maximise the safety of service users.	**2B.M2** Explain why risk assessment is important in health and social care.	**2B.D2** Evaluate the importance of the use of risk assessments in health and social care, using selected examples.
2B.P4 Describe how the right to confidentiality is protected in health and social care.	**2B.M3** Explain why the right to confidentiality is protected in health and social care, using examples.	**2B.D3** Justify occasions where there is a need for an employee to breach confidentiality, using examples.

A.1 The rights of individuals using health and social care services

The rights of individuals

People who use health and social care services have the right to be:

- respected

Respect for an individual's views

Mary has learning difficulties and lives in sheltered accommodation. A holiday is planned. She decides where she wants to go on holiday. Her views are respected.

- treated as an individual

Treating people as individuals

Javed is overweight and needs to manage his diet. He is vegetarian. The dietician should treat him as an individual and not make him adopt a non-vegetarian diet.

- treated with dignity

Maintaining a sense of dignity

Douglas lives alone and has problems managing personal hygiene since his stroke left him paralysed down one side. Dave, his carer, helps him to have a shower but also helps Douglas to do what he can for himself. Dave puts soap on the flannel but then Douglas can wash himself and maintain his dignity.

- treated equally and not discriminated against

Treating people equally

Sam and Toni are a lesbian couple. Sam has to go into hospital for an operation and only next of kin are allowed to visit. Toni is allowed to visit as she is the civil partner. This is an example of treating people equally.

- allowed privacy and confidentiality

Privacy and confidentiality

Zara goes to the surgery to make an appointment with her GP. The receptionist asks what the problem is. Zara complains to the surgery manager and the system is changed so that patients are allowed privacy and do not have to disclose confidential information at the reception desk. This change allows privacy and confidentiality for patients.

- allowed access to information about self

Access to own medical records

Saif has complex health needs. He is worried that his GP is not taking his health needs seriously. According to the NHS website:

'If you want to view your health records, you may not need to make a formal application. Nothing in the law prevents healthcare professionals from informally showing you your own records. You can make an informal request during a consultation, or by phoning your GP surgery or hospital to arrange a time to see your records.'

- given choices, for example to communicate in preferred method or language

Choice of preferred language

Chantelle is deaf from birth. She uses BSL to communicate. When she needs to go into hospital the NHS provides a signer so that Chantelle can use her own language.

- allowed independence

Independence in a care home

May is going into a residential care home for the first time. She wants to stay as independent as possible and after discussion with the care manager she decides to manage her own medication.

- safe

Maintaining safety

Violet is 75 years old and lives at Poppydene Care Home. She has dementia and came into care because when she lived at her own home she would go out and forget where she lived. In order to keep her safe at Poppydene, the carers always make sure the front door is locked. Violet likes to go out so spends a lot of time in the garden, where she can be safely supervised.

- able to take risks

Managing risks and maintaining independence

May is happy in the care home but wants to keep her independence. She takes the bus and meets friends once a week for coffee in town. May decides she can manage the risk and she is able to stay independent.

- involved in own care.

Good care involves people in their own care

May, Chantelle, Sam and Douglas are involved in their own care. They are more likely to understand what they need to do and in this way they will remain healthier.

Legislation that protect the rights of service users

Current and relevant legislation protects the rights of service users.

Human Rights Act

The Human Rights Act (1998) states that your human rights are:

1. the right to life
2. freedom from torture and degrading treatment
3. freedom from slavery and forced labour
4. the right to liberty
5. the right to a fair trial
6. the right not to be punished for something that wasn't a crime when you did it

7. the right to respect for private and family life
8. freedom of thought, conscience and religion, and freedom to express your beliefs
9. freedom of expression
10. freedom of assembly and association
11. the right to marry and to start a family
12. the right not to be discriminated against in respect of these rights and freedoms
13. the right to peaceful enjoyment of your property
14. the right to an education
15. the right to participate in free elections
16. the right not to be subjected to the death penalty.

If any one of these rights and freedoms is breached, you have a right to take the person to court, even if the breach was by someone in authority such as a police officer.

Mental Health Acts

Studied

Where people have mental health issues, care can sometimes infringe some of these rights unless we are careful. The Mental Health Act 1983 and parts of the Mental Capacity Act were amended by the Mental Health Act 2007. The 2007 Act defined mental disorder as 'any disorder or disability of the mind' but to prevent discrimination and protect people, this definition cannot be used against people with learning disabilities unless that disability is 'associated with abnormally aggressive or seriously irresponsible conduct'.

Guiding principles in the Act recognise individual rights. These include:

- *Purpose principle*: decisions must be taken with the purpose of maximising the safety and well-being (mental and physical) of patients, promoting their recovery and protecting other people from harm.
- *Least restriction principle*: people taking action without a patient's consent must minimise the restrictions they impose on the patient's liberty
- *Respect principle*: the diverse needs, values and circumstances of each patient must be respected, including their race, religion, culture, gender, age, sexual orientation and any disability.
- *Participation principle*: patients must be involved in planning and reviewing their own treatment where possible.
- *Effectiveness, efficiency and equity*: People taking decisions under the Act must use resources in the most effective, efficient and equitable way.

Figure 8.01 Teenagers with mental health issues must be offered age appropriate services

The 2007 Act ensures patients are given choice – are involved in their own care and that independent mental health advocacy is there to support patients. Patients have a right to refuse certain treatment such as electroconvulsive therapy (ECT). Those under 18 years old must be offered an age-appropriate service, which means they cannot be put into care that is meant for older people.

Some people with mental health issues realise they are unwell and volunteer to go into hospital. Others are forcibly detained, which conflicts with the right to liberty. A key part of the 2007 Act is the section about the Deprivation of Liberty Safeguards (DOLS). These ensure that the right to liberty is respected where possible. Safeguards include age – the person must be at least 18 years old, with a mental disorder, and lacking capacity to decide where to be for the treatment. The proposed deprivation of liberty is in the person's best interests.

Once individuals are released out into the community on supervised community treatment, they can be forcibly brought back if they do not take their medication. On the other hand, someone cannot be detained for treatment unless *appropriate treatment* is available. This shows the difficult balance between maintaining individual rights and protecting the public.

The Equality Act 2010

 Studied

The Equality Act 2010 protects the rights of people who use health and social care services, as we saw in Unit 7. The Equality Act 2010 protects people from discrimination, harassment and victimisation on the grounds of age, disability, gender reassignment, marriage and civil partnership, pregnancy and maternity, race, religion or belief, sex and sexual orientation.

Check your understanding

1. Which Act gives the right to be free from torture and degrading treatment?
2. Which Act defined mental disorder as 'any disorder or disability of the mind'?
3. Which Act protects people from harassment?
4. Which Act says that people under 18 years of age cannot be treated alongside older people?
5. Which Act has a section about deprivation of liberty?

A.2 How care workers can uphold the rights of service users

Examples of upholding service users' rights

In the unit on health and social care values we met residents of Poppydene Care Home. Now we see how care workers uphold the rights of service users at Poppydene and that it is not always easy to do so.

Anti-discriminatory practice

`Studied ☐`

We saw anti-discriminatory practice in Unit 2. Poppydene residents who returned late from the Sikh Gurdwara were also offered tea, and times for serving tea were adjusted to include everyone, even though this meant a little disruption for the cook. We saw how the Poppydene activities coordinator planned a trip that included everyone. Mr Jones in his wheelchair could also attend. It was not easy to find a coach that could take wheelchairs but eventually one was found.

Ensuring privacy during personal care

`Studied ☐`

Mr Zaid's dementia means that he does not always communicate his need for the toilet in time. He is incontinent. The carers take him to his room; in the privacy of his own bathroom he can be helped to have a shower and change his clothes.

Offering a person-centred approach

`Studied ☐`

In earlier units we learned that Mrs Khan is diabetic, likes an early shower, and prefers to speak English rather than Urdu. She is treated with respect and dignity by having her preferences met. Sue the manager involves Mrs Khan in her own care by negotiating a safe time for her to have her shower. Together they assess the risks of a home visit and managing Mrs Khan's diabetic routine. She is able to take risks in a safe environment, going out with relatives for a visit and independently deciding when she has her meal and insulin. She is treated equally and not discriminated against when she expresses choice. Mrs Khan likes to keep control of her diabetes herself, does her own blood sugar tests and manages her insulin with the help of the nurse.

Mrs Khan's case study shows person-centred care in practice. It is not always easy to give this type of care because it costs more and takes time to plan, but it is better care.

Showing empathy

Studied ▢

The right to privacy and confidentiality was breached in one example of care at Poppydene, but since then Sue, the manager, has done some training for the staff and they now realise that each person has a right to privacy and confidentiality.

They also know that individuals are entitled to know what information is held about them. Mrs Khan keenly follows what is written about her in the report but does not have access to other people's information.

Empathise with service user

Mr Zaid has dementia and at times undresses in the sitting room at Poppydene, thinking it is his own home. He is treated with dignity and respect, and led to his own room when this happens. Carers show empathy. They try to put themselves in Mr Zaid's situation and think what he would prefer. At times, other residents complain about this behaviour and ask what is wrong with him and why he does it. The carers understand the right to privacy and confidentiality, so just explain that Mr Zaid is not well. They do not tell the other residents that he has dementia. They empathise with him and his condition, maintain confidentiality and respect him as an individual, even though at times he is verbally abusive to them.

Being honest

Studied ▢

Being honest is very important. Honesty such as not stealing is of course essential and criminal record checks are carried out on all care workers. That type of honesty is vital. So is telling the truth, but it is important to know when to be totally open and when to wait before giving information.

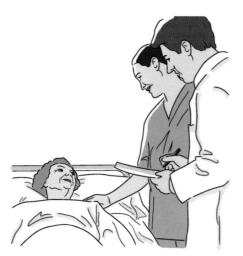

Figure 8.02 It is important to be honest and open when giving patients news

Knowing when to speak out

One of the residents at Poppydene, Mrs Burton, has lost a lot of weight and has to be admitted to the local hospital. She is a very alert lady, and used to be a headmistress of a local school. Several tests are done and the results come back. Staff Nurse Jenny sees the report, as Mrs Burton is her patient, and she sees the suggested diagnosis but waits until the doctor is available to speak to Mrs Burton. He comes to discuss the results with Mrs Burton. Nurse Jenny is there to support her.

The doctor is very honest with Mrs Burton. The results show that she has advanced cancer of the stomach. There are a range of options, but because the cancer has spread the treatments cannot cure her. Nurse Jenny knew the results indicated this but waited until the doctor had told Mrs Burton, because it is the doctor's job to give the diagnosis. The nurse's job is to help the patient understand what the doctor has said.

Being honest with a patient is important, but it takes a great deal of skill to know when to speak out and when to keep quiet. It is not easy. Difficulties occur. It is emotionally very demanding. Upholding rights and providing person-centred care is expensive and takes time. Another difficulty is that it requires training so that carers know what rights patients have. The benefits do, however, outweigh the difficulties, as patients become more independent, healthier and empowered to take care of their own health.

Check your understanding

Match the start with the correct sentence ending:

1. The rights of individuals using health and social care services are protected by _____
2. Rights include _____
3. Care workers uphold the rights of service users through _____

   a. to be respected, treated as an individual, with dignity

   to be treated equally and not discriminated against

   to be allowed privacy and confidentiality

   to be allowed access to information about self

   to have account taken of own choices, for example to communicate in a preferred method or language

   to be allowed independence

   to be safe

   to be able to take risks

   to be involved in own care.

   b. anti-discriminatory practices, ensuring privacy during personal care, offering person-centred approach, showing empathy and being honest.

   c. The Human Rights Act 1998, Equality Act 2010, Mental Health Act 1983 revised 2007.

Key learning points

Laws cover rights of individuals

 Revised

The rights of individuals using health and social care services are covered by laws such as the Human Rights Act 1998, the Equality Act 2010 and the Mental Health Act 1983.

Rights of individuals using health and social care services

Revised

These include the right to be: respected; treated as an individual; treated with dignity; treated equally and not discriminated against; allowed privacy and confidentiality; allowed access to information about self; given choices, for example to communicate in preferred method/language; allowed independence; safe; able to take risks; involved in own care.

Care workers can uphold the rights of service users

Revised ☐

Care workers can uphold the rights of service users through: anti-discriminatory practices such as including everyone in activities; ensuring privacy during personal care; offering a person-centred approach, such as a choice of bath or shower; showing empathy, that you understand how they would like to be treated; being honest.

Difficulties in upholding individuals' rights

Revised ☐

The difficulties in upholding the rights of service users are expense, time and more training requirements.

Benefits in upholding individuals' rights

Revised ☐

The benefits are that service users are empowered to take some responsibility for their own health and so they are more likely to be healthy.

Assessment activity

Create a leaflet

Create a leaflet to help service users in your local area. It will be displayed in the local health centre. Use note form, and spider diagrams where possible to increase the visual impact.

Include sections on:

Pass

Tested ☐

● Individual rights in health and social care – provide a summary of the individual rights of care service users. Include links to current and relevant legislation. Give examples to show how current legislation protects their rights.

Merit

Tested ☐

● Ways to uphold rights – explain three ways in which the rights of service users can be upheld in care centres by care staff. Include maintaining service-user confidentiality.

Distinction

Tested ☐

● Benefits to service users – assess the benefits to service users of having their rights upheld, and assess any difficulties this may create for care staff.

B.1 Responsibilities of employers and employees in ensuring safety

Those who work in care must ensure the safety of patients, residents, staff and members of the public.

Ways of ensuring safety include:

- risk assessment
- safeguarding
- other ways such as controlling substances harmful to health; using protective equipment; controlling the spread of infection; reporting and recording accidents and incidents; complaints procedures; providing toilets, washing facilities and drinking water; providing first aid facilities
- current and relevant legislation such as the Health and Safety at Work Act 1974.

Risk assessment

This is a 5-step process to examine the workplace and prevent or reduce the risk of harm. An example is shown in Table 8.01.

Table 8.01 An example of a 5-step process in risk assessment

5-step process				
Step 1	**Step 2**	**Step 3**	**Step 4**	**Step 5**
Identify the hazards	Decide who might be harmed and how	Evaluate the risks and decide on precautions	Record your findings and implement them	Review your assessment and update if necessary
Loose carpet	Residents, staff and visitors may trip and fall	High risk – so decide whether to fix the carpet at once or remove it at once	Record findings Remove carpet	Carpet removed for immediate safety. But a carpet is needed so one is ordered and a fitter is coming to fix it next week.

Changing circumstances

Sue, the manager of Poppydene Care Home, carries out risk assessments whenever circumstances change; for example, a new member of staff starts, a new resident arrives, or a change happens to require an assessment.

Step 1: Identify the hazards

P3

Studied ☐

A hazard is anything that may cause harm, such as loose carpet, wet floor or trailing cord. The risk is the chance, high or low, that somebody could be harmed by these and other hazards, together with an indication of how serious the harm could be.

Sue the manager looked around Poppydene Care Home. She noted there was a temporary hazard. When the cleaner vacuumed the sitting room, the flex from the vacuum cleaner trailed across the hall, creating a hazard. There was a high risk of people tripping over it.

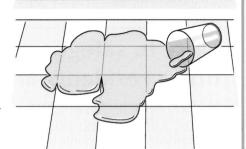

Figure 8.03 A spill could cause someone to fall over

Step 2: Decide who might be harmed and how

Studied ☐

Sue realised that the care workers, visitors, and residents were all people who might trip over the cable and have a nasty fall.

Step 3: Evaluate the risks and decide on precautions

Studied ☐

She realised the trailing cable posed a high risk, and there was a nearer socket that could reduce the risk posed by trailing cables. She explained the risks to the cleaner and that the nearer socket must be used to reduce risk.

Step 4: Record your findings and implement them

Studied ☐

Sue noted the incident, told the staff and then put up a notice telling the staff to use the nearest socket for electrical equipment so they would not forget.

Her risk assessment recorded what the hazard was, whether it was high or low risk, and what might happen. She then noted what action was needed, what was done, by whom and when.

Sue had to prioritise and deal with those hazards that were high-risk and had serious consequences first. She then looked at other hazards and assessed the risks in the same way.

M2

Step 5: Review your assessment and update if necessary

Studied ☐

Sue reviewed the risk assessment. One of the cleaners had been on holiday when Sue drew staff attention to the hazard, and later a new cleaner started working at the home, so Sue had to review the risk assessment again to make sure everyone was following safe practice.

The right to take acceptable risks is part of choice. Sue carried out a risk assessment when Mrs Khan's family wanted to take their mum out. The potential hazards were that Mrs Khan could eat the wrong foods and not take her insulin on time. After making sure that Mrs Khan and her relatives understood the importance of the right food and timing of insulin, Mrs Khan decided for herself that the risks were acceptable. This was her choice.

D2

Safeguarding

This is part of the duty of care. It is important to prevent harm.

Duty to safeguard the individual, other residents and staff

Mr Zaid has dementia, gets confused and at times can be violent. Sue has a duty to safeguard the other residents, the staff and Mr Zaid himself. She does this by risk assessing the situation. Mr Zaid gets particularly upset when he wants the toilet. He becomes agitated; because he is confused, he cannot always express his needs. At these times he becomes verbally abusive and can lash out at staff. Other residents get annoyed with him and have threatened him. The situation poses a risk to everyone.

Sue asks staff to take Mr Zaid to the toilet every two hours so that reduces the risk of his being incontinent, and reduces the risk of him becoming agitated and aggressive. This works up to a point. Sue reviews the situation and decides to allocate Mr Zaid a main carer, Bill, who has had training on dementia care. Bill is able to understand Mr Zaid and can help him to communicate his needs. Gradually, as people begin to understand Mr Zaid's needs, his frustration and anger are reduced.

Other ways of ensuring safety

Other ways that employers and employees ensure safety are by taking responsibility.

Control of substances harmful to health

Studied ☐

Safety is everyone's job. **The control of substances harmful to health** is very important and is guided by COSHH regulations. Substances may include bleach or cleaning fluids. They must be stored in a locked cupboard and not put into other containers. The cleaner who uses the bleach has a responsibility to lock it away. The manager has a responsibility to provide a place where it can be locked.

In health and care settings all tablets and medication must be kept in a locked cupboard, which can be secured to the wall. A record is kept of which medication is given when and by whom. Controlled drugs must be stored in a specially designed double-locked cupboard and a strict record kept of what is used. Any medicines left over must be properly disposed of by the pharmacist. Only people trained to give medication may do so.

Figure 8.04 Potentially harmful products should be stored with care

Protective equipment and infection control

Studied ☐

Protective equipment such as gloves and aprons must be provided by the employer and employees must use them. Infection control, especially hand washing, is everyone's responsibility. Employers may have written procedures but it is care workers' responsibility to wash their hands before and after care procedures, and after going to the toilet.

Reporting and recording accidents and incidents

Studied ☐

This is again everyone's responsibility. Employees such as care workers must report accidents and incidents. Each health and care setting has a procedure for this, and has an accident or incident book. The person in charge may take a verbal report from people involved and complete the written report.

Complaints procedures

Studied ☐

Complaints procedures must be in place in a health and care setting. This is something that inspectors look for. A good care setting will act promptly and ensure issues are dealt with as soon as possible.

Provision of toilets, washing facilities and drinking water

Studied ☐

This is an employer's responsibility. Staff should never share patient toilets or washing facilities.

Provision of first-aid facilities

Studied ☐

This is an employer's responsibility. There must be a trained first aider. All staff should know where the first aid box is kept and who the trained first aider is.

Current safety legislation

Health and Safety at Work Act 1974

Studied ☐

Legislation about workplace safety stems from the Health and Safety at Work Act 1974, which makes the following requirements.

Employers must:

- make the workplace safe, ensure machinery is safe and that safe systems of work are set and followed
- ensure articles and substances are moved, stored and used safely
- provide adequate welfare facilities
- train workers on health and safety
- consult workers on these matters.

Reporting of Injuries, Diseases and Dangerous Occurrences Regulations (RIDDOR) 1995

Studied ☐

These regulations state that employers must report serious workplace accidents, occupational diseases and specified dangerous occurrences (near misses).

Safe lifting

Studied ☐

The following regulations govern safe lifting:

- The Manual Handling Operations Regulations 1992 (amended 2002)
- Lifting Operations and Lifting Equipment Regulations 1998 (LOLER)
- Workplace, Health, Safety and Welfare Regulations 1992

Storage of substances

Studied ☐

The Control of Substances Hazardous to Health Regulations (COSHH) 2002 govern the storage of substances.

More information about current health and safety legislation is available at www.hse.gov.uk

Check your understanding

1. A. The five steps to risk assessment are:

1 _____

2 _____

3 _____

4 _____

5 _____

2. B. Safeguarding means: (choose one of the following)

    (i) stopping people doing anything they want

    (ii) protecting people from harm

C. COSHH is short for _____

D. Protective equipment includes _____

E. Who is responsible for reporting and recording accidents and incidents?

F. Name four things an employer must provide

G. One of the main laws about workplace safety is _____

Employers and employees must make sure information is confidential. Their responsibilities are as follows.

Accurate recording and proper storage and retrieval of information

This includes electronic methods, written records, use of photographs, mobile phones and social media.

Confidentiality or privacy of information relates to Article 8 of the European Convention of Human Rights. It extends to written and spoken information, as well as electronically held material.

Information must be accurately recorded, stored safely and be retrievable. Written records must be factual, readable and signed and dated by the person making the record.

Figure 8.05 Information should be stored safely

Photographs may only be taken with permission and for relevant purposes; for example, to record injuries after an attack on a person. They may not be taken on personal equipment such as a camera phone, but must be taken by the official photographer using official equipment.

Photographs form part of the medical record. Care professionals must maintain confidentiality. Using mobile phones to take photographs of patients and their relatives is unethical. Care workers must never discuss patients on social media such as Facebook, just as they are not allowed to discuss patients outside the work environment.

Maintaining confidentiality

It is important to maintain confidentiality to safeguard service users, to adhere to legal and workplace requirements, and to respect the rights of service users. Mrs X is a victim of domestic violence. She is discharged from hospital to a refuge. Her husband demands to know where she is. In a case like this confidentiality must be maintained to protect Mrs X. Professional codes of conduct demand confidentiality and it is Mrs X's human right under the law.

Disclosure

Disclosure means the giving of information.

Disclosure may refer to when a person discloses confidential information to a care professional. Disclosure may involve a care worker passing on information. According to the Nursing and Midwifery Council guidance, disclosure is only lawful and ethical if the individual has freely and fully given consent to the information being passed on. Consent may be explicit or implied. It may be required by law or be capable of justification by reason of the public interest.

When breaches of confidentiality are appropriate

Occasionally, it may be necessary to breach confidentiality; for example, to safeguard others and prevent criminal activities, or to safeguard the service user. In such circumstances, protocol must be followed. Police do not automatically have the right to access information. Here is an example where a breach of confidentiality may be needed.

Professional concern

A child is admitted to hospital with recent injuries and injuries sustained over time. She says her aunt and aunt's boyfriend beat her. Professionals should raise concerns. This is where it is appropriate to breach confidentiality.

Current legislation that protects confidentiality

This includes the Data Protection Act 1998, which covers the processing of information that identifies living individuals. Processing includes holding, obtaining, recording, using and disclosing of information and the Act applies to all forms of media, including paper and electronic.

A further important law is the Freedom of Information Act 2000, which came into force in 2005 and grants people rights of access to information not covered by the Data Protection Act 1998; for example, information which does not contain a person's identifiable details.

The Police and Criminal Evidence Act 1984 allows nurses and midwives to pass on information to the police if they believe that someone may be seriously harmed, or death may occur if the police are not informed. There is a formal procedure that must be followed for this.

Real life connection

Careers in health informatics – Administrative assistant

Staff working in health informatics in the NHS are employed in four main groups. These are:

- clinical informatics
- information and communication technology (ICT)
- information management
- knowledge management.

The NHS employs many administrative assistants. An assistant may be involved with the Informatics Learning Networks (ILN), which provides networking and continuous professional development opportunities for healthcare staff in health informatics. This administrator would support network staff, help to organise events, use Microsoft Office software and update the website (no technical experience would necessarily be required).

Check your understanding

Match the start with the correct sentence ending given in the list below:

1. Risk assessment _____
2. Current legislation about work place safety _____
3. The right to take acceptable risks _____
4. Safeguarding _____
5. It may be necessary to breach confidentiality _____
6. Confidentiality _____
7. Laws about confidentiality include _____

  a. is part of choice.
  b. is a 5-step process to examine the workplace and prevent or reduce the risk of harm.
  c. is part of the duty of care.
  d. safeguards service users and respects the rights of service users.
  e. includes Manual Handling Operations Regulations 1992 (amended 2002), Lifting Operations and Lifting Equipment Regulations 1998 (LOLER) and the Workplace, Health, Safety and Welfare Regulations 1992.
  f. to safeguard others and prevent criminal activities or to safeguard the service user.
  g. the Data Protection Act 1998, the Freedom of Information Act 2000 which came into force in 2005 and the Police and Criminal Evidence Act 1984.

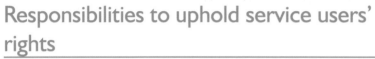

Key learning points

Responsibilities to uphold service users' rights

Revised ☐

Employers and employees have responsibilities to uphold service users' rights in health and social care.

Employers and employees must ensure safety

Revised ☐

Employers and employees must ensure safety through:

- risk assessment, taking into account the right to take acceptable risks
- safeguarding and preventing harm; for example, if a patient has dementia, staff must protect the patient from hurting himself or others
- control of substances harmful to health; for example, locking away cleaning fluids
- use of protective equipment, such as gloves and aprons
- infection control
- reporting and recording accidents and incidents, including RIDDOR reports
- ensuring complaints procedures are available
- provision of toilets, washing facilities and drinking water, provision of first-aid facilities
- working to current and relevant legislation, such as the Health and Safety at Work Act 1974.

Employers and employees must ensure confidentiality

Revised ☐

Employers and employees must ensure confidentiality through:

- accurate recording and proper storage and retrieval of information, both electronic and written records, avoiding the use of photographs, mobile phones and social media
- appropriate disclosure
- knowing we maintain confidentiality to safeguard service users, to adhere to legal and workplace requirements and to respect the rights of service users
- knowing when breaches of confidentiality are appropriate, to safeguard other individual(s), to safeguard a service user or to report criminal activities
- knowing current and relevant legislation; for example the Data Protection Act 1998 and the Freedom of Information Act 2005.

UNIT 8 Individual Rights in Health and Social Care

Assessment activity

Add two sections to the leaflet you started in the previous activity.

Section 1

Pass/Merit/Distinction

Tested

Use notes and mind maps to show the responsibilities of care staff in dealing with service users.

Include:

- a description of one example, from a particular care setting, of how an employee can plan to maximise the safety of care service users
- an explanation of why the use of risk assessment is important for the well-being of service users in health and social care settings
- an evaluation, using two examples, of why it is important to carry out risk assessments in care settings.

Section 2

Pass/Merit/Distinction

Tested

Maintaining confidentiality

Include notes on:

- a description of how service-user confidentiality is promoted in a particular care setting
- an explanation of why the right to confidentiality is important in care settings
- two examples, from a care setting, of where a breach of confidentiality could be justified.

Model assignment

This assignment will assess the following learning aims:

A investigate the rights of individuals using health and social care services
B examine the responsibilities of employers and employees in upholding service users' rights in health and social care.

Scenario

You are a student on a health and social care course. One of your elderly relatives wants to know what rights she has as a service user. Write a handbook of rights for an elderly relative who uses health and social care.

Section 1

Include sections on:

- Individual rights in health and social care: a summary of the individual rights of care service users. Include links to current and relevant legislation. Give examples to show how current legislation protects their rights.
- Ways to uphold rights: explain three ways in which the rights of service users can be upheld in care centres by care staff. Include maintaining service-user confidentiality.
- Benefits to service users: assess the benefits to service users of having their rights upheld and assess any difficulties this may create for care staff.

Section 2

Add two more sections to your booklet
1 The responsibilities of care staff in dealing with service users.

- Include an example from a particular care setting of how an employee can plan to maximise the safety of care service users.
- Include an explanation of why the use of risk assessment is important for the well-being of service users in health and social care settings.
- Add an evaluation, using two or more examples, of why it is important to carry out risk assessments in care settings.

2 Maintaining confidentiality

- Include a description of how service user confidentiality is promoted in a particular care setting.
- Include an explanation of why the right to confidentiality is important in care settings.
- Give two or more examples, from a care setting, of where a breach of confidentiality could be justified and say why each is justified.

References

www.dh.gov.uk/prod_consum_dh/groups/dh_digitalassets/@dh/@en/documents/digitalasset/dh_087073.pdf   - Code of Practice Mental Health Act 1983 revised.

www.dh.gov.uk/health/files/2012/07/Post-Legislative-Assessment-of-Health-Act-2007-Accessible-version-17June-2012.pdf

www.hse.gov.uk/pubns/indg163.pdf

www.hse.gov.uk

www.nmc-uk.org/Nurses-and-midwives/Advice-by-topic/A/Advice/Confidentiality/

Unit 9

Healthy Living

This unit explores how healthy and unhealthy lifestyle choices impact on health and well-being. While some of the choices people make can have a positive effect on their lives, health and well-being are also influenced by the negative choices people make in their everyday lives. In this unit you will also consider the barriers and limitations that may have an impact on the success of measures taken to improve health and well-being.

Learning aims

In this unit you will:

✓ explore the factors that contribute to healthy and unhealthy lifestyles and their effects on health and well-being.

✓ explore ways of improving health and well-being.

Learning Aim A

A.1 Defining a healthy lifestyle
A.2 Defining effects of an unhealthy lifestyle

Definition of health

The term 'health' has been defined by the World Health Organization as: 'a complete state of physical, mental and social well-being and not merely the absence of disease or infirmity'.

Health should be seen from a holistic point of view, which means taken as a whole. When we look at someone we should not only see his or her physical problem, but also include other areas of the individual's health.

Consider the example below.

A short stay in hospital

Joe, who is 25 years old and lives alone, has just started his first job as a buyer. Unfortunately, while travelling to work he fell off his motorcycle and sustained a broken leg and fractured ribs.

Joe had a short stay in hospital, where his leg was pinned and plastered. He was given painkillers and then allowed home.

This seems to be a good solution to his physical problem, but if we were to consider Joe holistically then we should look at the following factors:

- His financial situation: he may have no work and therefore no money.
- How will he get around?
- His hygiene arrangements at home – is his bathroom upstairs?
- Can he cook and get to shops?
- How close are his social contacts?
- He lives alone – he may become anxious or depressed about his situation.

All areas of health impact on one another. However, in this unit we will be looking at each area as separate items so that you can identify them easily.

The effects of a healthy and unhealthy lifestyle

Both healthy and unhealthy lifestyles have an effect on an individual's physical, intellectual, emotional and social needs. See Figure 9.01.

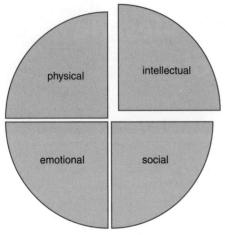
Figure 9.01 Physical, intellectual, emotional and social needs

Positive and negative effects of our choice of lifestyle

Having a healthy lifestyle will have positive effects on all areas of health and an unhealthy lifestyle will negatively affect health. Consider the information given in Table 9.01 and look at the physical, intellectual, emotional and social effects of a healthy and unhealthy lifestyle.

Table 9.01 Effects of a healthy and an unhealthy lifestyle

Effects	Healthy lifestyle	Unhealthy lifestyle
Physical	To keep our bodies in the best condition possible we need to supply them with basic needs, which are food, shelter, warmth rest, exercise and personal hygiene. If we follow a healthy diet and exercise regime we are less likely to suffer from illness and disease, for example colds and anemia. Our body systems work with a good supply of oxygen, balanced diet and the correct amount of exercise and rest. If we avoid smoking and poor lifestyle choices we will have improved energy and fitness levels.	If we do not provide the body with its basic needs and choose unhealthy lifestyle choices then we may possibly suffer from illness and disease. Smoking can lead to a range of cancers and lung conditions such as bronchitis. Not having the correct energy balance may cause weight gain, or weight loss. Both conditions are detrimental to the body and over a long period of time may cause long-term conditions such as Type 2 diabetes. Short-term conditions such as chest infections and skin infestations may be the result of poor housing and environment.
Intellectual	To keep our brains active we need to keep them stimulated. We can do this with education, employment, and activities like quizzes and reading. This will give us: ● improved concentration ● clearer thinking and the ability to learn ● improved memory and recall skills.	If we are not exposed to good educational opportunities, positive images of education and access to good education then: ● we may have low self-esteem so be unable to reach our full potential and goals ● it may impact on career prospects ● our mind may not be stimulated fully so the ability to think clearly and logically could be reduced.
Emotional	We all require things to help us feel confident, relaxed and happy. We need to feel secure about sharing feelings and showing feelings. If we are emotionally healthy then we are more likely to: ● have greater levels of happiness ● have improved mood, self-esteem, and self-image ● experience less stress, as we are able to use strategies to deal with emotions and be resilient ● feel stable and comfortable with ourselves and be less likely to experience mental health problems.	A negative impact on emotional health can begin from a very early age and have a long-lasting detrimental effect on the individual. This can lead to: ● low self-esteem and self-image ● general unhappiness with life ● mental health issues like stress, anxiety and depression may occur. Those who suffer with a low self-image may affect close family and sexual relationships. Mental ill health may lead to a dependence on medication, therapy and counselling.
Social	We need to enjoy opportunities with friends and family to build relationships and learn how to socialise with others. Having a good social outlook will enable us to: ● build close relationships ● develop and maintain appropriate intimate and sexual relationships ● develop a wide circle of varied friendships.	Social relationships are important to all of us and mostly we find that the feeling of isolation and loneliness is not natural. If we live in isolation and do not make friendships then we may suffer: ● isolation from family and friends ● reduced opportunities to be involved in activities. People who are socially isolated are more likely to be involved in crime, accidents and personal injuries.

A.3 Factors that contribute to healthy or unhealthy lifestyles and their effects

This section covers specific factors that can lead to an unhealthy lifestyle. There is also a discussion about the physical, intellectual, emotional and social areas of health that will be affected by the choice of an unhealthy lifestyle.

Diet and nutrition

We saw in Unit 1 and Unit 6 that diet and nutrition play an important role when considering factors that lead to an unhealthy or healthy lifestyle. It is important to look back at these units to make sure that you fully understand the different food groups, their sources and recommended daily intakes.

Our diet should be balanced, which means that it contains the right nutrients in the correct proportions. Nutrients are naturally occurring chemicals that can be found in our food. As we age, or our health status changes, we may require these nutrients in differing amounts to keep us healthy.

The main nutrients are:

- protein
- carbohydrates
- fats
- vitamins
- minerals
- fibre
- water.

Physical effects

Studied ☐

A healthy diet will allow the body to work and fight infections appropriately. If we understand the nutrients we take in and the work they do, then we can give our body what it needs accordingly. So, for example, in pregnancy we may need to take in a high protein diet and folic acid. As an older person we may need to cut down on carbohydrates if we are not as active as we used to be. We need a correct energy balance to give us energy.

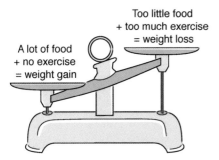

Figure 9.02 Correct energy balance

If we do not have a balanced diet over a long period then our body will suffer and stop working properly.

Some diseases that may occur are: coronary heart disease, obesity and diabetes. There is further information about these topics in Unit 6 and Unit 10.

Excessive weight loss can also be a consequence of poor nutrition. Malnutrition is a term used to describe the effects of under- or over-eating for a long period. Poverty can lead to a poor diet and some parents may forfeit meals in order to feed their children. But this is unwise, as just as a car needs petrol, so too the body needs food. An undernourished body will be susceptible to infections, tiredness and loss of energy.

Exercise

Regular exercise is important. It has been found that exercising for at least 20 minutes three times a week can be beneficial for us. If you have not exercised for a long time, however, you should not go straight into demanding and strenuous exercise, as it can damage muscles, especially your heart. It is recommended that you start with gentle exercise and gradually build up, so your heart, lungs and other muscles get used to the increased demand. Of course, we need to remember that children should take regular daily exercise and be encouraged to move away from television or computer games and get involved in physical exercise, indoors or outdoors. This will burn off the energy they take in their diet. An elderly person is still encouraged to exercise, but it may be gentler according to their health status.

Topic A3

Physical effects

Generally, exercise can be seen to reduce the likelihood of obesity, coronary heart disease (as discussed in Unit 6 and Unit 10) and improve lung disorders like asthma. Asthma is a common respiratory condition in which the airways become inflamed and reduce the passage of air into and out of the lungs. It is the muscles around the airways that are strengthened as part of an exercise regime, and this will help someone who has asthma to breathe.

Body mass index

Body mass index (BMI) is calculated in the following way:

- BMI = weight (kg) divided by height (m)^2

Therefore, someone who weighs 65 kg and is 1.72 m tall would have a BMI of 22 (rounded up) and would be in the normal weight range.

- 1.72^2 (i.e. 1.72 x 1.72) = 2.96
- 65 divided by 2.96 = 21.9

However, the body mass index calculation does have some limitations. If someone has a high level of muscle it may lead to a higher reading, which could indicate that an individual is overweight when this is not the case.

To remind yourself how BMI is measured, i.e. what is meant by underweight, normal, overweight and obese, refer to section A2 in Unit 6.

> **Key terms**
> **Body mass index (BMI):** This measures the body fat on an individual. It is determined using the height and weight of an individual.

Home environment

The environment is the surroundings in which a person lives. It refers not just to a house, village or town, but the wider environment, such as the area or country. If the country someone lives in is at war, or politically unsettled, then such factors will affect many areas of the individual's life, including safety, education, health and freedom of movement. If the house is in a rural location then access to shops and medical facilities may prove difficult. Poor housing and overcrowding are usually found in socially deprived areas so levels of crime, drug and alcohol abuse may be apparent in that area.

Physical effects

Poor housing can lead to an increased risk of physical illness (e.g. damp increases respiratory problems) and the stress of living in poor housing and overcrowding can increase the risk of mental illness, for example depression. Vulnerable people like young children and older people are particularly at risk from health problems caused by poor housing. Overcrowded conditions will lead to the spread of illness and, if not treated, illnesses may become worse.

Work environment

Our health can be affected by our work and the income we get from it will provide us with the finance to live accordingly. However, an income earner who has to work long hours, away from home, for example, may have a lot of money but not be able to enjoy it; this can have physical and emotional effects. People in lower paid jobs may be stressed for other reasons, which may include trying to have a healthy diet and enjoy family life with a limited income.

Physical effects

Studied

Health problems associated with working shifts include peptic ulcers, cardiovascular disease, chronic fatigue, excessive sleepiness and difficulty in sleeping. Shift workers also tend to be more overweight due to poor eating habits and lack of exercise. They also have a higher divorce rate, worse rates of substance abuse and depression and are more likely to view their jobs as stressful. However, some family incomes depend on anti-social work and the economy of the family is improved, so these working patterns can be seen as having a positive effect on the family.

Depending on the type of job, accidents and injuries may be more apparent. For example, a manual job as a builder, miner or fisherman may be more hazardous than a job in an office. Other hazardous occupations that are well paid include jobs within the police force, the ambulance service and social work. People who work in these roles may not only be open to physical injuries but they are also exposed to abuse, violence and racial attacks.

In some environments workers may be exposed to sexual abuse, bullying and discrimination, which can be stressful and cause sickness and absence from the workplace.

Alcohol consumption

The effects of alcohol and guidelines for consumption are discussed in Unit 1 and Unit 5.

Alcoholism is an uncontrolled habit of drinking alcohol, which causes health problems for the individual. You may also see terms such as 'alcohol dependence' or 'alcohol abuse' used in discussions about the effects of alcohol on individuals.

Binge drinking means taking in a large amount of alcohol in a short space of time. For example, it may mean that an individual drinks all of his or her recommended weekly units in one night, on a regular basis.

For further information have a look at the following website:

www.nhs.uk/change4life/pages/alcohol-lower-risk-guidelines-units.aspx

Topic A3

Cancer

According to the Cancer Research UK website, it has been shown that consuming alcohol above your weekly limits over a long period results in a greater risk of seven different types of cancer. Those are: mouth cancer, oesophageal cancer, pharyngeal cancer, laryngeal cancer, bowel cancer, breast cancer and liver cancer. While not everyone who drinks will get cancer, there has been found to be an increased risk in those who drink alcohol.

www.cancerresearchuk.org

Mental health issues

Alcohol is a depressant not a stimulant, so drinking excessive amounts to cope with situations, or to relieve our stresses, may have a reverse effect on us. This can lead to severe feelings of anxiety and depression and an inability to cope. People who have mental illness are more likely to drink as a way of forgetting problems rather than facing them. After a long period, alcohol changes the chemistry of your brain and how it works; this can affect memory and the ability to deal with feelings and emotions. The more a person drinks to feel better, the more alcohol is required to give the same boost each time. Alcohol can damage relationships, families and lead to unemployment.

Weight gain

Alcohol is made from yeast and sugar so excessive amounts gives you a high calorie intake and can lead to obesity, for example:

- A glass of white wine (175 ml) = 130 calories (You could have a slice of cake or a serving of blueberries, greek yoghurt and honey.)
- A pint of lager (5 %) = 250 calories (You could have a burger or a chicken salad sandwich.)
- Alcopops (275 ml) = 200 calories (You could have a small chocolate bar or at least 3 apples.)

Liver disease

It is the liver which breaks down alcohol and cleans it out of the bloodstream. The liver gets rid of alcohol at the rate of one unit per hour, so light drinking allows the liver to recover. If you drink heavily each day, this does not allow the liver to repair so it may stop working effectively; this can cause a disease called cirrhosis, which if not treated can be fatal.

Drinking excessive amounts of alcohol can lead to risk taking, including violent behaviour, drink driving and unsafe sex. In turn, this may cause accidents, injuries and unplanned pregnancies, as well as sexually transmitted infections. See Unit 1 for more information about these topics.

Benefits of alcohol

We may read about the benefits of alcohol. It is claimed that a small amount of alcohol can help to avoid coronary heart disease, although it is not clear why. However, according to the drinkaware website the negative affects of drinking alcohol outweigh the benefits.

www.drinkaware.co.uk

Emotional and social effects

Studied ☐

Alcohol can affect the way people react in situations and some individuals may also use alcohol as a coping mechanism in an attempt to help them face the stresses and strains of life, which they may feel unable to cope with. This dependence may be at the cost of family and relationships.

Smoking

As we saw in Unit 5, an individual may smoke to relieve stress and avoid situations of conflict, so to ask or advise someone to give up smoking may not be as easy as it looks. Underlying issues need to be addressed before giving advice about smoking; certainly a substitute needs to be considered. Obviously the amount an individual smokes and the length of time he or she has smoked for will be a key to how easy or difficult it will be to give up.

Physical effects

Studied ☐

Bronchitis

Bronchitis is an infection of the main airways of the lungs (bronchi), which causes them to become irritated and inflamed. The main symptom is a cough, which may bring up yellow-grey mucus. Bronchitis may also cause a sore throat, wheezing and a blocked nose. Smoking is the most common cause of chronic bronchitis. Over time, tobacco smoke can cause permanent damage to the bronchi, causing them to become inflamed.

Coronary heart disease

Coronary heart disease (CHD) is the UK's biggest killer; around one in five men and one in seven women die from the disease. CHD causes around 94,000 deaths in the UK each year. Coronary heart disease is the term that describes what happens when your heart's blood supply is blocked or interrupted by a build-up of fatty substances in the coronary arteries. Smoking is a major risk factor. Carbon monoxide (from the smoke) and nicotine both put a strain on the heart by making it work faster. They also increase your risk of blood clots. Other chemicals in cigarette smoke damage the lining of your coronary arteries, leading to furring of the arteries. If you smoke, you increase your risk of developing heart disease by 24 per cent.

Lung cancer

Smoking is a big risk factor for many types of cancer. Cancer Research UK states that smoking causes 85–90 per cent of lung cancers. People who smoke are 15 times more likely to die from lung cancer than people who have never smoked.

Emphysema

Chronic obstructive pulmonary disease (COPD) is the overall term used to describe a variety of illnesses, including chronic bronchitis, emphysema and chronic obstructive airways disease. People with COPD have permanently damaged lungs and find it difficult to breathe most of the time. COPD is closely linked with smoking in many cases. The changes in smoking habits several decades ago mean that although COPD is more common among men, cases are rising three times as fast among women. COPD is the sixth most common cause of death in England and Wales, causing over 30,000 deaths a year. But it's estimated that by 2020 it will be the third biggest killer in the world. COPD is the only major cause of death that has increased significantly in recent years.

Emotional and social effects

`Studied` ☐

If the underlying reason for smoking is not treated, then a dependency on tobacco will lead to an addiction and quitting smoking becomes even harder for the individual. The social effects of smoking are becoming more apparent as smoking is banned in public houses, eating places and many workplaces. People who wish to smoke have to do so separately from others, or endure outdoor weather. Other social effects are that secondary smoking may also cause diseases. This means that although you may not smoke you can acquire an illness because of the smoking habits of someone you live or work with. Young children are particularly vulnerable to the ill effects of secondary smoking.

Recreational drug use

An explanation of drugs is given in Unit 1. For more information see the following website: www.talktofrank.com/sites/default/files/The%20truth%20about%20drugs%20v1.2.pdf

Physical effects

`Studied` ☐

Some recreational drugs contain substances you may be unaware of and our bodies may react in extreme ways when exposed to them, resulting in injury or death. For example, an inquest heard that a 15-year-old girl who died after taking ecstasy she found in a university lecturer's drug stash during a house party would not let friends call an ambulance because she was scared of getting into trouble. For more information see the following web link:

This is an extreme case, but the influence of drugs can cause people to take risks they would otherwise not take and can lead to accidents and injuries, including driving under the influence of drugs and violent behaviour. Drugs can leave people with no sense of danger and they may have unprotected and unsafe sex in a casual manner.

Emotional and social effects

Studied ☐

An addiction or dependency on drugs may develop from having just one smoke, tablet or pill. This can spiral out of control and lead to financial problems and possibly to crime, loss of relationships and employment.

Safe and unsafe sexual practices

Contraception and safe sexual practices are now taught early in young people's education so they have an informed choice about sexual behaviours, which should be reinforced positively by parents and main carers. If an individual has numerous sexual partners, he or she is exposed to risks including unplanned pregnancies, as well as sexually transmitted infections. It is important to keep sexually healthy by not only attending regular personal screening and taking treatment, if required, but also by having an awareness of the sexual history of your partner. You may be responsible and take this area seriously but others may not. Barrier methods of contraception are important to protect against sexual infections, as well as pregnancies.

Physical effects

Studied ☐

Sexually transmitted infections and cervical cancer require diagnosis and treatment (these are all detailed in Sections B1 and B2 in Unit 10). When considering the factors related to safe sexual practices it is important to remember that they relate to same-sex couples, as well as heterosexual couples. Although pregnancy is not a physical effect of same-sex relationships, all the sexually transmitted infections can be passed from one person to another.

Emotional and social effects

Studied ☐

Within relationships, commitment and trust should be formed and this leads to close sexual relationships. These relationships can enhance the bond between a couple and form a dependency. Relationships between teenagers may be short lived, but during the late teens, longer relationships will form that prepare individuals for adult life. A stable relationship with love and trust will provide a positive environment for family life.

Topic A3

Personal hygiene

Poor or inadequate personal hygiene may impact upon a person's health. You should bathe or shower daily and more frequently in some situations, for example, after exercise. Hand washing is important, as failure to ensure your hands are clean can lead to serious illness. The odour of perspiration may remain on clothing, so it is important to change and wash your clothes regularly. It is important for workers in health and social care to have good personal hygiene to prevent the spread of infection.

Physical effects

Studied ☐

Poor personal hygiene can have physical consequences and lead to an increased risk of infection and illness. Furthermore, bacteria and fungus on skin that is not washed can lead to acne, body odour or athlete's foot.

Emotional and social effects

Studied ☐

People may not want to befriend someone who has poor personal hygiene. Some people may find it hard to tell someone about poor personal hygiene and may choose to avoid that individual. This, in turn, can impact upon an individual's emotional health and well-being. For example, the individual may become isolated and feel left out. In extreme circumstances, the person may experience difficulty in finding employment and suffer depression as a result.

Sleep patterns

Sleep and rest are required so that our bodies are able to recharge and recover. The amount of sleep needed varies between age groups.

Table 9.02 Amount of sleep needed by age group

Age group	Sleep
Babies and young children	Sleep patterns are short and frequent throughout the day and night.
Adults	Average of 7–8 hours a night. Some adults also require a short rest during the day.
Older people	Less sleep required. Older people have wakeful periods in the night but may require sleep in the daytime.

Sometimes employment will affect sleep patterns, which can be quite stressful for those whose work requires that they have to sleep at irregular times of the day.

Physical effects

Studied ☐

A nurse or firefighter may have to do shift work, so sleep patterns can be varied. As a nurse you may be required to work a morning shift, afternoon shift and a night shift in the same month. This can be a cause of stress if you are unable to get the required amount of sleep. Accidents could occur if you are not as alert as you should be.

Factors that affect lifestyle choice

Adopting a healthy lifestyle may not always be easy. Sometimes there are factors beyond our control that we cannot change and which may affect our lifestyle choices. These are discussed below.

Partners and family

Our family may have a positive influence on our growth and development. The family is responsible for our early socialisation, which can be positive or negative depending on our role models. Peer pressure means the influence that people similar to us, such as friends or co-workers, have on our behaviour. For example, we may be influenced to study, work hard and achieve or we could be influenced to choose to smoke or take illegal drugs. Both these options can dramatically change our health, development, well-being and lifestyle choices.

Culture and religion

Your beliefs, morals and values will depend on where you grow up and the community in which you live – your cultural influences. Religion can be included with these influences as faith and customs are linked to religion. For example, some women in the Muslim faith cover their faces as part of their culture. Some families have strict religious rules and teach their children that sex before marriage is wrong. Some parents who do not drink or smoke will discourage their children from doing so. Therefore, adopting the cultures around us can influence our choices to be healthy or not.

We live in a multicultural society, so it is important to allow individuals to express their cultural beliefs without fear of discrimination. This is particularly true if we are caring for individuals within a care environment.

Peer group pressure

As adolescents grow away from their family they are influenced by their friends or peer groups. These influences, which may be positive and negative, can mould a young person's life and choices from this age. Teenagers need a strong sense of self-esteem to be able to consider pressures around them and so their lifestyle choices. A person who has low self-esteem may take up smoking or drugs as a desire to belong as part of a group. Peer pressure will affect individuals' choices in, for example, fashion, music, food, sexuality and relationships. Adolescence can be a very impressionable time, so it is important to allow teenagers to explore areas of their life but within safe surroundings and with education about those choices.

Role models

Studied ☐

As we are growing up, it is important to have positive **role models** to show us how to behave or act in certain situations and to accept positive views of society. There may be good and bad role models, but as we are growing we look to parents and teachers for our positive influences. If we see parents resolving arguments in an aggressive way, then we may assume that is correct behaviour and do the same ourselves. Positive behaviour from role models will allow us to grow up with an open and respected view of society.

> **Key terms**
>
> **Role model:** A person we look up to who may influence our behaviour or lifestyle.

Media influence

Studied ☐

The media (forms of mass communication such as television, books, magazines, newspapers and the internet) has a huge influence on our attitudes and behaviour. The positive aspects of the media, for example in delivering education, are clear. This is evident in Unit 5 in the discussion about health promotion. However, the media can have a negative influence on our lifestyle choices. Individuals may read in a newspaper or magazine about a celebrity's poor lifestyle, which may include smoking, binge drinking and drug taking. It is possible that these individuals will see the celebrity behaviour as acceptable and adopt a similar lifestyle as a result.

Self-esteem levels

Studied ☐

The way we see ourselves may be completely different to how others see us. Imagine looking at yourself in the mirror. How do you see yourself? Is it different to how other people see you?

Many factors can affect our self-esteem, either positively or negatively. When individuals feel good about themselves, they feel the world is a good and happy place to live in. Having a good self-esteem helps us to succeed in education and society. Poor self-esteem may lead to fear, anxiety and low achievement in education and society. Children and young people should have positive experiences around them to help develop their self-esteem and reinforce a positive self-image.

Education and understanding

Studied ☐

A positive experience of education can benefit an individual. It can lead to a sense of achievement and well-being and can increase a person's job prospects in later life. Education may also have an impact on health and well-being. For example, if a member of one family has some knowledge of healthy diets and lifestyles, he or she can educate the whole family about how to avoid certain illnesses and diseases. However, deadlines and exam times can be a source of stress. People may experience bullying, which can negatively impact upon their self-esteem and well-being. A lack of education can negatively impact upon someone's achievement. It may also damage the individual's job prospects and financial prospects in later life.

Personal and family finances

Income is the money that comes into the home. This may be from paid employment, savings, investments or inheritance, or from benefits that come from the government if a person is unemployed or has a disability. Expenditure is money spent to provide for living needs. Clearly, the amount of expenditure is determined by the amount of the household income.

A high income allows a better choice of housing, education, health services, diet, clothes, transport, and so on. However, we should remember that a higher income does not always mean that better lifestyle choices are made. Government and other research show that people on a lower income are more likely to suffer ill health. In areas where income is low, the choice of housing may be limited. There may be a higher than average incidence of crime, which leads to stress in the family. Groups of people on a low income include unemployed people, some single-parent families, people with long-term illnesses, disabled people and older people.

Genetic inheritance

All humans carry a pattern of genes, which controls how our bodies develop and grow, so when we are formed we acquire half of our genes from each parent. Some of these genes can be information that determines diseases like sickle cell anemia and cystic fibrosis. Sometimes the genes are 'mutated'; this means a sudden and rare change that can happen and a condition like Down's syndrome can occur. Adults with a genetic disorder in the family may decide not to have children in order to avoid passing on serious illnesses. Some couples may require genetic counselling, which means they may talk to a specialist and calculate how likely the chance is of the disease happening. Some genetic disorders are sex linked. The mother may be a carrier of the disease but the illness will only occur if she has a male baby, for example haemophilia.

Mental health and illness

Mental illness can be so severe that individuals are unable to hold down a job, relationship or sometimes care for themselves. Other mental health problems can be treated and individuals carry out routine daily living activities, with the support of medication and therapy, for example depression. When people have mental health problems they may find it difficult to concentrate on certain areas of their life, so exercise and healthy eating may be a chore. If they have anxiety or depression they may be more inclined to use alcohol or drugs to make them feel able to cope with daily situations.

Check your understanding

Read the following case studies and decide which factors are contributing to their healthy or unhealthy lifestyles? Are these factors physical, intellectual, emotional or social?

Case study 1

Emma and Christopher are three-year-old twins. Their mother works full time as a nurse so works shifts and their father takes care of the household and childcare duties. He smokes occasionally but waits until the twins are asleep and goes out into the garden to smoke. The children have a strict routine, with mealtimes and bedtime always at the same time. The family sits down to enjoy a meal together once a day. Dad enjoys watching television while the twins are playing, but Mum worries about how this may influence the twins. Emma and Christopher play regularly with the children from next door, whose rules and manners are not as strict as theirs. Occasionally, the twins are confused when they see other children doing things they are not allowed to do.

Case study 2

Judith is a single mother, living in a small flat with her three-year-old son Thomas. Judith tries to budget on her low income but sometimes is forced to cut back on fresh fruit and vegetables. Sometimes she has to buy more expensive food from the local store as she cannot afford the bus fare to the supermarket, where cheaper brands and offers may be available to her.

The local environment where Judith lives has high unemployment and it is hard for her to find part-time work. She also struggles to afford suitable childcare arrangements. Judith would like to join a gym but cannot afford the time or money so is feeling quite unfit.

Key learning points

Healthy lifestyle

Revised

As defined by the World Health Organisation we should have all areas of our health in good working condition so that we can term ourselves healthy. Individuals with genetic or chronic ill health conditions should be termed healthy within their own boundaries and not discriminated against because of it.

Physical effects

Revised

Physical effects are to do with how our body works and whether it is affected by healthy or unhealthy lifestyles. Illnesses and diseases may become apparent from the way we treat our bodies with diet, exercise and drugs.

Intellectual effects

Revised ☐

Intellectual effects are those impacting on how our brain works and how we learn. Being healthy will mean being able to learn and think clearly. If this area is affected by an unhealthy lifestyle then an individual may not succeed in education, so may not fulfill their careers and goals.

Emotional effects

Revised ☐

Emotions are about our feelings and a healthy emotional lifestyle will affect our moods, self-confidence and self-esteem. Emotional issues may affect our mental health and the way we deal with issues.

Social effects

Revised ☐

Social effects can be shown in relationships and maintaining close relationships. A healthy social lifestyle means an individual will have close friendships. An unhealthy social lifestyle will cause loss of friendships, isolation and possible criminal behaviour.

Factors affecting a healthy or unhealthy lifestyle

Revised ☐

Many different factors – both healthy and unhealthy – can affect our lifestyles, some of which are more difficult to change than others. Underlying issues may cause someone to have an unhealthy lifestyle. For example an individual may drink excessive amounts of alcohol in order to cope with issues in their life.

Assessment activity

Work out the BMI for the following people:

1 Jim is 1.70 m and weighs 57 kg.
2 Billy is 1.83 m and weighs 121 kg.
3 Sian is 1.62 m and weighs 45 kg.
4 Sam is 1.55 m and weighs 70 kg.

Use the following guidelines to see whether they are under or overweight:

- Underweight: below 20
- Normal: 20–25
- Overweight: 25–30
- Obese: 30+

www.bbc.co.uk/health/tools/bmi_calculator/bmi.shtml - BMI calculator

Learning Aim B

B.1 Ways to improve health and well-being

Identify areas for potential improvement

Once we have identified and agreed to improve a particular area of our own or others' health, we need to develop plans to implement change. Suggested areas that an individual may wish to improve are set out below. See Figure 9.03

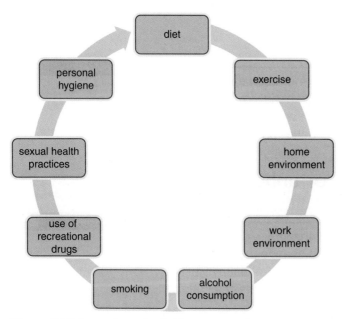

Figure 9.03 Areas for potential improvement

Improving health and well-being

Once an area for improvement has been identified and the individual has agreed to it, then it becomes the individual's own. This is important because some individuals will not improve their lifestyle if just told to do so; they have to take ownership of their problem and will then have some responsibility for the planning and setting of targets. These will be discussed in this section.

Assess difficulties

You then need to assess the difficulties that might be encountered in starting and keeping to a healthy lifestyle. It is all very well identifying areas of our lives that we need to improve on; the biggest problem is often sticking to the plans made to bring about change. How many times, for example, have you planned to join a gym, stop smoking, or cut down on alcohol consumption?

Getting started

Studied

It is important to set realistic and achievable goals, otherwise you will not see any progress and the plan may be lost. Support from professionals is important, as they can show you evidence about your achievements. For example, by doing a peak flow at the doctor's surgery you are able to see that your lung function is improving after cutting down smoking. Group support from family and friends, or specific group support like Weight Watchers, will provide the moral support to encourage you to keep going and seeing others in a slimming group lose weight will motivate you to carry on.

Time commitment

Studied

This is one of the biggest difficulties that prevents people from keeping to a healthy lifestyle. It is important to set time aside to exercise, attend slimming classes and visit clinics and professionals in order to stick to the plan. Planning ahead to fit in activities is important, as it is all too easy to say 'I haven't got time today'. You need to consider whether there is any likelihood of events occurring that may disrupt your plans. For example, if you are on a weight loss plan and an important celebration is coming up, you need to look at how you are best going to accommodate this within your lifestyle, while enjoying the celebration at the same time.

Motivation

Studied

Before individuals can be persuaded to change they need to be motivated. This means they want to make the necessary changes to improve their lifestyle. They also need to accept that they may encounter some short-term difficulties and it may be tough at first. Keeping and sticking to a plan is hard work so providing incentives may help when working towards a goal. For example, when losing weight you could have a photograph of a favourite or new piece of clothing you are going to fit into displayed in a prominent position. The plan must be achievable so that the outcome is realistic. By first setting a short-term goal you will be motivated to keep going. When you reach this goal you can set another one.

Setting realistic targets for improving health and well-being in different areas

Consider the areas mentioned above in which individuals may wish to improve themselves. After having decided on which areas to focus on, it is important not only to set realistic targets, but also to have an open mind about how people change their behaviour. For example, some people may want to stop smoking altogether, while others may need to cut down gradually. It is always the individual's choice and the plan should reflect this. Remember it is the individual's plan that is made with your advice, not your plan.

Remember that goals should be:

- S – Specific
- M – Measurable
- A – Achievable
- R – Realistic
- T – Timely.

Intervention strategies and their effects on health improvement

In order to keep people on target we need to suggest strategies to help them stick to their plan.

Healthy lifestyle plans

Studied

If the individual owns the plan and has been part of the planning process then he or she is more likely to stick to it. Keeping a diary to record how they are doing each day will enable individuals to reflect on their progress and it may help to motivate them. If they regularly review the plan with a professional, this will provide encouragement and help them to stay motivated.

Support strategies

Studied

Hypnotherapy and **acupuncture** can be used as specific strategies to help an individual to give up smoking or alcohol. These techniques can change people's behaviour and be a very effective method of improving lifestyles.

Key terms

Hypnotherapy: This aims to reprogramme patterns of behaviour within the mind, enabling irrational fears, phobias, negative thoughts and suppressed emotions to be overcome. Hypnotherapy is a state of induced trance-like condition. It is not a deep sleep as some may believe.

Acupuncture: This is a method of encouraging the body to promote natural healing and to improve functioning. This is done by inserting needles and applying heat or electrical stimulation at very precise acupuncture points.

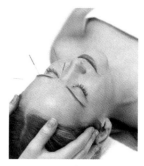

Figure 9.04 Acupuncture

Specific techniques

Studied ☐

Nicotine replacement therapy

Nicotine replacement therapy (sometimes called NRT) provides a supply of nicotine to your body. It gives you a smaller, short-term supply of the drug than your body is used to getting from cigarettes. Most people use it for the first three months after stopping smoking, although you can use it for as long as you need to. NRT is supplied as patches, gum, inhalers, tablets that you put under your tongue, lozenges, and a nasal spray.

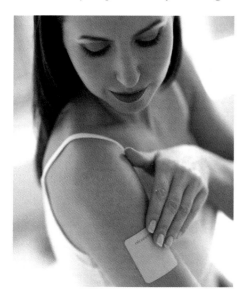

Figure 9.05 Nicotine replacement therapy

Face-to-face support

This type of support is required for behaviours that can be harmful and cause mental health issues, such as alcohol consumption and use of recreational drugs. Support can be provided through groups or one-to-one counselling sessions that will include discussion about how to change behaviour and how to deal with withdrawal from drugs or alcohol. This type of support is essential, as individuals may experience detrimental effects to their health if they just withdraw immediately from drugs or alcohol without any support.

Topic B1

219

B.2 Types and sources of support available to help promote healthy lifestyles

Forms of support

For most people, tackling an area of their lifestyle that requires change is not easy and help and support should be made available.

We can give support in many different ways, depending on whom we are supporting and how we are providing support.

Listening

Listening is a skill and is a great support to someone who requires help. If you can listen, respond and understand someone's situation and point of view you will be invaluable. In too many cases we hear that people have no time to listen to others.

Empathy

This is the ability to understand another person's feelings. It is not to feel sorry for the person but to show that you are aware of what it may be like to be in his or her situation. Perhaps you have been in the same situation, which may help you to be empathetic towards others.

Encouragement

This can be in the form of verbal encouragement but also can be displayed in other ways. If one of your family members gives up smoking, for example, you may want to show encouragement by giving your relative a hug or booking a meal out at his or her favourite restaurant. To know that someone is on your side, giving you encouragement, can be a tremendous help and support.

Advice and guidance

You may adopt an educational approach when offering advice and guidance, giving practical information about ways to follow a healthy lifestyle. Some people may prefer to receive advice and guidance from someone who has had a similar experience. For example, an individual who is trying to give up smoking may find it beneficial to talk to someone who has been through the process and stopped smoking. Written advice may be given in leaflet form, or a doctor, nurse or counsellor may prescribe advice.

> **Key terms**
> **Empathy:** Experiencing and feeling other people's situations and sharing an understanding.

Formal support

Studied ☐

This is usually organised support from a professional body, which will provide support for a particular illness, disease or condition. Formal support may be provided by the NHS or be a paid-for service from a private source. Examples of formal support are shown in Figure 9.06.

Informal support

Studied ☐

This support is usually provided by friends, family and community organisations such as charities or local churches. The support offered may be basic but necessary; it may include shopping, cleaning or chatting, in addition to transport to and from hospital appointments. Examples of informal support are shown in Figure 9.07.

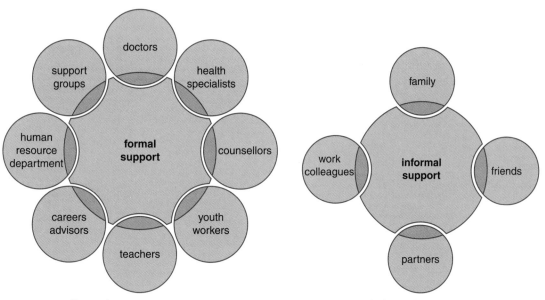

Figure 9.06 Formal support

Figure 9.07 Informal support

Support in maintaining positive change

Studied ☐

Whether the support is formal or informal, it is important that the aim is to:

- keep to the plan for healthy lifestyle changes
- maintain a positive outlook.

The types of support may vary and differ in their approaches and lengths and they may be adapted according to the needs of the individual, for example, someone who is trying to lose weight may first need medical advice and a strict dietary plan. As this begins to have an effect he or she may need help and support from a local slimming group, as well as family and friends.

B.3 The barriers to achieving a healthy lifestyle

Limitations

Sometimes change is very difficult and although individuals may see the benefits of change, they may sometimes encounter barriers which stop them from making the change. These are discussed below.

Genetic factors

Studied ☐

In Section A4 we saw that if individuals have a genetic condition which predisposes them to ill health this will stop them from having optimum health. This is something that cannot be changed and is part of their genetic makeup. However, many people with genetic conditions live a full and active lifestyle.

> **Key terms**
> **Genetics:** Factors we inherit from our parents that we cannot change and make us who we are.

Current physical condition

Studied ☐

Medical conditions may be a barrier to optimum health but many people live with chronic conditions like diabetes and epilepsy and with medication they are well. It is when the individuals do not take care of their condition and ignore medical advice that they may suffer ill health. Individuals who have medical conditions because of an unhealthy lifestyle may feel they are unable to change their lifestyle as it may be 'too late'. A smoker who has had heart surgery and has chronic obstructive airways disease may have to live with these consequences, which can be seen as a barrier to improving their lifestyle.

Unrealistic goals

Studied ☐

It is all too easy to say how we are going to change, but if we make goals that we are unable to achieve it may cause us to move away from the plan. There is no harm in having a long-term goal but it needs to be achievable and realistic. A few short-term interim goals will help us towards a healthy lifestyle.

Motivation to change

Studied ☐

Motivation to change is an important factor. This has been discussed above in Section B1.

Influence of partners and family

The behaviour of those around you in your immediate environment may be a barrier to changing your lifestyle. If those people close to you smoke, drink, or have unhealthy eating habits it becomes very difficult to focus on change by yourself and the reasons for change become difficult to appreciate.

Peer group pressure

As we saw in Section A4 negative peer pressure can lead individuals to choose unhealthy lifestyles because of those around them. The need to be part of a group as a teenager is more important than change and the benefits of change may be unimportant at this time.

Media influence

The media can be a negative influence that prevents people from wanting to aspire to achieving a healthy lifestyle. The media may portray celebrities enjoying a life with alcohol and drugs, and music may contain lyrics that condone the use of drugs; for example, 'We Are Young' by the group Fun talks about the effects of drugs, saying '*My friends are in the bathroom getting higher than the Empire State*'. These images and influences do not encourage individuals to change; in fact they may sometimes have the opposite effect.

Self-esteem levels

Self-esteem is a term used to judge your attitudes and values towards yourself. So an individual who has low self-esteem will not have the confidence to change and may be unable to see the reasons for change. Having low self-esteem will affect the person's pride and worthiness and may have a negative impact on their body image.

Time available

This has been discussed in Section B1.

Lack of education or understanding

If individuals do not understand the reason for change or its benefits, it will be difficult to motivate them to change. Education will give the reasons for change. Research shows that people from a poor social background may live in a poor area with poor housing conditions. These areas often have schools with low levels of achievement and temporary teachers and this will affect individuals' career goals.

Topic B3

223

Addiction

Studied ☐

Addiction and dependency on substances such as illegal drugs, alcohol, or smoking are barriers to change, as these substances act on a person's brain and can become all consuming so the individual's thoughts are about the next cigarette, drink or drug. An individual in this condition may know he or she needs to change but is physically unable to do so.

Financial barriers

Studied ☐

The financial cost of making a change may prevent some individuals from doing so. For example, an individual may wish to increase his or her physical activity but be hindered by the cost of classes or joining a gym. Weight loss and choosing a different meal to others in a family also may be costly, as is joining a weekly weight loss class, which may also suggest eating specific food brands that are expensive.

Availability of negative lifestyle choices

Studied ☐

As with media and peer pressure, if an individual is surrounded by people at work and home who smoke, and they wish to give up smoking then the choice to have a cigarette in times of stress may be too easy.

Lack of access to support

Studied ☐

If an individual is trying to achieve a healthy lifestyle single handed then it can be a difficult task. If people do not have close support and encouragement, it may be very easy for them to stop the plan to change, especially if they are feeling lonely or fed up and unsupported.

Real life connection

Pharmacy assistant

Pharmacy assistants work alongside pharmacy technicians and under the supervision of a registered pharmacist. They work in hospital and community settings. In the community sector their job titles may include 'dispenser', 'dispensing assistant', 'pharmacy assistant' and 'healthcare assistant'. Within the hospital sector, the titles 'pharmacy assistant' and 'assistant technical officer' are more commonly used.

To be considered for a pharmacy assistant role, applicants will usually need to have a good standard of education and some GCSEs at grade C or above (or equivalent) can be an advantage. Some posts may require specific GCSE grades (or equivalent), such as A–C in English, maths and a science subject.

Adult nursing

Adult nurses work with old and young adults with a variety of health conditions. They use skills of caring, counselling, managing, teaching and all aspects of interpersonal skills to improve the quality of care. They work in hospital wards, clinics or community settings and do shift work including night shifts, bank holidays and weekends. Nurses study for three years at university and must be registered with the Nursing and Midwifery Council in order to practice. The starting salary for a nurse is around £21,000 and there are opportunities for progression into management or teaching.

Check your understanding

Case study

Mark and Susan live in a large detached home in the suburbs of a town. Mark earns a high salary, but his work takes him away from the family for most of the week. Susan works part time and is able to take and collect her teenage daughter Louise from high school. Their lives are extremely busy and have little routine. Susan buys a lot of convenience foods to save time on cooking, but she always provides a hot meal for her daughter. Mark eats out a lot while entertaining clients in restaurants. He also drinks alcohol more than he should during his meetings with clients, and though he is aware of his weekly limits he often exceeds them. He sometimes misses meals because of his work commitments, or eats 'on the go' while travelling. Although he works very hard and is hardly ever at home, he feels it is worthwhile to provide money for family holidays abroad twice a year.

Look at the case study above and consider the following points:

1. Identify areas for improvement for Mark and Susan.

2. Suggest support that could be offered – is it formal or informal?

3. What influences are there which will encourage a healthy lifestyle? What barriers could you suggest that may stop Mark from achieving a healthy lifestyle?

Key learning points

Realistic targets

Revised ☐

These are usually a mixture of short-and long-term goals that are appropriate for the individual.

Intervention strategies

Revised ☐

Methods which can be used alongside health plans; these may include technical and alternative methods.

Formal support

Revised ☐

This is support that may be organised professionally, or on a regular basis. It can be funded by the NHS or paid for privately.

Informal support

Revised ☐

This is support from friends, family and organisations in the community; for example, churches and local charities.

Limitations

Revised ☐

This means a barrier that inhibits an individual from leading a healthy lifestyle.

Influences

Revised ☐

These can be positive or negative aspects which can lead to a healthy or unhealthy lifestyle.

Sample assessment paper

Health and social care

Unit 9: Healthy Living

Sample assessment paper

Time: 1 hour

Total marks: 50

1 When considering healthy and unhealthy lifestyles, we have to look at the impact that it has on the four different areas of health. Can you name all four areas? (4 marks)

2 (a) Exercise has many benefits and leads to a healthy lifestyle. Suggest two benefits. (2 marks)

   (b) If an individual does not take regular exercise, he or she is more likely to suffer negative effects. Suggest two effects. (2 marks)

3. Sleep patterns can affect a person's physical and emotional health. Suggest two reasons why. (2 marks)

   (a) Physical
   (b) Emotional

4 The use of recreational drugs can have a negative effect on an individual's lifestyle. Suggest two reasons why. (2 marks)

5 (a) A healthy diet is essential for our bodies to grow and develop and it has a positive effect on our lifestyles. Suggest two reasons why. (2 marks)

   (b) A diet which is high in saturated fats may cause ill health. Choose the item from the list below that best describes the condition you may suffer from. (1 mark for the correct answer)

   - Body odour
   - Weight loss
   - Anxiety
   - Obesity

   (c) A diet high in sugar can also have negative effects on the body. Choose the item from the list below that best describes the condition you may suffer from. (1 mark for the correct answer)

   - Tooth decay
   - Constipation
   - Pregnancy
   - Lung disease

6 A good home environment with personal space and positive influences within it is important to all of us. This allows us to develop and grow as individuals.

(a) Suggest two benefits of a positive home environment. (2 marks)

(b) If the home environment is overcrowded, damp and has high levels of anxiety and conflict within it, there may be a negative impact on family life. (1 mark)

7   Janine is 18 years old and drinks alcohol on a regular basis. She is unaware of the recommended limits for women and drinks each night to unwind from her busy job. Below is a guide to the numbers of units alcohol contains. The recommended units for women is 21 units per week, or 2–3 units a day, with at least 2 days without alcohol.

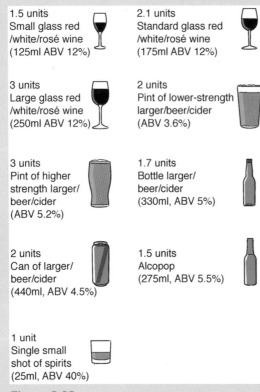

Figure 9.08

(a)   Janine drinks the following amounts of alcohol:

- Monday – 2 pints of larger
- Tuesday – 3 alcopops
- Wednesday – none
- Thursday – 3 small glasses of white wine (125 ml)
- Friday – 3 large glasses of white wine (175 ml)
- Saturday – 4 shots of vodka and diet coke
- Sunday – none.

(i)   What is Janine's unit intake per week? (1 mark)

(ii)   Is this over or under the weekly recommendation? (1 mark)

(iii)   By how much? (1 mark)

(b) If Janine carries on with this lifestyle, how may it affect her health? Give two suggestions.(2 marks)

(c) Janine enjoys drinking, as she finds it a good way to relax and unwind from a stressful day at work. Explain what barriers Janine may come across if she decides to reduce her alcohol intake? (6 marks)

(d) If Janine changed her habits what positive effect would this have on her physical and emotional health?

    (i) Physical (1 mark)

    (ii)Emotional (1 mark)

(e) Janine may need support to change her lifestyle. Can you suggest some support she could access?

    (i) 2 types of formal support (2 marks)

    (ii)2 types of informal support (2 marks)

8 Smoking is harmful to health. Liam has been smoking since he was 12 years old. He is now 21 years old.

    (a) Suggest two risks to health caused by regular smoking. (2 marks)

    (b)Suggest two techniques that could be used to help Liam reduce his smoking habit. (2 marks)

9 The Stephenson family do not do any physical exercise at the moment. Anita and Sam, who both work full time, are aged 30. They have 3-year-old twins Charlie and Carole. Before the twins were born Anita and Sam were members of the local badminton club and went swimming twice a week. Their current very busy lifestyles have hindered their exercise regime. Anita and Sam now feel they need to get the family into a healthy exercise programme that meets all their needs.

    (a) What strategies can be used to support their new exercise plan? (5 marks)

    (b)What potential barriers can you foresee which may hinder the family's exercise plan? (5 marks)

Unit 10

Human Body Systems and Care of Disorders

It is important for people working in Health and Social Care to understand how human body systems work so that they can offer the right care to individuals with particular problems. This unit will provide knowledge and understanding about the way our bodies work and will look at the way in which the main body systems work and their relationships with each other. It will also look at disorders that can happen to these systems and the ways in which routine care can be provided to treat these disorders.

Learning aims

In this unit you will:

✓ understand the structure and function of main body organs and major body systems, and their relationships

✓ explore routine care of disorders relating to body systems.

Assessment criteria

Level 2 Pass	Level 2 Merit	Level 2 Distinction
Learning aim A: Understand the structure and function of main organs and major body systems, and their interrelationships		
2A.P1 Describe the structure and function of the main organs in the human body.	2A.M1 Explain the function of component parts of one major system in the human body.	2A.D1 Analyse how body systems interrelate to maintain one example of homeostasis in the human body.
2A.P2 Describe the structure of major systems in the human body.	2A.M2 Explain how two major body systems interrelate.	
2A.P3 Describe the functions of major systems in the human body.		
2A.P4 Describe the relationship between major body systems.		
Learning aim B: Explore routine care of disorders relating to body systems		
2B.P5 Describe one common disorder related to each major body system.	2B.M3 Explain in detail the effects of three common disorders on the major body systems.	2B.D2 Recommend and justify appropriate routine care for a selected individual with a common disorder.
2B.P6 Describe the routine care given for one common disorder related to each major body system.	2B.M4 Discuss the impact of routine care given to individuals, with reference to a selected example.	
2B.P7 Carry out and record over a period of time one routine observation that can be used to support care, interpreting your results in relation to norm values.		

Learning Aim A

A.1 Structure and functions of main body organs

The main body organs and their functions are given in Table 10.01

Table 10.01 The organs of the body

Organ	Main function	System
Skin	Protects the body from harmful bacteria with a waterproof barrier. It controls body temperature and has the ability to repair itself.	Excretory
Heart	A specialised muscle that contracts regularly and continuously, pumping blood to the body and the lungs. The pumping action is caused by a flow of electricity through the heart that repeats itself in a cycle.	Cardiovascular
Lungs	We have two lungs, which supply our bodies with the vital oxygen required for our bodies to function properly. They are also responsible for getting rid of the waste product carbon dioxide.	Respiratory
Brain	The main control centre for the body, which is responsible for all functions within the body, whether under voluntary or involuntary control.	Nervous
Eyes	Our eyes are moved by muscles, which allows us to look up and down and from side to side without moving our head. Normally, both eyes work together to form a picture on the retina, which is then interpreted by the brain.	Nervous
Ears	The organs of hearing and balance. Our ears have three sections: outer ear, middle ear and inner ear. Noise or sound waves enter our outer ear and are channelled down the canal until they reach our eardrum. Once the sound wave reaches our eardrum, it vibrates and the sound waves then pass into the middle ear. Our middle ear is an air-filled cavity that links the outer ear with the inner ear.	Nervous
Stomach	A food bag that stores, warms and softens food and drink. It is able to expand and contract in response to how much it contains. It converts solids into fluid to promote digestion, squeezes food towards its exit and then squirts it rhythmically into the next part of the intestine.	Digestive
Pancreas	Produces digestive juices (enzymes) that continue the process of breaking down foods that begins in the stomach. The pancreas also produces hormones and insulin, which controls the balance of glucose between the blood and the rest of the body.	Digestive
Intestines	In the small intestine the food mixes with vital enzymes secreted by the liver and the pancreas. Fats and proteins are mainly digested in the small intestine. The large intestine receives the end products of the digestion process where water and other nutrients are absorbed. Waste products to be excreted are stored in the end segment known as the rectum.	Digestive
Liver	The centre of your metabolism. Complex chemical processes take place in the liver and it controls the body's absorption of food. It carries out more than 500 separate processes concerned with regulating all the main chemicals in the blood and many other life-supporting functions.	Digestive

Kidneys	Filter the blood, clean it and keep its composition balanced. They maintain appropriate levels of fluids, minerals and other substances, including salt and water. They react to hormones from the brain and produce vital hormones of their own.	Excretory
Bladder	Urine drains from the kidneys into the bladder via two tubes – ureters. It is then stored in the bladder. The bladder stretches and fills and at a convenient time is emptied via another tube (urethra).	Excretory
Ovaries	There are two ovaries, one at each end of the fallopian tubes. The ovaries are responsible for the storage and release of eggs (ova). They produce the female hormones oestrogen and progesterone.	Reproductive
Testes	Men have two testes, which are responsible for the production, storage and release of sperm. They produce the male hormone testosterone.	Reproductive
Uterus	Also known as the womb, it is a hollow, pear-shaped organ, which has a thick blood supply and allows the implantation of the developing foetus and growth of the newborn.	Reproductive

Check your understanding

As a class, divide into small groups, each taking one of the organs listed below. Each group should draw the organ, label it and give a brief description of its function. On a large piece of paper, draw the outline of a simple 'gingerbread person'. Place your organ and description in its correct location. Display this in your classroom as help for P1 of your assignment.

- skin
- heart
- lungs
- brain
- eye
- ear
- stomach
- pancreas
- intestines
- liver
- kidneys
- bladder
- ovaries
- testes
- uterus.

Visit www.bbc.co.uk/science/humanbody and follow the interactive body link to play the organs game.

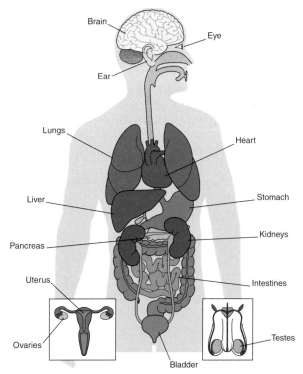

Figure 10.01 The organs of the human body

Circulatory system

The main function of the circulatory system is to transport oxygen and nutrients to the tissues and take away from the tissues carbon dioxide and other waste products. The cardiovascular system consists of the:

- heart
- blood
- blood vessels.

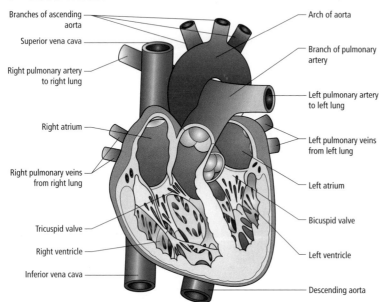

Figure 10.02 The structure of the heart

The heart

Studied

The heart is a large muscle, which contracts rhythmically so that the blood can be transported to the lungs to collect oxygen, then to the body, organs and tissues to deliver the oxygen. It then collects carbon dioxide from the body organs and tissues, taking it back to the heart and lungs. The heart is split into four chambers: two upper chambers (atria) and two lower chambers (ventricles).

The right side of the heart pumps the blood to the lungs to collect oxygen, while the left side pumps blood around the body. The heart can be called a double pump. The left side of the heart muscle is much larger and thicker, as it has a greater distance to pump the blood around.

The 'heartbeat' is the sound of blood being pushed through the valves of the heart through its four chambers.

How blood flows through the heart

Blood flows through the heart in the following way:

- **Oxygenated** blood from the lungs returns to the heart and enters the left atrium.
- Blood is forced out of the aorta (main artery of the blood) and carries the oxygenated blood to the rest of the body.
- **Deoxygenated** blood returns from the body to the right atrium.
- The blood is then pushed into the right ventricle.
- Blood is forced through the pulmonary artery, which carries the deoxygenated blood to the lungs.
- The whole process is a cycle and begins again.

Oxygen-rich blood is carried in arteries to all tissues in the body; then blood with carbon dioxide from the tissues is taken back to the heart in veins.

> **Key terms**
>
> **Oxygenated:** Blood which is combined with oxygen
>
> **Deoxygenated:** Blood which has no oxygen and is combined with carbon dioxide

Blood vessels

Studied ☐

There are three types of blood vessels in our bodies:

1. Arteries
2. Veins
3. Capillaries

Table 10.02 shows the differences between arteries and veins.

Table 10.02 Differences between arteries and veins

Arteries	Veins
Carry blood away from the heart	Carry blood towards the heart
Carry oxygenated blood	Carry deoxygenated blood
Blood flows rapidly	Blood flows slowly
Blood flows under high pressure	Blood flows under low pressure
Blood flows in pulses	Blood flows by squeezing action
Walls are thick	Walls are thin
Valves absent	Valves present
Internal diameter small	Internal diameter large
Cross-section round	Cross-section oval

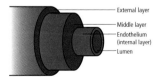

Figure 10.03 An artery

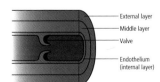

Figure 10.04 A vein

Capillaries

Capillaries are thin-walled vessels that consist of a single layer of cells that allows oxygen, vitamins, minerals and water to be exchanged into the tissues to nourish the cells. Carbon dioxide and water then pass out of the cells to be excreted.

Figure 10.05 A capillary

Blood

Blood is made up of 55 per cent plasma and 45 per cent blood cells. Plasma is the liquid portion of your blood. It has a number of vital functions in bleeding and infection control. It contains proteins and antibodies, which are produced by the immune system to fight diseases. Blood cells are suspended in the plasma. An average adult has around 5 to 6 litres of blood in their vessels.

Red blood cells make the blood look red and it's these that deliver oxygen to the cells in the body and carry back waste gases in exchange. The red blood cells look like tiny inner tubes or donuts under a microscope. In the middle is where the oxygen sits.

Figure 10.06 Red blood cell

White blood cells are part of your body's defense against disease. Some will attack and kill germs by devouring them and others will attack and kill by manufacturing and producing chemical agents against disease.

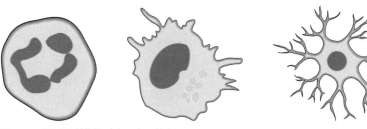

Figure 10.07 White blood cells

Platelets are other cells that help your body to repair itself after injury. Platelets play an important role in blood clotting. When a small vessel is injured, platelets stick to each other and the edges of the injury and form a plug that covers the area. The plug or blood clot formed stops the loss of blood.

Figure 10.08 Platelet

The functions of blood

The functions of blood include:

- *Transportation* – blood carries nutrients from the **digestive system** to the body cells. It carries oxygen from the lungs to the working muscles. It removes waste like CO_2 via the lungs and other waste products, like excess water, via the kidneys. Blood transports hormones to where they are needed.
- *Protection* – blood carries white cells to areas of infection. It carries antibodies to fight germs. It carries platelets to injured areas to form clots.
- *Temperature regulation* – Blood carries heat away from working muscles and the centre of the body to the skin. It maintains the temperature within the body.
- *Body equilibrium* – blood reduces the effects of lactic acid that is produced in the muscles. It regulates fluid balance.

Respiratory system

The function of the respiratory system is to deliver oxygen into the body by breathing in and to remove waste carbon dioxide and water from the body by breathing out. These actions are called inspiration (breathing in) and expiration (breathing out).

The respiratory system consists of:

- mouth
- nose
- larynx (voice box)
- trachea
- lungs (x2)
- bronchus (x2)
- bronchioles
- alveoli.

The respiratory system has a similar structure to the trunk and branches of a tree (see figure 10.09). Oxygen is breathed into the body and carbon dioxide is breathed out of the body via the trachea and bronchus. These are similar to the main trunk of the tree. As air travels down the trachea, bronchus and bronchioles, any particles of dust are trapped by tiny hairs that line these tubes. The exchange of oxygen and carbon dioxide takes place at the end of the branches (bronchioles) in the alveoli. The alveoli are structures like bunches of grapes, which allow maximum crossover of gases back and forth to make the process efficient.

The process of **inhalation** is automatic – you don't have to think about breathing.

Muscles in the rib cage and a special muscle underneath the lungs, called the diaphragm, also help with the process of respiration.

Put your hands on your ribcage and feel your breathing. Can you explain what happens when you breathe in and then breathe out?

> **Key term**
>
> Inhalation: This is the process of breathing in oxygen and exhalation is the process of breathing out carbon dioxide.

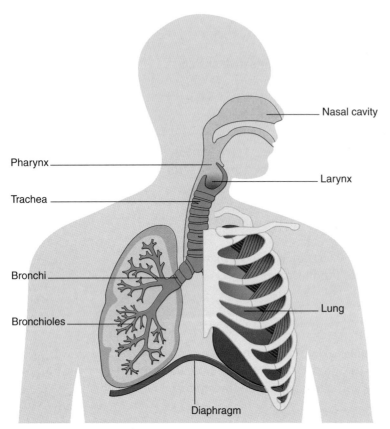

Figure 10.09 The respiratory system

- Nasal cavity
- Pharynx
- Larynx
- Trachea
- Bronchi
- Lung
- Bronchioles
- Diaphragm

Nervous system

The main functions of the nervous system are:

- to *receive* information from our external and internal environment
- to *interpret* (make sense of) this information
- and then to *take actions* accordingly.

This could be actions like walking, talking or running away. Or it could be actions such as reducing body temperature, increasing heartbeat or regulating water balance. In this way, your nervous system is similar to a telephone exchange: it receives messages from all over the body, interprets them and sends out messages with answers to make changes.

The nervous system is split into two parts: the central nervous system – brain and spinal cord – and the peripheral nervous system – nerves. All messages are sent from sensory receptors via a sensory nerve to the brain or spinal cord. The brain or spinal cord then interprets the message and responses are made by the motor neurones to the effectors to make the change or movement.

The brain

The brain consists of billions of nerve cells. It is responding all the time to external and internal messages – those outside you and within you. For example, as you are reading this book your brain is interpreting information and allowing you to understand new ideas and perhaps make pictures. It will also be responding to external things. For example, are you feeling hot or cold? Your brain adjusts the internal environment to help you to feel comfortable, as well as creating feelings or emotions.

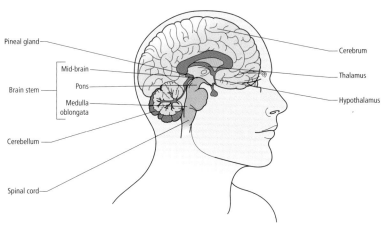

Figure 10.10 The brain

Spinal cord

This runs from the base of the brain to the lower part of the back (lumbar region). It is a bundle of nerve fibres, nerve cells and blood vessels. The spinal cord is protected by the spinal vertebrae in the spinal column. The spinal cord is also protected by a tough outer membrane and between this and the spinal cord is a fluid that acts as a shock absorber, called cerebrospinal fluid.

Nerves

There are 43 pairs of nerves that make up the central nervous system. Twelve of these pairs are the cranial nerves, which supply the brain, and the other 31 pairs are spinal nerves, which supply the rest of the body. Nerves vary in thickness and consist of bundles of nerve cells.

Nerves are made up of nerve cells or neurones and there are three basic kinds:

1. Sensory neurones relay impulses from the sense organs to the central nervous system.
2. Motor neurones relay the impulses from the central nervous system to the muscles or glands.
3. Relay neurones transport impulses between nerves.

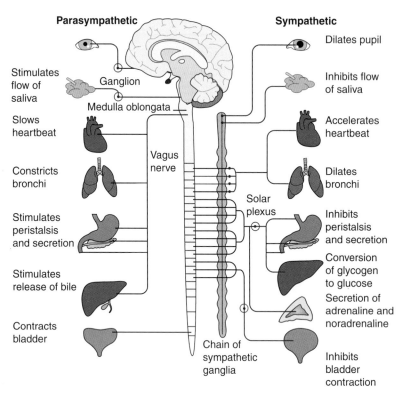

Parasympathetic

Stimulates flow of saliva

Ganglion

Medulla oblongata

Slows heartbeat

Constricts bronchi

Vagus nerve

Stimulates peristalsis and secretion

Stimulates release of bile

Contracts bladder

Chain of sympathetic ganglia

Sympathetic

Dilates pupil

Inhibits flow of saliva

Accelerates heartbeat

Dilates bronchi

Solar plexus

Inhibits peristalsis and secretion

Conversion of glycogen to glucose

Secretion of adrenaline and noradrenaline

Inhibits bladder contraction

Figure 10.11 The nervous system

a. **Reflex actions** are movements that you do without thinking, such as blinking or your mouth watering. These actions are done in response to external stimuli, but you do not always have control over them. Have you ever tried not blinking for a few minutes?

b. **Voluntary actions** are actions that we do have control over. You can decide to walk, run, sit down, read or write. These actions are under your control.

The autonomic nervous system

Studied ☐

This part of the nervous system is not under our control. It has two parts, called the sympathetic and parasympathetic nervous systems, which together are responsible for maintaining vital organs and the stability of the body internally (homeostasis). This is discussed later in the unit.

The sympathetic nervous system prepares our bodies for fright, flight or fight situations, so this means our bodies will be prepared for immediate action. Study Figure 10.11 to see what effect the hormone adrenaline has on the body.

The parasympathetic nervous system has the opposite effect. It slows down the heart rate and allows the body to relax and recover.

We also rely on our five senses to help us understand the world around us. These are:

- sight
- hearing
- touch
- taste
- smell.

Renal system

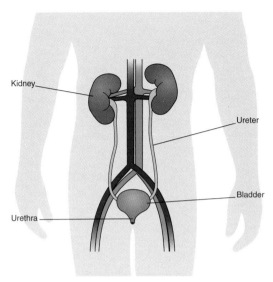

Figure 10.12 The renal system

The kidneys

Studied ☐

You have two kidneys, which filter the blood like a sieve. The kidneys keep in substances that are useful to the body and excrete waste substances together with water, which is called urine. Your kidneys also adjust the water, salt and acid balance of your blood through a process called osmoregulation. The kidneys are bean shaped and are situated on either side of the vertebrae (spine). They are about the size of a clenched fist. The right kidney is slightly lower than the left one, as it is below the liver.

The nephron is the working part of the kidney and spans all three regions of the kidney.

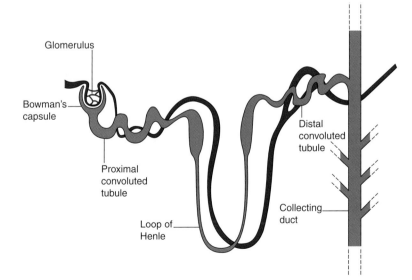

Figure 10.13 How a nephron works

The inside of a kidney has three regions:

1. cortex
2. medulla
3. pelvis

The ureters

These lead from each kidney and take urine to the bladder. They are long, muscular tubes that move the urine along by peristalsis. They are around 30 cm long.

The bladder

This is the muscular storage sack for urine and when full (adult) can hold up to 500 ml. Emptying the bladder, or urination, is under voluntary control in most adults. It is triggered by the sensory nerves in the bladder, which send messages to the brain that the bladder is ready to be emptied.

The urethra

This is the muscular tube that runs from the bladder to the outside of the body. In women the urethra is about 4 cm long and in men it is about 20 cm long, as it runs through the penis.

Digestive system

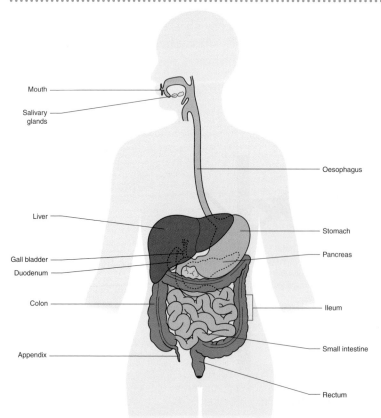

> **Key term**
>
> **The digestive system or alimentary canal:** This runs from your mouth to your anus and is approximately 8 m long.

Figure 10.14 The digestive system

The digestive system consists of the mouth, salivary glands, pharynx, oesophagus, stomach, duodenum, ileum, colon, liver and pancreas.

Physical and chemical digestion take place at the same time – while the teeth and tongue are grinding and mashing the food, the enzymes can mix with the food to break it down even more.

Watch the digestive system in action by visiting the website www.constipationadvice.co.uk and go to the section called 'How it works'.

The process of digestion is as follows:

1. *Ingestion* – food is taken into the mouth and digestion starts. Chemical and physical breakdown of food takes place. Food is cut and ground into small pieces. The food is made into a soft bolus with the help of saliva. Food is pushed to the back of the mouth and is swallowed; from here it travels into the oesophagus to the stomach by a process called peristalsis.
2. *Digestion* – when the food reaches the stomach it is further broken down by gastric juice; it is now a thick liquid called chyme. Food stays in the stomach for around 3 to 5 hours.
3. *Absorption* – as the food is passed into the small intestine more enzymes from the pancreas further break down the food, and bile from the liver breaks down fats. It is then taken from the gut wall into the bloodstream.
4. *Assimilation* – this is the process where nutrients are used within the cells.
5. *Elimination* – this is when the food that has not been digested moves into the large intestine. This leaves a semi-solid mass called faeces. It is eliminated via the anus.

Endocrine system

The endocrine system produces chemical messages called hormones. These hormones are released by glands into the bloodstream. Once in the bloodstream, they target organs and can affect the structure and function of that part of the body. There are 39 hormones, which work with the nervous system to maintain homeostasis in the body. This is discussed further in this unit in A4 under 'Coordination of systems through homeostasis'.

The glands that secrete these hormones work in a system called negative feedback. Negative feedback means the gland is stimulated to produce more of the hormone when needed and to stop producing it when there is enough of the hormone in the body. It is a balancing act, which is carried out effectively by our bodies.

The endocrine system is responsible for the production and release of hormones into the blood stream, which control growth, metabolism, sex characteristics, pregnancy, milk production and water balance. See Table 10.03

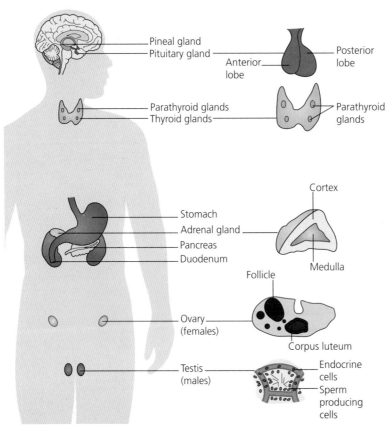

Pineal gland
Pituitary gland
Anterior lobe
Posterior lobe

Parathyroid glands
Thyroid glands
Parathyroid glands

Cortex

Stomach
Adrenal gland
Pancreas
Duodenum

Medulla

Follicle

Ovary (females)

Corpus luteum

Testis (males)
Endocrine cells
Sperm producing cells

Figure 10.15 The endocrine system

> **Key term**
> **Hormones:** These are chemical messages released into the blood stream to affect organs and their functions.

Table 10.03 Hormones and their effects

Name of gland	Hormone	Effect
Hypothalamus	The hypothalamus is a collection of specialised cells that forms the link between the endocrine system and the nervous system; it is situated in the lower central part of the brain.	With the pituitary gland, it controls the amount of hormones in the bloodstream.
Pituitary (master gland) Anterior lobe Posterior lobe	Growth Hormone (GH)	Stimulates growth of bones and muscles
	Prolactin	Stimulates breast milk production
	Thyroid Stimulating Hormone (TSH)	Controls secretion of thyroxine
	Adrenocorticotropic Hormone (ACTH)	Controls secretion of adrenal glands
	Follicle Stimulating Hormone (FSH)	Controls production of eggs/sperm
	Luteinising Hormone (LH)	Controls secretion of sex hormone
	Oxytocin	Stimulates uterus to contract at end of pregnancy
	Anti-diuretic Hormone (ADH)	Controls urine production

Pineal gland	Melatonin	Affects wake and sleep patterns
Thyroid gland	Thyroxine	Controls metabolic rate
Parathyroid gland	Parathyroid hormone	Controls blood calcium levels
Adrenal glands	Corticosteroids	Controls chemical balance
		Prepares body for physical action
Pancreas	Insulin	Reduces blood sugar level
	Glucagon	Raises blood sugar level
Testes	Testosterone	Sperm production
		Secondary sex characteristics
Ovaries	Oestrogen	Secondary sex characteristics
	Progesterone	Prepares for and maintains pregnancy

Reproductive system

This system is involved in the production of specialised cells called sex cells or gametes (eggs and sperm). When an egg and sperm join together it is called fertilisation and the combined cells are known as a zygote. It now contains characteristics (genes) from both parents.

The male reproductive system

Studied ☐

The male reproductive system has three main functions:

1. The testes produce sperm.
2. The penis deposits sperm inside the female reproductive system.
3. The testes produce the hormone testosterone (you will have investigated this in the endocrine system).

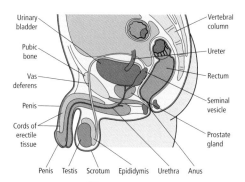

Figure 10.16 The male reproductive system

Sperm is produced in the testes, which are located in the scrotum. The testes are external organs that keep sperm at a temperature lower than body temperature to keep it alive. When sperm is needed, it is released and travels along the vas deferens and past the prostate gland, where it receives nutrients and fluid to keep it alive. In sexual intercourse, during ejaculation, sperm travels along the urethra of the erect penis and is deposited in the female vagina.

The female reproductive system

Studied ☐

The female reproductive system has four main functions:

1. The ovaries produce eggs or ova.
2. The uterus provides a safe environment for the developing foetus where it can be nourished.
3. The ovaries produce the hormones oestrogen and progesterone (you will have investigated these in the endocrine system).
4. The mammary glands (breasts) produce milk for the newborn baby.

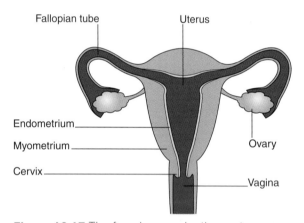

Figure 10.17 The female reproductive system

The female reproductive system is made up of two ovaries, two fallopian tubes, the uterus, the cervix and the vagina. An ovum (egg) is released from alternate ovaries each month (approximately every 28 days). The egg travels along the fallopian tube where it can be fertilised. When it is fertilised by a sperm, the ball of growing cells travels into the uterus where it embeds to begin the formation of a foetus. After approximately 40 weeks the baby is born.

Musculoskeletal system

This system contains the muscles and bones of the body. Its function is to provide support and movement of the body, as well as protection of vital body organs.

The skeleton

Studied

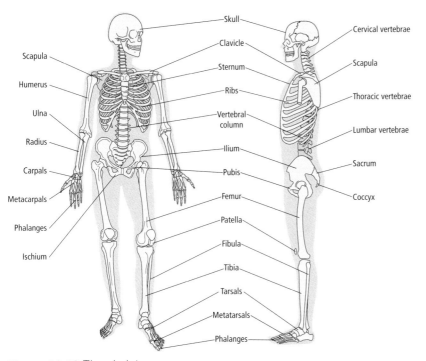

Figure 10.18 The skeleton

This is made up of 206 separate bones and has the following functions:

- It provides movement and something for muscles to attach to.
- It protects vital organs such as the brain, heart and lungs.
- Some bones produce new blood cells.
- It assists with blood clotting, as it produces calcium.

Joints

Studied

Where the ends of two bones meet is called a joint. There are over 200 places where this happens in your body. There are three types of joints:

1. Moveable joints: for example, shoulder, elbow, knee and hip, i.e. hinge and ball and socket joints.
2. Slightly moveable joints: for example, spine, wrist and ankles, i.e. sliding joints.
3. Immoveable joints: for example, skull.

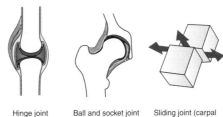

Hinge joint   Ball and socket joint   Sliding joint (carpal bones in the wrist)

Figure 10.19 The three types of joint

Muscles

Muscles are controlled by nerves and always work in pairs. This is because muscles pull bones; they do not push bones, so they have to work together to make movements. See Figure 10.20.

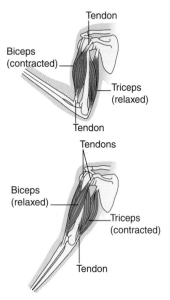

Figure 10.20 Muscle pairs flexing and extending a bone

Check your understanding

Match each system to the correct statement given below.

1. Circulatory system
2. Respiratory system
3. Nervous system
4. Digestive system
5. Renal system
6. Endocrine system
7. Reproductive system
8. Muscular system
   a. Filtering blood and maintaining fluid balance
   b. Development of foetus and birth of a baby
   c. Control of muscles, bones and coordination
   d. Release of hormones, maintenance of homeostasis
   e. Reprocessing information with the help of five senses
   f. Absorption and elimination of nutrients
   g. Balance of carbon dioxide and oxygen
   h. Supply of oxygen to the whole body

A.4 Relationship between major body systems

How systems rely on other body systems

Although the systems you have just read about all work to provide a main function for the body, it is clear that their job cannot be done without the help of other body systems. Therefore systems within the body rely on each other to maintain correct body functioning.

Circulatory and respiratory system

Studied ☐

The circulatory system relies on the respiratory system to provide oxygen from the lungs to give to the heart to pump around the body. The cardiovascular system then returns deoxygenated blood to the heart, then the lungs, to drop off the carbon dioxide and pick up new supplies of oxygen.

Musculoskeletal and nervous system

Studied ☐

Movements of muscles, bones and joints are all controlled by the nervous system. Skeletal muscles such as your arms and legs are under voluntary control, which means that you control them. For example, if you want to run, jump or dance then your brain sends specific message controlled by the brain to make the muscles move. Some muscles in our body are under involuntary control; this means we have no control over them but they are still controlled by the brain and nerves but react also to hormone levels and our senses. For example, if our bodies sense we are cold our small muscles move quickly (shivering) to warm us up; also other muscles like the heart and lungs work without our control – they work for 24 hours a day every day of our lives.

Digestive and endocrine system

Studied ☐

As we eat carbohydrates they are digested by enzymes from the mouth and intestine, into sugars, the smallest sugar being glucose. The pancreas, which belongs to the endocrine system, secretes insulin, which is a hormone. Insulin controls the amount of sugar in our blood stream. If we are low in glucose, insulin allows it to be taken to the cells to be used. If we have sufficient glucose, insulin controls the storage of excess glucose in the liver until it is required. This is a fine balancing act so that the blood sugar level remains constant.

Endocrine and reproductive system

The reproductive system is controlled by oestrogen; ovum (eggs) are released from alternate ovaries each month (approximately every 28 days).

If the egg is not fertilised it is shed with the monthly menstruation.

The diagram below shows the changes of the uterus lining during the menstrual cycle. This is due to the hormone oestrogen from the endocrine system.

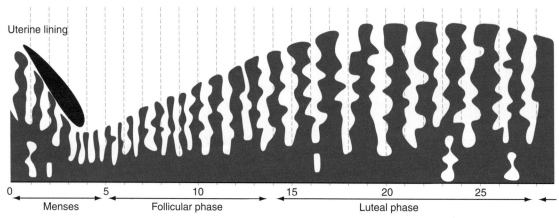

Figure 10.21 Changes in the uterus during the menstrual cycle

Coordination of systems through homeostasis

Homeostasis is the mechanism in our bodies that regulates and maintains a stable and constant internal environment. To help us understand homeostasis, imagine your body is similar to your home and your homeostatic mechanism is your central heating system. Within the system is a thermostat which regulates the heating system; it is similar to the hypothalamus in our brain, which regulates our internal environment. The hypothalamus is the control centre.

Our bodies are continuously making adjustments to regulate normal body functions. Fortunately, these adjustments are done automatically; otherwise we would be very busy people, regulating our internal environment frequently.

Homeostasis is described as a negative feedback system. This simply means that the system is able to take corrective action to maintain a constant environment. This can be further explained in Figure 10.22.

UNIT 10 Human Body Systems and Care of Disorders

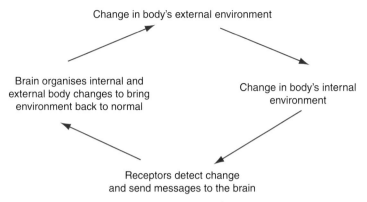

Change in body's external environment

Brain organises internal and external body changes to bring environment back to normal

Change in body's internal environment

Receptors detect change and send messages to the brain

Figure 10.22 Homeostasis: a negative feedback system

A good example of how the endocrine system controls our internal environment is in keeping the body temperature stable.

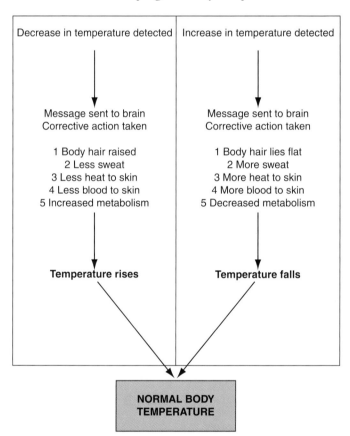

Decrease in temperature detected	Increase in temperature detected
Message sent to brain Corrective action taken	Message sent to brain Corrective action taken
1 Body hair raised 2 Less sweat 3 Less heat to skin 4 Less blood to skin 5 Increased metabolism	1 Body hair lies flat 2 More sweat 3 More heat to skin 4 More blood to skin 5 Decreased metabolism
Temperature rises	**Temperature falls**

NORMAL BODY TEMPERATURE

Figure 10.23 Body temperature control

Homeostasis cannot take place without detectors and correctors. Look at Figure 10.23 and the corrective action the body takes to maintain a constant body temperature.

There are also behavioural actions that we take in response to a rise or fall in body temperature, for example:

- have warm or cold drinks
- put on or take off clothing
- take exercise
- switch on a fan.

Check your understanding

Fill in the missing words in the following four statements from the list below.

1. The circulatory and the respiratory system work together to transport _____ oxygen to all cells and _____ carbon dioxide out of the body.
2. The muscular and nervous system work together to enable the body to_____.
3. The digestive and endocrine system work together to allow _____ to absorb glucose from the _____.
4. The endocrine and _____ system work together to allow _____ to regulate the menstrual cycle in _____ and sperm production in _____.

- insulin
- expired
- reproductive
- hormones
- females
- move
- males
- inspired
- diet

Key learning points

Circulatory

Revised ☐

This system is concerned with the transport of oxygen and removal of carbon dioxide from the blood stream. It transports nutrients to the cells and removes waste products.

Respiratory

Revised ☐

The respiratory system is closely linked with the circulatory system, as it receives oxygen as we breathe in and gets rid of carbon dioxide as we breathe out.

Nervous

Revised ☐

This system is concerned with the transmission of signals to and from the brain via the nerves, so we can move and respond to our senses.

Renal

Revised ☐

The renal system removes waste products from the blood via the kidneys which are eliminated via the bladder as urine.

Digestive

Revised ☐

The digestive system breaks down our food and extracts the beneficial nutrients, which are sent to our cells, and gets rid of waste via the large intestines as faeces.

UNIT 10 Human Body Systems and Care of Disorders

252

Endocrine

This system is a balancing system that controls levels of hormones, which affect all body systems.

Assessment activity

Detailed wall display

Pass

With a body outline as your central display, identify where all of the organs of the body are situated. Add names and pictures and include a brief description of the structure and function of each organ.

Learning Aim B

B.1 Disorders relating to body systems
B.2 Routine care of disorders

Circulatory system disorders

Hypertension

This is high blood pressure. The heart has to work harder to pump blood around the body. This can weaken the heart and over time can lead to life-threatening conditions. The increased pressure can damage the walls of arteries, which can result in a blockage or cause the artery to split (haemorrhage). High blood pressure can be caused by a diet high in animal fats, smoking, stress and excessive intake of alcohol.

Routine care

Regular blood pressure checks will be done at the GP surgery with the practice nurse or GP. Blood pressure will then be monitored and treated.

Lowering blood pressure will mean lifestyle changes and in some instances medication. Lifestyle changes will include:

- Cut your salt intake to less than 6 g a day.
- Eat a healthy, low-fat, balanced diet, including plenty of fresh fruit and vegetables.
- Be physically active.
- Cut down on alcohol.
- Stop smoking.
- Lose weight.
- Drink less coffee, tea or other caffeine-rich drinks such as cola.
- Try relaxation therapies, e.g yoga, meditation and stress management.

Blood pressure-lowering medication may have to be taken for life. Medication may include:

- Diuretics – sometimes known as water pills, diuretics work by flushing excess water and salt from the blood stream.
- Beta-blockers – they work by making your heart beat more slowly and with less force, thereby reducing blood pressure.

Coronary heart disease

Coronary heart disease (CHD) is usually caused by a build-up of fatty deposits on the walls of the coronary arteries. The coronary arteries are the heart's own supply of blood and nutrients, so if this supply is reduced it may lead to heart conditions like 'angina' or 'myocardial infarction' (heart attack). The fatty deposits, called atheroma, are made up of cholesterol and other waste substances. This process is called atherosclerosis.

Routine care

CHD cannot be cured but it can be managed with lifestyle changes, medicine and in some cases surgery. Lifestyle changes will include:

- stopping smoking
- eating a healthy diet
- being physically active.

Medication may include:

- Beta blockers – they block the effects of a particular hormone in the body which slows down the heartbeat and improves blood flow.
- Statins – if you have a high blood cholesterol level, cholesterol-lowering medicine may be prescribed.
- Low-dose aspirin – this type of medicine will help prevent your blood clotting and can help to reduce your risk of heart attack and angina.

Deep vein thrombosis (DVT)

Studied

This is a blood clot in one of the large veins of the body, usually the lower leg around the calf area. It can cause pain and swelling and if left untreated a piece of the clot may break off and block a smaller artery, such as in the lungs (pulmonary embolism); this can be fatal. It can be caused through obesity, inactivity or from other conditions like heart disease.

Routine care

If you have DVT you will need to take a medicine called an anticoagulant. This will prevent a blood clot from getting bigger. It can also help to stop part of the blood clot from breaking off and becoming lodged in another part of your bloodstream (an embolism). Compression stockings prevent calf pain and swelling and lower the risk of ulcers developing. Raising the leg during resting will help to relieve the pressure in the veins of the calf and stops blood and fluid pooling in the calf itself.

Stroke

Studied

A stroke can be described as an interruption to the blood supply in the brain. This can be caused when a blood vessel is blocked by a clot or the blood vessel bleeds, so the brain tissue is not fully supplied with oxygen and nutrients. Strokes can cause loss of movement which can be isolated to one side of the body and also cause confusion and speech difficulties.

The National Stroke Strategy produced the FAST campaign. Do a search and study the signs and symptoms and help that can be given.

www.nhs.uk/NHSEngland/NSF/Pages/Nationalstrokestrategy.aspx

Routine care

Medicines that dissolve the clot are given to the individual but are most effective when given in the first 48 hours.Other medication includes aspirin and an anticoagulant which thins the blood.Professionals who will be involved in the care of a service user who has suffered a stroke will include physiotherapists, occupational therapists, speech therapists, medical doctors and nurses.

Respiratory system disorders

Bronchitis

Studied ☐

The term bronchitis refers to inflammation of the air passages in the lungs; this can be acute which means a short illness that can usually be treated and relieved. Chronic, as we learned earlier, means over a long period of time so the lungs have been inflamed over a long period of time; this can be from irritants like smoke or from repeated lung infections.

Routine care

Most cases of bronchitis do not require treatment from a GP and the symptoms can be easily managed at home.

There is no cure for chronic bronchitis but healthy living will help. If you have bronchitis:

- Get plenty of rest.
- Drink lots of fluids. This helps prevent dehydration.
- Treat headaches, fever, and aches and pains with paracetamol or ibuprofen.

If you smoke, you should stop immediately. Smoking aggravates bronchitis and increases your risk of developing a chronic (long-term) condition.

The GP will not routinely prescribe antibiotic treatment as bronchitis is nearly always caused by a virus.

Asthma

Studied ☐

Asthma is a condition that causes the airways of the lungs (the bronchi) to become inflamed and swollen. It is a very common lung condition. Most cases begin in childhood. The lungs become irritated by common triggers, which cause an allergic response in the tissue linings of the muscular bronchi in the lungs. When the bronchi are irritated, they become narrow and the muscles around them tighten, which can increase the production of sticky mucus, or phlegm. This makes it difficult to breathe and causes wheezing and coughing, and it may make the chest feel tight.

Routine care

The aim of treatment is to get your asthma under control and keep it that way. Everyone with asthma should be able to lead a full and unrestricted life. The treatments available for asthma are effective in most people and should enable you to be free from symptoms.

Medication will include inhalers to keep the airway open and not inflamed; sufferers should also avoid any triggers which aggravate the asthma such as animal fur, pollen or dust. Care at your GP surgery is provided by doctors and nurses trained in asthma management and it should be regular.

Nervous system disorders

Parkinson's disease

Studied ☐

Parkinson's disease is a disorder of the central nervous system which limits a person's ability to control some of his or her muscles. It is caused by a slow, gradual loss of certain cells in the brain. These cells make a chemical called dopamine. This chemical is needed for muscles to work normally. Parkinson's disease causes movement and muscle problems. This may be a slight, uncontrolled shaking of the arms and legs, called tremor. Muscles feel stiff and rigid. The person may have difficulty moving his or her arms and legs, or may have shaky hands. Eventually, walking may become a process of taking small steps and slow movement, which is called a shuffling gait.

Routine care

Specialised medication called Levadopa is given to relieve some of the symptoms of Parkinson's disease. Other care will include trying to limit the effects of this condition. This will include speech and language therapy and also physiotherapy, which will improve muscle tone and so fitness levels. Individuals suffering from Parkinson's may require aids to help with daily living, for example walking aids, kitchen and eating aids.

Multiple sclerosis

Studied ☐

Multiple sclerosis is a condition of the central nervous system, which controls the body's actions and activities, such as movement and balance. Each nerve fibre in the central nervous system is surrounded by a substance called myelin. Myelin helps the messages from the brain to travel quickly and smoothly to the rest of the body. In multiple sclerosis, the myelin becomes damaged, interrupting the transfer of these messages.

Routine care

Medication will include steroid treatment and painkillers. Care from a physiotherapist who will provide stretching exercises to alleviate muscle spasms will be helpful. Mobility aids around the house will also improve the lifestyle of those living with multiple sclerosis.

Sensory impairment

Studied ☐

Sensory impairment is when one of your senses, sight, hearing, smell, or touch is no longer normal. For example, if you wear glasses you have sight impairment; if you find it hard to hear or have a hearing aid then you have a hearing impairment. A person does not have to have full loss of a sense to be sensory impaired. Sensory impairment refers to a defect in sensing and passing on the impulse. This leads to absence of sensation. People with sensory impairment may not be able to react to the stimuli given to the respective sensory systems. The impairment may be caused by aging and other physiological changes, accident or injury.

P5
P6
P7

M3
M4

D2

Digestive system disorders

Bowel cancer

This is a general term for cancer that starts in the large bowel. Depending on where the growth is found, it can also be called colon cancer or rectal cancer. Signs of bowel cancer can be blood in your stools and changes in your bowel habits; for example, diarrhoea and constipation. Also there could be unexplained weight loss. Bowel cancer is one of the common cancers in this country and is more common in those over 60 years old.

Routine care

People with cancer should be cared for by a multidisciplinary team (MDT). This is a team of specialists who work together to provide the best treatment and care.

The team often consists of a specialist cancer surgeon, an oncologist (a radiotherapy and chemotherapy specialist), a radiologist, pathologist, radiographer and a specialist nurse. Other members may include a physiotherapist, dietician and occupational therapist, and you may have access to clinical psychology support.

There are several treatments for bowel cancer, including:

- surgery
- chemotherapy
- radiotherapy
- biological therapy.

Surgery is usually the main treatment for bowel cancer, but in about one in five cases, the cancer is too advanced to be removed by surgery. If you have surgery, you may also need chemotherapy, radiotherapy or biological therapy, depending on the particular case.

Cholecystitis

This is inflammation of the gallbladder. This happens when the bile duct becomes blocked with a gallstone so bile is unable to flow into the small intestine. It is a very painful condition with sharp pain in the right upper area of the abdomen and is usually accompanied by a high temperature. Eating high fat foods brings on a bout of cholecystitis, so it is usually common for the person to have a low fat diet to avoid the gallbladder becoming inflamed before an operation can take place.

Routine care

You will first be given an injection of antibiotics into your vein if the symptoms are particularly severe or there is a high risk of complications. You may be referred for surgery a few days after antibiotic treatment.

A cholecystectomy is the most widely used type of surgery for cases of acute cholecystitis. This is surgical removal of the gallbladder.

Irritable bowel syndrome

Studied

Irritable bowel syndrome (IBS) affects a large number of the population and more commonly young adults and is twice as common in women. IBS is a functional disorder of the bowel so no abnormality is seen in the structure of the bowel, which means diagnosis may be quite difficult. Service users with IBS may suffer abdominal pain that is spasmodic, wind, bloating, swelling, and a changing stool pattern.

Routine care

IBS symptoms can often be reduced by changing your diet and lifestyle.

It may be helpful to keep a food diary and record whether certain foods make the condition better or worse. Once the food has been identified it can be avoided.

If you have IBS with diarrhoea, you may find it helps to cut down on the insoluble fibre you eat. It might also help to avoid the skin, pith and pips from fruit and vegetables, too.

If you have IBS with constipation, it can help if you increase the amount of soluble fibre in your diet and increase the amount of water you drink.

A number of different medications are used to help treat IBS. The medication will include painkillers and muscle relaxants, in addition to treatments for constipation if required.

Renal system disorders

Urinary tract infections (UTIs)

Studied

These are very common infections, particularly in women. They can be very uncomfortable but are easily treated. UTIs cause a burning and stinging sensation when passing urine and also create the feeling of wanting to urinate frequently, but only small amounts of urine are passed. Pain can also be felt in the lower part of the abdomen.

Routine care

If you have a UTI that needs treating, your GP will prescribe a course of antibiotics for up to a week. This will be confirmed with a urine specimen. You will also be given painkillers with the antibiotics.

Renal failure

Studied ▢

This condition occurs when the kidneys are no longer able to carry out their job of filtering the blood. It is possible to live with one kidney if one is damaged. However, if the damage is due to a chronic disorder like diabetes or high blood pressure, it is likely that both kidneys will be affected. This condition is incurable and may require dialysis or even a kidney transplant. Treatment of the underlying condition is necessary to relieve symptoms and so reduce damage. Acute renal failure can arise from an accident or an injury and can usually be treated.

Routine care

Effective treatment of kidney disease can prevent the condition from getting worse and can save lives. However, in some cases dialysis or kidney transplant may have to be considered.

Endocrine system disorders

Type 1 and Type 2 diabetes

Studied ▢

Glucose is absorbed from the blood by a hormone called insulin, which is secreted from the pancreas. In diabetes mellitus this process does not work, so cells cannot take in glucose and the blood glucose remains high.

There are two types of diabetes: Type 1 and Type 2.

Type 1 diabetes (insulin dependent diabetes) occurs from damage to the pancreas, from infections, or occurs genetically; it is a less common form of diabetes. The pancreas does not produce any insulin at all, so the service user will always require insulin injections to control his or her blood glucose levels. Type 1 diabetes usually occurs in younger people.

Type 2 diabetes (non-insulin diabetes) is more likely to occur in people who are overweight; the pancreas does not produce enough insulin or the cells are resistant to insulin. Type 2 diabetes is more common and increasing in society today. The symptoms can be controlled with a healthy diet and exercise.

Routine care

1. *Type 1 diabetes*: Diabetes cannot be cured, but treatment aims to keep your blood glucose levels as normal as possible and to control your symptoms to prevent health problems developing later in life.

    - Treatment will include insulin therapy, which will be either injections or via a small insulin pump which is located around the abdomen area. These pumps are given to younger people whose body and lifestyle is changing and whose insulin levels are irregular.
    - A balanced diet and regular monitoring of blood sugar levels will be carried out by specialist nurses, dieticians and doctors and reviewed regularly.
    - As diabetes can damage nerves, care of eyes and feet, in particular, is suggested.

2. *Type 2 diabetes*: People who are diagnosed with type 2 diabetes will be advised to change their lifestyle. This includes taking regular exercise, eating a healthy diet and losing weight if you are overweight or obese. Doing this may be enough to keep your blood glucose at a safe and healthy level, without the need for other treatment.

- If you have Type 2 diabetes, you may need medicines that reduce high levels of blood sugar. At first, this will usually be tablets, sometimes a combination of more than one type of tablet. It may also include insulin injections.
- Specialised doctors and nurses and dieticians will regularly review the condition.

Underactive/overactive thyroid gland

Studied

(For more information about thyroid glands, their position and function, see Sections A2 and A3 in this unit.)

An **underactive thyroid gland** means the gland is producing an insufficient amount of the hormone thyroxine. As thyroxine is responsible for control of heart rate and metabolic rate the individual will feel sluggish, tired, depressed and have weight gain. Treatment is simple, with medication to replace the hormone thyroxine in tablet form.

An **overactive thyroid gland** means there is too much thyroxine hormone being produced. As this hormone is responsible for metabolic rates, individuals will suffer with anxiety, hyperactivity and weight loss. As the gland is overactive it may swell and can sometimes be a visible lump in the throat area called a 'goitre'. Treatment is simple with medication, and occasionally surgery is required to remove part of the gland.

Routine care

1. An *underactive thyroid* (hypothyroidism) is usually treated by taking hormone-replacement tablets called Levothyroxine. This replaces the thyroxine hormone which your thyroid does not make enough of. You will initially have regular blood tests until the correct dose of Levothyroxine is reached. This can take a little while to get right.

2. The most widely used treatments for an *overactive thyroid* are outlined below.

- Thionamides are tablets used to control the condition.
- Once the production of thyroid hormones is under control, your specialist may gradually reduce the medication.
- Radioiodine treatment is a form of radiotherapy used to treat most types of overactive thyroid. Radioactive iodine shrinks your thyroid gland, reducing the amount of thyroid hormone it can produce.
- Surgery to remove all or part of the thyroid gland is known as a total or partial thyroidectomy. It is a permanent cure for recurrent overactive thyroid.

Reproductive system disorders

Cervical cancer

Studied ☐

The cervix is the entrance to the womb from the vagina. Cervical cancer often has no symptoms in its early stages. The most common is unusual vaginal bleeding, which can occur after sex, in-between periods or after the menopause. It's important to see the GP as soon as possible.

Routine care

Regular cervical smears should be done after the age of 25 years. This will identify any concerns. It is important that these checkups are done so regular attendance is vital.

If diagnosed with cervical cancer, the degree of the condition will determine the treatment, but it could include laser treatment, a small biopsy (area of cervix removed) or chemotherapy and radiotherapy.

Professionals involved will include oncologists, specialist nurses, surgeons and radiologists.

Testicular cancer

Studied ☐

Cancer of the testicles is one of the less common cancers. It usually affects younger men between the ages of 15 and 44. The most common symptom is a painless lump or swelling in the testicles. Other symptoms can include:

- a dull ache in the scrotum
- a feeling of heaviness in the scrotum.

Routine care

The first treatment option for all cases of testicular cancer, whatever the stage, is to surgically remove the affected testicle. In some cases, a single dose or short course of chemotherapy and radiotherapy may then be given.

Infertility

Studied ☐

Infertility is when a couple cannot conceive (get pregnant) despite having regular unprotected sex.

Around one in six couples may have difficulty conceiving. This is approximately 3.5 million people in the UK.

Routine care

Lifestyle changes are recommended as infertility may be caused by obesity, smoking and alcohol intake.

Depending on the cause, treatment can vary. Blocked fallopian or sperm ducts may require surgery. Medication may be needed for women who have ovulation problems or men who may have low sperm counts.

Assisted pregnancies can be sought through the NHS and privately.

Sexually transmitted diseases/infections

Studied ☐

Sexually transmitted diseases/infections (STIs) are diseases passed on from one person to another through unprotected sex (sex without a condom) or sometimes through genital contact.

Some common ones are listed below.

Chlamydia

Most people who have chlamydia do not notice any symptoms and will not know they have the infection. Otherwise, symptoms may include pain when urinating, unusual discharge and, in women, bleeding between periods or after sex. Diagnosing chlamydia is easily done with a urine test or a swab of the affected area. Chlamydia is easily treated with antibiotics, but can lead to serious long-term health problems.

Genital warts

Genital warts are small fleshy growths, bumps or skin changes that appear on or around the genital or anal area. Treatment will include specialised creams and liquids, which need to be applied to the affected area regularly.

Genital herpes

Genital herpes is a long-term condition caused by the herpes simplex virus. There are often few or no initial symptoms. However, certain triggers can activate the virus, causing outbreaks of painful blisters on your genitals and the surrounding areas. There is no cure for genital herpes, but the symptoms can usually be effectively controlled using antiviral medicines.

Gonorrhoea

Gonorrhoea is a bacterial infection that can cause an unusual discharge from the vagina or penis, and pain when urinating. Gonorrhoea can be easily diagnosed through a simple swab test and treated with antibiotics. If left untreated, it can lead to more serious long-term health problems and infertility.

Syphilis

Syphilis is a bacterial infection that causes a painless but highly infectious sore on the genitals, or sometimes around the mouth. Secondary symptoms, such as a skin rash and sore throat, then develop. These may disappear within a few weeks, after which you have a symptom-free phase. If diagnosed early, syphilis can be easily treated with antibiotics, usually penicillin injections. But if it is left to progress untreated, syphilis can go on to cause serious conditions such as stroke, paralysis, blindness or death.

HIV

HIV is a virus most commonly caught by having unprotected sex or sharing infected needles to inject drugs. AIDS is the final stage of HIV infection, when your body can no longer fight life-threatening infections. There's no cure for HIV, but there are treatments to enable most people with the virus to live a long and healthy life.

Pubic lice

Pubic lice ('crabs') are tiny blood-sucking insects that live in coarse human body hair, most commonly pubic hair. They cause itching and red spots. They can usually be successfully treated with insecticide medicines available over the counter in most pharmacies, or from a GP or GUM clinic.

Musculoskeletal system disorders

Osteoarthritis

Studied

This condition affects joints. It is caused by inflammation of the surrounding tissues; the cartilage then becomes damaged and the joints do not move smoothly. Bony growths can develop around the joints, making movement painful and slow. Joints commonly affected are hips, knees and small joints in the hands. This condition is more common in those over 50 years of age.

Routine care

Osteoarthritis cannot be cured, but treatment can ease your symptoms and prevent them from affecting your everyday life.

Exercise is the most important treatment for people with osteoarthritis, whatever your age or level of fitness. Being overweight or obese makes osteoarthritis worse.

The type of painkiller (analgesic) your GP may recommend for you will depend on the severity of your pain and any other conditions or health problems you have. These may include tablets, creams and injections of steroids into the joints to relieve pain and swelling.

Professionals involved will include a physiotherapist and occupational therapist.

Individuals may use mobility aids, such as frames, sticks or chairs.

Osteoporosis

Studied

This condition is more common in older people and affects bones, causing weakness and fragility. This condition may then be compounded as changes in hormone levels affect bone density, so as female oestrogen falls during the menopause, bones can become thin and weak.

Routine care

A specialised scan will determine the level of osteoporosis and treatment is given accordingly.

Healthy eating which includes calcium and vitamin D-rich food will avoid rapid decline of the bone density.

Weight-bearing exercises such as walking, dancing and jogging will also stop the condition from getting worse.

Individuals with osteoporosis need to keep safe from falls and trips, as any bone fractures will be difficult to mend.

Check your understanding

Which system does the disorder belong to?

1. circulatory
2. respiratory
3. reproductive

4. nervous
5. digestive
6. renal

a. cervical cancer
b. urinary tract infection
c. Parkinson's disease

d. asthma
e. deep vein thrombosis
f. irritable bowel syndrome

The impact of care on people with disorders

Caring for service users will have both positive and negative impacts. Study Figures 10.24 and 10.25 below and discuss in your class the positive and negative effects of care.

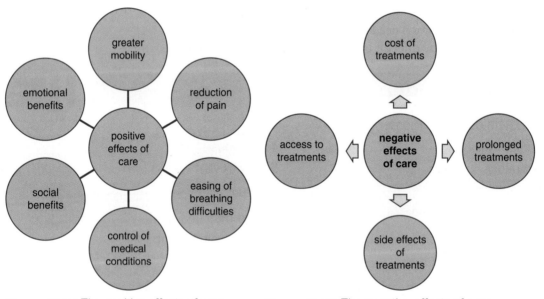

Figure 10.24 The positive effects of care   **Figure 10.25** The negative effects of care

Carrying out and recording routine observations that support care

Studied ▢

Taking temperature

The temperature of the body needs to be kept fairly stable as dramatic changes can seriously affect the body's systems. Body temperature monitors how effectively the homeostatic mechanisms are controlled in your body. Temperature is measured in °C.

There are different ways to measure a temperature as well as different places on the body where temperature can be taken:

● tympanic thermometers – in the ear
● liquid crystal display (LCD) strip thermometers – on the forehead
● digital thermometers – in the mouth or under the arm.

Normal temperature for an adult is 36 °C to 37.2 °C.

Figure 10.26 Different types of thermometers

Taking pulse

The pulse is the rhythmical beat from the heart as the arteries expand and contract. It gives an idea of how well the cardiovascular system is working. A pulse can be felt anywhere in the body where an artery travels over a bone. The most common places for feeling a pulse are wrist-radial pulse and neck-carotid pulse.

The pulse is recorded in beats per minute (bpm). When taking a pulse rate, the beats should always be counted for a full minute.

When taking a pulse rate it is important to assess if the beat you are feeling is regular. Some medical conditions can affect the rhythm of the heartbeat. It is also important to note whether the beat is strong or weak. Abnormalities should always be noted and reported.

In an adult normal pulse rate is 60 bpm to 80 bpm (beats per minute).

Measuring respiration rates

Breathing is the process by which the body gains oxygen and gets rid of carbon dioxide. Breathing rate is measured by watching the movement of the chest – one breath in (inspiration) and one breath out (expiration) are counted as one respiration. When measuring breathing rate, it should be counted for a full minute. Occasionally respirations may be shallow, so it may be necessary (with permission) to rest your hand lightly on the person's chest. Again, it is important to note and report the strength and rhythm of the client's breathing rate. The normal respiration rate for an adult is 16 to 20 respirations per minute.

Measuring blood pressure

Blood pressure is the force exerted by the blood on the vessel walls. Again this is a measurement to monitor the cardiovascular system. Blood pressure can vary over the body, depending on where the pressure is taken. It is usually measured in the arm with a machine and an inflatable cuff. Nowadays, these are very often battery operated and will display the pulse rate as well (older styles tend to be manually operated).

Normal blood pressure reading for an adult can range between 110/60 mmhg to140/90 mmhg (millimetres of mercury).

Interpreting results in relation to normal values

It is important to establish what is called a 'baseline set of observations' to give to the doctors or supervisors in the care setting. This gives information to professionals to enable them to treat and diagnose service users and to follow improvement or decline of their condition. The observations will then be taken at regular intervals to show a pattern of measurements. We must remember that not all service users are the same. Many factors will alter readings and these have to be taken into account when taking observations from service users. When taking vital readings, it is important that we look at other physical signs the service user may be showing. If necessary, we should report these to our supervisors.

Look at Figure 10.27 and discuss what signs a care worker should look for. Discuss what possible reasons could be causing them.

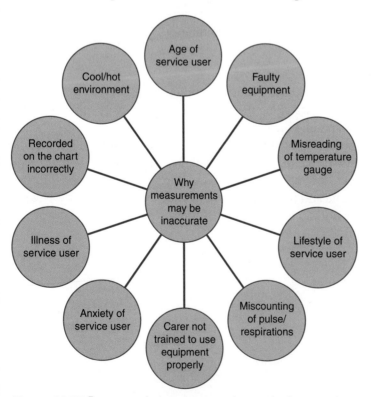

Figure 10.27 Reasons why measurements may be inaccurate

Real life connection

The role of a paramedic

Paramedics are often one of the first healthcare professionals on the scene of any accident or medical emergency. They are usually one of a two-person ambulance crew, either with a care assistant or ambulance technician. They might work on their own, using a motorbike, emergency response car or even a bicycle to reach their patients. With extra training, they could also become members of an air ambulance crew.

When they arrive at the scene, they will assess the patient's condition and take potentially life-saving decisions about any treatment needed before the patient is transferred to hospital. They then start giving the treatment, with the assistance of the emergency care assistant or ambulance technician. Paramedics use high-tech equipment, such as defibrillators (which restore the heart's rhythm), spinal and traction splints and intravenous drips, as well as administering oxygen and drugs.

They might be called out to someone who has fallen from scaffolding, for example, or an elderly person with a suspected stroke. Based at a local ambulance station or a large hospital along with other emergency crews, they work shifts, including evenings and weekends, going out in all weathers at all hours of the night or day. They work closely with doctors and nurses in hospital accident and emergency departments, briefing them as they hand their patient over to their care.

Check your understanding

Get into small groups and look into the following procedures. Find out all the important points and prepare an information leaflet for a care worker. Make sure you give them clear instructions about how to measure the following:

- pulse rate
- breathing rate
- temperature
- blood pressure
- peak flow
- blood glucose level.

Include the following information and draw up clear diagrams:

- how to position the service user
- how to take and record the above measurements
- what the normal range is for an adult
- what equipment you may need.

Tests

These can include investigations carried out at the GP surgery, for example blood tests, in addition to tests carried out at the hospital, for example scans and x-rays.

Use of aids

Aids are used to make an individual's lifestyle easier and can include hearing aids, glasses, walking frames and stairlifts.

Treatment

Treatment can include procedures carried out to treat or relieve conditions; for example, chemotherapy or radiotherapy.

Medication

Medication is usually prescribed and can be in tablet form like some painkillers, injection form like insulin, and creams and lotions like eczema treatment.

Lifestyle changes

These changes are usually suggestions made to improve life expectancy and relieve some conditions. Suggestions may include, stopping smoking, cutting down on drinking alcohol, reducing fats or salt in the diet or increasing exercise.

Normal values

These are a set of readings, which are a guideline to measure if the individual has any significant problems. For example a normal pulse rate for an adult is 60 bpm to 80 bpm.

Assessment activity

Produce an article for a health magazine which will inform people about common disorders and their routine care.

Pass

Tested

- Describe one common disorder which is related to each of the seven body systems. Include the care routines for each disorder.

Merit

Tested

- Choose three disorders and detail how this disorder can affect the major body system and how the care given will impact on the individual.

Distinction

Tested

- For the three disorders say why the routine care is necessary.

Model assignment

This assignment will assess the following learning aims:

A understand the structure and function of main organs and major body systems, and their interrelationships

B explore routine care of disorders relating to body systems.

Scenario

As a health and social care student you have been asked to give a talk to a visiting group of learners who wish to go into the nursing profession.

Section 1

1. Present a PowerPoint presentation which includes pictures with the following information

   - Describe the structure and function of the main ORGANS in the human body.
   - Describe the structure and function of major SYSTEMS in the human body (7 systems in all).

2. In the next part of your presentation you need to select ONE major system and explain the functions of the component parts (how and why does it work).

Section 2

In a poster for your classroom you need to describe the relationship between the major body systems listed below.

- Circulatory and respiratory system
- Musculoskeletal and nervous system
- Digestive and endocrine system
- Endocrine and reproductive system

This poster should describe the relationships between the systems. Include diagrams and pictures which will help you.

With the information from your posters, write a report which explains how two of the systems interrelate.

- (Choosing the circulatory and respiratory system will allow you to explain how these two important systems function together during exercise.)
- Higher level students should include in your report an analysis of how these two systems maintain homeostasis (for example the pulse rate).

Produce an information booklet

The local healthcare centre as asked you to produce an information booklet for their service users about common disorders of health.

Section 1

The first section of the booklet should mention each of the 7 systems in our bodies and relate a common disorder for each system; this should also include a description of the routine care required.

Section 2

Choose three of the common disorders and explain each one in further detail; for example, how multiple sclerosis affects the nervous system.

Role play

In a role-play situation prepare a scenario (which your tutor will observe) where you talk to a service user about his or her condition of 'high blood pressure'.

1. You will need to discuss your service user's condition of high blood pressure with that individual and how it may affect his or her body, in addition to what range of care routines he or she will be expected to receive and why.

2. You will need to demonstrate how to take and record blood pressure at least three times, and discuss your findings with your service user regarding what the normal values are against their readings.

3. Higher level students should prepare a transcript of the role play and reflect on the discussion.

Unit 11

Services in Health and Social Care

This unit explores the range of health and social care services available, the difficulties faced by some people in getting these services, and how we overcome the difficulties. It explores partnership working, firstly where professionals from different services work together to provide multi-agency care, and secondly where different professionals from the same service work together to provide multi-disciplinary care.

Learning aims

In this unit you will:

✓ understand the provision of health and social care services.

✓ explore factors that affect access to health and social care services.

✓ examine partnership working in health and social care.

Assessment criteria

Level 2 Pass	Level 2 Merit	Level 2 Distinction
Learning aim A: Design a personal fitness training programme		
2A.P1 Describe the provision of health and social care services.	**2A.M1** Discuss the differences in the different types of health and social care provision, with reference to examples.	**2A.D1** Compare national provision of health and social care services to local provision.
2A.P2 Outline how current and relevant legislation affects the provision of health and social care services.		
Learning aim B: Explore factors that affect access to health and social care services		
2B.P3 Describe factors which positively affect access to health and social care services.	**2B.M2** Assess how factors affect access to health and social care services.	**2B.D2** Make recommendations on how to improve access to health and social care services for a selected individual.
2B.P4 Describe factors which negatively affect access to health and social care services.		
Learning aim C: Examine partnership working in health and social care		
2C.P5 Describe how professionals could work together in partnership in health and social care, using selected examples.	**2C.M3** Explain the potential benefits of partnership working in health and social care to service users.	**2C.D3** Assess potential difficulties of partnership working in health and social care.

Structure of health and social care services

Primary care

Primary care is the first point of contact. This includes GPs, opticians, dentists, health visitors, and midwives. These professionals may treat a person themselves or may refer them for secondary care.

Figure 11.01 Primary care

Secondary care

Secondary care includes hospital care, therapists, counsellors and social workers. Sometimes people refer themselves to secondary care, for example by going straight to the emergency department of a hospital, or calling social services; but mostly people are referred from primary care. In secondary care, a person is assessed and may be cared for during the acute phase of the problem.

Figure 11.02 Secondary care

Tertiary care

Tertiary care includes day care, nursing homes, residential care homes, fostering arrangements, hospices and specialist care units (e.g. renal units, oncology units). Tertiary health care can involve specialist treatment. The Queen Elizabeth Hospital in Birmingham is a specialist regional centre providing specialist tertiary care for liver disease, cancer and trauma. Tertiary care in the social sector includes day care, residential care homes and nursing homes. When people are unable to return to their own home after secondary hospital care, they may be discharged to a care home in the tertiary sector.

Figure 11.03 Tertiary care

A case study illustrates the structure of health and social care services.

Primary, secondary and tertiary care

Jameela visits her GP because she feels unwell (primary care). Her GP does some blood tests then refers her to the local hospital for more investigations (secondary care). Unfortunately, the results show that she has a serious problem with her kidneys. She is referred to the regional specialist hospital for treatment (tertiary care). She is put on the waiting list for a transplant.

Informal care

Informal care provided by family, friends, and neighbours is the main way care is provided before statutory services become involved. It is estimated that there are about 6 million informal carers giving support in this country.

Types of provision

In addition to the three-layer structure above, provision of health and social care is classified into three types, as shown in Table 11.01:

Table 11.01 Types of provision in health and social care

Health and social care	
Statutory or state provision	This includes the NHS for health care and social services for social care.
Private and independent provision	This aims to make a profit. It includes private dentists, care homes, hospitals, physiotherapists, domiciliary care, and cosmetic clinics.
Voluntary services	These aim to cover costs but not make a profit. They include national and local charities such as the Salvation Army and the Samaritans.

Differences in types of provision

There are many differences between the types of provision.

Variation in cost

Studied ☐

Statutory services are free at the point of delivery. **Private** dentists and opticians, care homes, private hospitals, private physiotherapists, cosmetic services and domiciliary services charge for services and aim to make a profit. Some **voluntary** services make a small charge for their services to cover costs. Some do not charge.

Funding sources

Studied ☐

Statutory services are funded by national insurance contributions.

Private and independent provision is paid for by the person using the service at the time it is needed. Some people have private medical insurance to pay for these services.

Voluntary services rely on donations. Samaritans, a voluntary sector counselling service, relies on donations. Marie Curie cancer care offering home nursing and hospice care is funded by donations.

Waiting times

Studied ☐

Waiting times are longer for statutory services than for private services. NHS waiting times vary but can be as long as 18 weeks. Private services arrange appointments to suit the patient. Some voluntary services are immediately available, for example telephone support from Samaritans.

Availability/accessibility

Studied

Statutory services are subject to a 'postcode lottery'. This means that NHS treatment may not be available everywhere. If you do not have an address, you cannot get a GP.

Private services are available to those who can afford them and they may be more available in cities than in rural areas. **Voluntary** services may serve just one area.

National organisations

Studied

National organisations such as Social Services, Care Quality Commission, NHS, and the Department of Health serve the whole of the country, although there are differences for Scotland, Wales and Northern Ireland. The Care Quality Commission has a special role to check whether hospitals, care homes and care services are meeting national standards. www.cqc.org.uk

Local organisations

Studied

Local organisations such as children's trusts, ambulance trusts, and mental health trusts are organised locally but are part of the statutory sector.

The impact of different forms of health and social care provision

Studied

The impact of different forms of health provision is an unequal society. Those who are richer can get quicker healthcare; poorer people who rely on state provision wait longer and may get less health care. People relying on voluntary services may find the service reduced or withdrawn if donations dry up.

Check your understanding

Complete the table for your area; then compare your findings with a friend.

	Examples of state provision
Primary care	GP
Secondary care	Local hospital
Tertiary care	Regional specialist hospital

A.2 Current and relevant legislation

Attempts to reform health and social care

There have been many attempts to reform health and social care to reduce inequality. Rising demand for care and increased costs, the need for improvement and the lack of government finances are driving the need for change.

The Health and Social Care Act 2008

Studied ▢

This Act created the Care Quality Commission to regulate and inspect health and social care, improved the regulation of health and social care professionals and made changes to public health. The 2008 Act is about to be revised by the Health and Social Care Act 2012, which sets out key themes. Doctors will have more say in what services are provided. Private and voluntary services will have a greater role to play. Patients will have a stronger voice. There will be a new focus on public health to reduce ill health. Accountability locally and nationally will be stronger and there will be reduced tiers of management.

The Mental Health Acts

Studied ▢

The Mental Health Act 1983 and parts of the Mental Capacity Act were amended by the Mental Health Act 2007. We saw how these laws provided for individual rights in Unit 8. Provision for mental health needs is spread across statutory mental health trusts. There is also private provision, which must be paid for by the patient, and voluntary provision such as the charity Mind. Statutory provision must offer age-appropriate services. Where possible, people with mental health issues are treated in the community through primary care. If it is necessary an individual may become an informal inpatient in the secondary care sector. Sometimes people are *compulsorily* detained under a section of the Mental Health Act 1983 and lose some of the rights available to informal patients. Mental health tribunals, independent panels, decide whether a formal patient should be discharged into primary care under a supervised community treatment order.

Care Quality Commission Regulations 2009

Studied

These regulations, made under the Health and Social Care Act 2008, require health and social care providers to be registered with the Care Quality Commission (CQC) and set out the standards of care required. CQC inspect care providers, regulate them and monitor the use of the Mental Health Act.

The impact of legislation

The impact of legislation on the provision of health and social care services has been to set out the resources that must be provided to service users, set out the rights of service users, and set basic service level agreements of what service can be expected; for example, a maximum of 18 weeks waiting time between referral and seeing a hospital doctor. One intended impact of legislation is that by introducing greater competition and accountability the availability of services will improve as GPs can now refer patients to private hospitals if the waiting list is too long for the statutory sector.

Check your understanding

Match the start with the correct sentence ending.

1. The structure of health and social care services _____
2. A GP service _____
3. A general hospital _____
4. A specialist regional centre for liver transplant _____
5. A foster home _____
6. There are three types of provision _____
7. Funding for statutory care _____
8. Funding for voluntary care _____
9. Funding for private care _____
10. The NHS is _____
11. Children's trusts are _____
12. The Care Quality Commission _____
13. The Health and Social Care Act 2012 _____

a. ...statutory, private or independent, and voluntary provision.
b. ...is in three parts: primary, secondary and tertiary.
c. ...is an example of primary care.
d. ...is an example of tertiary social care.
e. ...is an example of secondary care.
f. ...is an example of tertiary health care.

MI

DI

g. ...comes from the person needing care.
h. ...comes from national insurance contributions.
i. ...comes from donations.
j. ...an example of a local organisation.
k. ...an example of a national organisation.
l. ...gives more power to doctors to choose the care that can be offered.
m. ...inspects and regulates health and social care provision.

Key learning points

Structure of health and social care services

Revised ☐

This is provided in three parts: primary, secondary and tertiary.

Types of provision in health and social care

Revised ☐

There are three types of provision. These are statutory, private and independent provision, and voluntary services.

National health and social care organisations

Revised ☐

These include Social Services, the Care Quality Commission, the NHS, and the Department of Health.

Local health and social care organisations

Revised ☐

These are specific to the local area; for example, children's trusts.

Impact of different forms of health and social care provision

Revised ☐

The impact of different forms of health and social care provision is more choice for those who can afford it, but inequality for poorer people.

Current legislation

Revised ☐

Current legislation for this area includes The Health and Social Care Act 2008 and 2012, Care Quality Commission Regulations 2009, The Mental Health Act 1983 and 2007.

Assessment activity

Information pack

The Husain family are moving into the area with their young children. To help them settle in, produce an information pack on the health and social care services available in the local area for the local service users. Remember to:

Pass

 Tested

- Describe the provision of health and social services.
- Outline how current and relevant legislation affects the provision of health and social care services.

Merit

Tested

- Discuss the differences between the types of provision, giving examples.

Distinction

Tested

- Compare the national provision of health and social care services to local provision.

Learning Aim B

B.1 Factors that affect access to health and social care services

In this section we look at how people get services, and what factors affect whether they can access health and social care services or not.

Geographical location

Where you live affects access. Living near to services, or having good transport links means a person is more likely to use the service. Local funding arrangements and how much demand there is affects access.

Socio-economic

Socio-economic factors of education, health awareness and lifestyle choices affect whether people know about health and social care services, and whether they choose to use them.

Equality and diversity

Disability

Studied ☐

Disability (sensory, physical and mental) may affect access to services. Someone who is visually impaired may not be able to read a letter sent to them for a hospital appointment. A deaf person will not hear radio campaigns on health. Someone with a physical disability may not be able to get out to attend appointments. A person with learning disabilities may not be offered advice on contraception or sexually transmitted infections, as it is assumed they do not have sex.

Cultural and religious factors

Studied ☐

Cultural and religious factors affect access to services. Mrs Husain's mother does not read or write and speaks very little English. A letter arrives inviting her to attend for breast screening. Her daughter translates the content, but cannot persuade her mother to attend as it involves taking her clothes off and the letter does not say if there is a same-sex carer.

Sexual orientation and gender, race, and age

Studied ☐

If we see professionals who are welcoming and non-judgemental we are more likely to use services. A government study found that women are

UNIT 11 Services in Health and Social Care

less likely to visit their GP when having heart problems, as they see a heart attack as a man's problem. Gay and lesbian couples may not seek help with relationship issues because they think services are not meant for them. African Caribbean and other Black people are more likely to have been referred for treatment by a stranger such as a police officer, rather than by a relative or a neighbour. The Irish have one of the highest rates of suicide of minority groups, yet they are often classed with white ethnicity, thus ignoring their needs.

An elderly woman with chest pain may not see her GP, as she does not want to make a fuss. A pregnant girl under 16 may not go to see her GP in case her boyfriend gets into trouble.

Communication affects access to services

The following example illustrates how communication may affect access to services.

> ### When English is an additional language
>
> Mrs Husain's mother has English as an additional language and does not understand what the doctor says. He also uses jargon like 'fasting blood sugar' when talking about her diabetes. She does not understand what her BMI is, as she is not familiar with acronyms, so she does not stick to her diet.

Financial

Financial aspects such as the cost of transportation can prevent people accessing services. Miss Smith has an appointment at the local hospital but cannot get a bus and cannot afford a taxi, so does not attend. The cost of services and availability of funding have an impact on what is offered. Several hospitals no longer offer emergency services but instead combine them at one central hospital.

Quality of care provision

Respect from professionals is a factor in whether people access care. Many older people dread the thought of having to go into residential care because they fear they will not be treated with respect. You can read the NHS Confederation and Age UK report on 'Dignity in Care' at www. nhsconfed.org/priorities/Quality/Partnership-on-dignity.

How provision can be adapted to improve access to health and social care services

Leaflets in other languages may help to improve access to health and social care services, but volunteers who are willing to read for those who cannot read may be a better solution. Alternative formats, such as pictures and taped messages will reduce the communication barrier. Domiciliary services for social care, and community-based health services will help those with mobility problems.

A district nurse may be able to visit Miss Smith to check her blood pressure. A volunteer may come out and explain the breast screening procedure to Mrs Husain's mother in her own language. A government report recommends more buses linking hospitals, linking timing of services to public transport, and volunteer car schemes offering lifts to people to get to hospital. Macmillan Cancer Care also suggests reduced car parking charges for those on long-term treatment programmes such as chemotherapy.

Check your understanding

Match the start with the correct sentence ending.

1. Geographical location affects access
2. Socio-economic factors
3. Equality and diversity factors
4. A financial barrier to services
5. The quality of care provision

a. ...because people have to travel further to get services.
b. ...include disability and cultural factors.
c. ...affects whether people use it.
d. ...include education, health awareness and lifestyle choices.
e. ...occurs when cutbacks affect services.

Key learning points

Factors that affect access to health and social care services
Revised

These are geographical, socio-economic, financial, and relate to equality, communication and the quality of care offered.

Services can be made more accessible
Revised

Changes can be made to make services more accessible. Examples include the provision of leaflets in other languages. Alternative formats, such as pictures and taped messages will also reduce the communication barrier.

P3

P4

Assessment activity

Report for local newspaper
A few weeks later you meet Mrs Husain and she tells you that she has had problems when trying to use health and social care services and knows that other people are having similar problems. Write a report for the local newspaper about these barriers to health and social care services and ways in which they can be overcome.

Include:

Pass
Tested

- a description of factors that positively and negatively affect access to health and social care services in the local area

Merit
Tested

- an assessment of how factors affect access to health and social care services, using examples of service users interviewed

Distinction
Tested

- recommendations on improving access for a selected individual.

M2

287

Learning Aim C

C.1 Partnership working in health and social care

Types of partnership working

Two types of partnership working are:

- multi-agency working
- multidisciplinary working

Multi-agency working

Multi-agency working works across different providers; for example, Social Services working with a mental health trust; and Children's Services working with the Justice system.

> ## Children's services work with the Justice system
>
> Jake was taken into care because his parents were unable to care for him. He has been caught stealing food at a local shop. The Children's Services will work with the police and the Justice system to provide care for Jake.

Multidisciplinary working

Multidisciplinary working is when health providers work together; for example, a health visitor working with a GP, or a psychiatric nurse with an occupational therapist.

Figure 11.04 Multidisciplinary working

> ## Health visitor works with GP
>
> Maisie the health visitor visits Mrs Husain and her new baby to check on baby's progress. While there she notices Mrs Husain is very tired. Maisie tells the GP who calls Mrs Husain in for a blood test.

Benefits of partnership working

The benefits of partnership working in health and social care include an effective mix of skills and best use of expertise. Social workers have expertise in social care. Health visitors, doctors and nurses have expertise in health care. Continuity of care and a seamless service lead to better care and cost reduction. It is cheaper to plan the right care first time rather than waste money giving the wrong care.

Potential difficulties of partnership working

- **Professional animosity** – The potential difficulties of partnership working happen when professionals do not understand each other's role.
- **Poor communication between professionals from different organisations** – Sometimes professionals are unclear about what information they can share and so vital information is not passed on. Victoria Climbie, a child looked after by her aunt, died because professionals did not share information about her care.
- **Manipulation by service users** – Sometimes there is manipulation by service users so they play one professional off against another.
- **Logistics** – The logistics of getting professionals together in one place to discuss a service user are difficult when each professional has a full caseload.
- **Financial constraints** – Financial constraints mean that at times cuts are made that affect services. Social workers may have a larger caseload than they can manage; nurses may have insufficient staff on a ward. This leads to a breakdown in services and abuse may occur.

Real life connection

Pharmacy technician

Pharmacy technicians in the NHS work in hospitals and in the community. They are part of the pharmacy team and work under the supervision of a pharmacist and supply medicines and products to patients. There are opportunities for management, administration and specialist roles as experience is gained. There are no minimum entry requirements to enter training, but you will usually be expected to have four GCSEs at Grade C or above, or the equivalent, including English, science and maths. Some trusts may offer the chance to train through an apprenticeship for pharmacy technicians.

Check your understanding

Match the start with the correct sentence ending.

1. Multi-agency working across different types of service
2. Multidisciplinary working
3. The benefits of partnership working
4. Difficulties arise when

a. …may include social worker, GP and youth justice team.
b. …may include GP, district nurse and pharmacist.
c. …include a better use of skills and continuous care.
d. …professionals do not work together.

Key learning points

Partnership working in health and social care

This includes: multi-agency working across different types of service; and multidisciplinary working within one service such as the health service, or within the social care service.

Benefits of partnership working

Benefits include an effective mix of skills, best use of expertise, continuity of care, seamless service and cost reduction.

Potential difficulties of partnership working

Revised

These are: professional animosity between agencies and professionals, poor communication between professionals from different organisations, manipulation by service users, logistics, financial constraints, and breakdown in services.

Assessment activity

Write an article

As a result of your previous report, the editor asks you to write an article looking into:

Pass

- how three professionals work together to provide care

Merit

- an explanation of the potential benefits for individual service users

Distinction

- an assessment of the potential difficulties of partnership working for individual service users in health and social care.

P5

M3

D3

Model assignment

This assignment will assess the following learning aims:

A understand the provision of health and social care services
B explore factors that affect access to health and social care services
C examine partnership working in health and social care.

Scenario

While on placement at your local health centre you are asked to prepare a resource file.

The first section is for new families with young children who are moving into the area. It should be attractive, clearly laid out and easy to understand for all ethnic groups in the practice.

The second and third sections of your resource file are for new staff including trainee GPs starting at the health centre and also for representatives on the patient's panel to help them understand factors affecting access to services.

Section 1: Understand the provision of health and social care services

This section must:

- Outline the provision of health and social care services.
- Describe the provision of health and social care services.
- Discuss the differences between the types of health and social care provision, with reference to examples.
- Compare national provision of health and social care services to local provision.
- Outline one effect of current and relevant legislation on the provision of health and social care services.
- Outline how current and relevant legislation affects the provision of health and social care services.

Section 2: Explore factors that affect access to health and social care services

- Identify factors that positively affect access to health and social care services.
- Describe factors which positively affect access to health and social care services.
- Assess how factors affect access to health and social care services.
- Identify factors that negatively affect access to health and social care services.
- Describe factors that negatively affect access to health and social care services.
- Make recommendations on how to improve access to health and social care services for a selected individual.

Section 3: Examine partnership working in health and social care

- Identify professionals who might work in partnership in health and social care.
- Describe how professionals could work together in partnership in health and social care, using selected examples.
- Explain the potential benefits of partnership working in health and social care to service users.
- Assess the potential difficulties of partnership working in health and social care.

References

www.samaritans.org

www.mariecurie.org.uk/en-gb/nurses-hospices/

www.dh.gov.uk/prod_consum_dh/groups/dh_digitalassets/@dh/@en/documents/digitalasset/dh_092041.pdf

www.macmillan.org.uk/Documents/GetInvolved/Campaigns/Campaigns/hospital_parking_report.pdf – The hidden price of getting treatment

https://nice.org.uk/nicemedia/documents/improving_patient_access.pdf

www.channel4.com/programmes/dispatches/episode-guide/series-14/episode-1 – Lost in care

Unit 12

Creative and Therapeutic Activities

At the end of this unit you should be able to identify appropriate **creative** and **therapeutic** activities for your service users and tailor them to their need by understanding, first of all, that your service users have needs and your activities have various benefits, so these can be sensitively and appropriately chosen and matched.

Giving service users' opportunities to take part in activities can improve **self-esteem** and lead to a range of physical, intellectual, emotional and social benefits; this in turn can improve conditions and aid recovery.

You will be aware of the variety of activities that can be selected and also in what settings they can take place.

As you plan and carry out activities, you will understand the need for risk assessment and your role within this area, to deliver and evaluate the activities from your point of view and the service user's experience. This will help you to plan for next time and evaluate how effective your role has been.

We should always reflect on our practice and strive to give our service users the best care and experience they can possibly have.

Learning aims

In this unit you will:

✓ explore different creative and therapeutic activities used in health and social care and their benefits.

✓ understand how professionals support and encourage individuals who take part in creative and therapeutic activities.

✓ be able to plan and implement appropriate creative and therapeutic activities in a health and social care setting.

Assessment criteria

Level 2 Pass	Level 2 Merit	Level 2 Distinction
Learning aim A: Explore different creative and therapeutic activities used in health and social care and their benefits		
2A.P1 Describe three creative and therapeutic activities suitable for individuals or groups in two different health and social care settings.	**2A.M1** Assess the suitability of creative and therapeutic activities for an individual or group, with reference to a case study.	**2A.D1** Make recommendations to improve creative and therapeutic activities for an individual or group, with reference to a case study.
2A.P2 Describe the benefits of three creative and therapeutic activities for individuals or groups in two different health and social care settings.		
Learning aim B: Understand how professionals support and encourage individuals who take part in creative and therapeutic activities		
2B.P3 Describe the role of professionals when planning and implementing activities in one health and social care setting.	**2B.M2** Compare and contrast the role of two professionals when planning and implementing activities in two different health and social care settings.	**2B.D2** Evaluate the impact of professional support on a selected individual participating in creative and therapeutic activities.
Learning aim C: Be able to plan and implement appropriate creative and therapeutic activities in a health and social care setting		
2C.P4 Describe factors that affect the selection, planning and implementation of creative and therapeutic activities in one health and social care setting.	**2C.M3** Assess the selection, planning and implementation of the creative and therapeutic activity.	**2C.D3** Recommend improvements to the planning and implementation of the creative and therapeutic activity.
2C.P5 Select, plan and implement one individual or one group creative and therapeutic activity for service users of one health and social care setting.		

A.1 Different creative and therapeutic activities used in health and social care

Examples of **creative** and **therapeutic** activities include:

- arts, craft and performing arts
- sport and exercise
- games and quizzes
- other activities.

Arts, craft and performing arts

Studied ☐

Drawing and painting

Drawing and painting activities allow service users to express their feelings and thoughts and they can be particularly helpful to those who lack vocabulary.

Photography

Photography is also useful when capturing service users enjoying other creative and therapeutic activities as photographs may be kept as memories.

Knitting, sewing, embroidery and tapestry

All these creative activities have a relaxing effect; they are repetitive in nature and can be a way of briefly escaping from traumatic events. Completion of tasks like this can be satisfying and so improve self-esteem.

Drama

This allows service users to explore stories and express feelings.

Singing

Singing is an activity that an individual can do alone or in a group, so it can bring social benefits. If service users sing together it can bring a sense of belonging and achievement for them.

Music

This may involve making music, listening to music or even music therapy, which uses music for therapeutic benefits. Like singing, music can offer service users the benefits of taking part in group activities and help with expression of feelings.

Key terms

Creative: The ability to make something using imagination and personal ideas.

Therapeutic: This is something that is given to a service user to help with the healing process and so will have a positive effect on the body and mind. It can also lead to a sense of well-being.

Swimming

This enables service users with limited mobility to enjoy freedom of movement. Hydrotherapy is a treatment process and differs from swimming because it involves special exercises that take place in a warm-water pool; this can be beneficial to those who have been injured or who have long-term muscle and movement problems.

Walking

Walking is a cheap and accessible form of exercise and can take place in organised groups such as Ramblers clubs, or a small group or as an individual activity. Regular walking has been shown to reduce the risk of chronic illnesses, such as heart disease, Type 2 diabetes, asthma, strokes and some cancers.

Running

This, like walking, is a cheap and accessible activity; correct shoes need to be worn and you should seek advice before starting this activity if you have a medical condition.

Yoga

This is described by the British Wheel of Yoga as a 'holistic approach to mind, body and spirit'. Classes generally exercise, stretch and flex the body and offer relaxation. For more information, go to www.bwy.org.uk.

Horse riding

This is a physical activity that can be beneficial for many service users. Horse riding must be carried out with authority and supervision, and using the correct equipment.

Dance

Dance is an all-round beneficial activity and it can obviously improve and strengthen large and small muscles. Follow this link to find out about other benefits to dance.

www.aarp.org/health/fitness/getmotivated/letsdancetohealth.html

Pilates

Pilates is an exercise system that can be used to strength and straighten muscles and can also improve balance and posture.

Games and quizzes

The following activities may prove beneficial for service users:

- crosswords
- board games
- jigsaw puzzles

- Sudoku
- general knowledge quizzes.

All these activities can be selected to suit any age group and varying abilities.

Other activities

Studied ☐

Gardening

This can be enjoyed by a range of service users. It can be used for learning with younger service users and can be adapted to suit most settings.

Cookery

This can be enjoyed by a range of service users and adapted to meet specific needs.

Information and communication technologies

Information and communication technologies (ICT) are a main driving source of communications at present and computers, televisions and mobile phones can all be used to relay messages and access the internet. Mobile phones can also be used to take photographs.

Reading

Reading can stimulate the imagination and extend vocabulary.

Massage

This is the manipulation of soft tissues, which can make changes in the body's surrounding structures. It can also provide relaxation benefits and is a popular therapy for babies. See the following web link for more information: www.urban-kneads.com/Benefits.html

Multi-sensory stimulation

This can be used for service users who have impaired senses or who suffer from dementia. It stimulates different areas of the brain to offer a sense of calm and improved mood. See the following web link for further information: www.nhs.uk/Conditions/Dementia/Pages/Treatment.aspx

Animals as therapy

Animals can provide companionship for elderly service users, particularly those living alone. However, animals can provide benefits to all age groups. See the following web link for further information: www.maturetimes.co.uk/node/9315

UNIT 12 Creative and Therapeutic Activities

Appropriate settings

The different health and social care settings where care is delivered and activities take place are an integral part of the service user's care package. Some examples are shown in Figure 12.01.

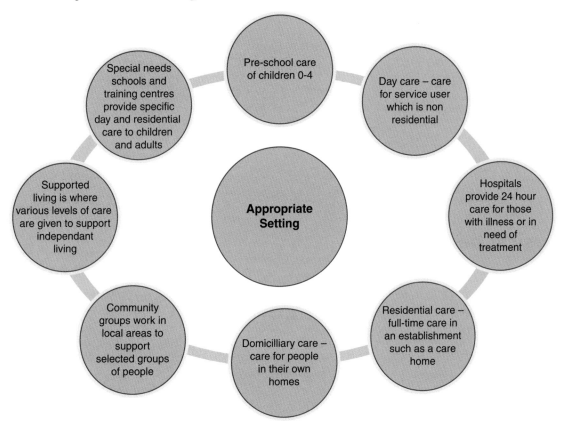

Figure 12.01 Appropriate health and social care settings

Check your understanding

Case studies

Consider the case studies below and suggest some appropriate creative and therapeutic activities for each one.

1. A group of pre-school children, who are learning how to interact with others, take turns and share.

2. An elderly gentleman who has just lost his wife; his family would like him to take up a new interest which would allow him to meet others. He lives at his own home.

3. A young adult who has learning difficulties and requires help with concentration skills. The individual attends a day centre regularly.

4. An elderly lady who lives in a retirement village, who would like to take part in an activity that would help to keep her hand and finger joints moving.

5. A teenager who is suffering with depression and wants to improve self-esteem and self-confidence. The individual has been visited at home by the community psychiatric nurse.

A.2 Benefits of creative and therapeutic activities

There are a number of benefits that service users may gain from creative and therapeutic activities. Some of these are listed below.

- Physical
- Intellectual
- Emotional
- Social

New skills can be developed or existing skills can be maintained. Benefits could also include promoting independence or being supportive.

Physical benefits

The physical benefits of creative and therapeutic activities may include improved **fine motor skills**, such as dexterity (e.g. picking up small objects), or **gross motor skills**, such as those performed by major muscle groups in legs or arms.

Activities that have physical benefits such as ball games, or that involve small muscle movements such as jigsaws and sewing can improve hand–eye coordination.

Keeping large and small muscles moving can improve mobility for some service users.

Some service users may have conditions such as arthritis that they will never fully recover from but small and large physical movements will maintain their condition; in other words, the condition should not get any worse.

Intellectual benefits

By repeating activities such as crosswords, quizzes and board games, we can encourage memory skills and organisational skills, which are very important when promoting independence with our service users.

Because some of these activities require input from one or more people, communication and language skills will be encouraged, whether learning new words and phrases or repeating questions and answers to improve memory skills. Such activities will benefit all age groups. One of the ways children learn is from repetition of activities; a good example would be reading with a child.

> **Key terms**
>
> **Fine motor skills:** These apply to small muscle groups which help with smaller movements like pencil drawing, cutting, holding utensils, threading beads and sewing activities.
>
> **Gross motor skills:** You may also see this as large motor skills and it applies to large muscles that move and coordinate the body in activities like walking, jumping, running and balance.

Emotional benefits

Emotional benefits may include improved **self-esteem** for the individual who completes, or takes part in, an activity and this can give a great sense of achievement. This positive feeling will motivate service users to develop new interests and maintain existing ones. As carers, if we display service users' paintings, for example, this will give them a sense of pride and positively encourage their self-concept (how they feel about themselves).

Social benefits

Social benefits will include the development of new friendship groups and learning to cooperate and share with others. Children take time to learn how to share.

Group activities will improve service users' confidence and ability to work with others. Taking part in a group activity can sometimes be difficult for people, as they may not fully understand the activity, so to avoid embarrassment they may show difficult behaviour or refuse to join in.

Working as a group and completing a task such as a drama production will enable the service user to enjoy achievement and a sense of pride, as the whole group will be given praise.

> ## Key terms
> **Self-esteem:** This is how you feel about yourself, in other words your self-pride; this can be affected in the short term, for example if you have not been chosen to play in a school team but also in the long-term, possibly if you are being bullied.

Check your understanding

Complete the following chart with appropriate activities. An example is included to start you off.

Check your answers with your class. Discuss the range of activities you have suggested for each area.

Activity	Area of benefit	Actual benefit
Swimming	Physical	Improves body strength and coordination
	Intellectual	
	Emotional	
	Social	

Key learning points

Physical benefits

These result from activities which improve strength and movement in small and large muscles.

Intellectual benefits

These result from activities that stimulate memory and improve and maintain problem-solving skills.

Emotional benefits

These result from the provision of activities that will improve a person's self-concept and give a feeling of pride and achievement.

Social benefits

These result from activities in which service users can develop relationships and interact with others to have a sense of belonging.

Assessment activity

Posters

Pass

Design two detailed posters for your classroom, which describe a range of suitable creative and therapeutic activities that can be carried out in health and social care settings.

Choose two settings from the list below:

- preschool
- day care centre
- hospital
- residential care
- domiciliary care
- community group
- supported living
- special needs school

Assessment activity

Information booklet

Using the information from the posters you have designed, select three activities from each setting and describe their benefits (PIES – physical, intellectual, emotional, social).

Merit

Consider each activity and say why you have chosen it. Is it suitable? Refer to a case study.

Distinction

Tested

In your booklet recommend how these activities can be changed or adapted to use with a group or an individual. Refer to a case study

B.1 The role of the professional in supporting and encouraging individuals

Professionals and ways they support activities

While planning and carrying out therapeutic activities, care workers should be part of the activity; this ensures health, safety and security and allows the carer to motivate and encourage reluctant service users, offering physical and practical help when needed.

There are a wide range of professionals involved in supporting and encouraging individuals who will benefit from creative and therapeutic activities in their setting.

Activity coordinator

Studied

The primary role of an activity coordinator is to keep service users involved, entertained, enthusiastic and active. Depending on the setting, the coordinator may also plan group sessions that include activities such as craft-making, painting or card games. Many coordinators not only need to come up with ideas, but also make the ideas relevant to the age groups and genders with which they are working.

Physiotherapist

Studied

When supporting creative and therapeutic activities it is the physiotherapist's role to select or suggest appropriate activities, offering expert advice, which will assist and benefit that service user. The physiotherapist will be able to offer practical help, for example aids and adaptations, so that service users can be involved in activities. A service user with limited mobility who wishes to join in with carpet bowls, for example, may be offered a frame to walk with and support. It would be the physiotherapist's role to show how the frame should be used and adapt it accordingly.

Occupational therapist

Studied

Occupational therapists' role in delivery of activities is to select activities that will enable service users to be as independent as possible. The occupational therapist may select activities for a purpose; for example, cooking activities for young adults with learning disabilities will not only be enjoyable, but also equip them with skills necessary for a more independent lifestyle.

Speech and language therapist

Studied ☐

The role of a speech and language therapist is to assess and treat speech, language and communication problems in people of all ages to enable them to communicate to the best of their ability. They may also work with people who have eating and swallowing problems. When selecting appropriate activities speech and language therapists will use their expertise in adapting activities to meet service users' needs, improving speech at the same time. For example, a service user who has suffered a stroke and needs assistance with speech may be given simple reading books with large print and pictures to encourage reading and speech.

Health and social care assistant

Studied ☐

When supporting clients who are engaged in creative and therapeutic activities, a health or social care assistant's role would be preparing areas for the activity and assisting with setting up the activity. Any service users who require help or encouragement could be assisted and motivated by the healthcare assistant.

The healthcare assistant would also be responsible for reporting any difficulties service users have, or any feedback about the activity itself.

Naturally, the care assistant's role would also be to ensure health and safety and support the professional who is conducting the activity itself.

Principles and values

As health and social care workers, we are responsible for providing adequate and appropriate resources for the service users.

So the careful selection of activities should ensure equality and **empowerment** of our service users.

> ## Key term
> **Empowerment:** This is a process where clients who have previously been dependent on care and support are enabled to make decisions and choices to take control of their own lives.

Anti-discriminatory practice

Studied ☐

Whatever our role is with the service user, we should always uphold anti-discriminatory practice and provide opportunities that offer choice and support independence. We should make sure our care gives the same choice to all service users alike. (See Unit 2, Topic A1)

Respect for cultural diversity and beliefs

Studied ☐

Care workers should show understanding of the various backgrounds our service users come from. (See Unit 2, Topic A1)

P3

M2

D2

Equality of opportunity

Studied ☐

We should make sure that the service user is aware there is an equal choice available to all. (See Unit 2, Topic A1)

Empowerment

Studied ☐

Care workers should encourage service users to be independent and use skills to control their own care. (See Unit 2, Topic B1)

Ensure dignity

Studied ☐

Care workers may ensure service users' dignity by treating them as they wish to be treated. (See Unit 2, Topic A1)

Promote independence

Studied ☐

Care workers should encourage choice and service users' involvement in their own care. (See Unit 2, Topic B1)

Confidentiality

Studied ☐

It is important to keep service users' information private. (See Unit 2, Topic A1)

Ways professionals support inclusion

Inclusion is a basic human right and should embrace all service users irrespective of race, gender, culture or age. For care workers to be 'inclusive' in their practice with service users, they should give equal access to all activities and opportunities. This removes barriers and promotes new experiences, friendships and encourages communication.

Inclusion activity

Studied ☐

As a class or small group play a simple game; for example, cards, bingo or a board game.

After completing the activity, some members of the group should assume one of the following roles and **play the game again**.

1. A person who does not speak English
2. A person with sight impairment
3. An individual who has suffered with depression and is extremely shy
4. An individual from a reserved cultural background who makes very little eye contact
5. A person who is confident, expressive and vivacious.

After this activity discuss how you felt while taking part and whether or not you now have a different view point than you had earlier.

- Discuss times in your life when you have felt you may have had an unfair advantage in a situation.
- How did this make you feel?
- As carers, how could you be aware of these differences?
- How will this activity change your practice?

Check your understanding

Read the following case study, then as a small group answer and discuss the questions which follow.

Case study

Mr Khan has been unstable on his feet, following a recent hip replacement. His wife died last year so a decision was made, involving Mr Khan and his family, for him to move in to the nearby Cherry Tree Retirement Village. Cherry Tree caters for varying levels of care and was happy to provide a care package for Mr Khan.

Mr Khan is a private person and is mostly happy with his memories and having contact with his family. However, his family are keen for Mr Khan to interact more with others and possibly take up a hobby.

Questions

1. Which professionals should be involved in Mr Khan's care package?
2. What support can these professionals offer?
3. What values and principles should be particularly respected?
4. How can these professionals support inclusion in this case?

Key learning points

Anti-discriminatory practice

Revised ☐

This means making sure that you are fair to all service users.

Cultural respect

Revised ☐

Showing an understanding of different cultures and that we all have different ways of living our lives.

Equal opportunity

Revised ☐

This means ensuring that activities are accessible and are available to all service users.

Empowerment

Revised ☐

This means allowing service users choice and control over their activities.

Key learning points

Dignity

Revised ☐

This means ensuring that all service users are treated with respect, according to their wishes.

Independence

Revised ☐

Encouraging service users to use their skills and be involved.

Confidentiality

Revised ☐

This means keeping personal information safe.

Assessment activity

Advert for activities coordinator vacancy

In your work placement, interview the person responsible for planning the activities and write a brief summary of the job role.

Use this information to create an advertisement for a new activities coordinator within a health and social care setting.

Your advert should include:

Pass

Tested ☐

- The role required.

Merit

Tested ☐

- A comparison with what they may already have done in another setting.

Distinction

Tested ☐

- A statement about the importance of the role in supporting service users.

Adhere to current and relevant sections of legislation

You should check that you adhere to current and relevant sections of **legislation**, **regulations** and guidelines during the implementation of creative and therapeutic activities. See Table 12.01

Table 12.01 Legislation that is relevant to creative and therapeutic activities

Relevant legislation, regulations and guidelines	Brief description	How this relates to creative and therapeutic activities
Health and Safety at Work Act 1974.	Main piece of legislation covering workplaces. Both employers and employees have responsibilities to ensure health and safety.	All activities in workplaces.
Manual Handling Operations Regulations 1992.	Relates to any activities that may involve moving objects (including people).	Any activities that may involve heavy objects or moving a patient.
Control of Substances Hazardous to Health 2002 (COSHH).	Ensures substances are kept safe. This includes storage, use and disposal. There should be guidelines and risk assessments in place.	Activities that involve the use of substances such as glue or paint.
Reporting of Injuries Disease and Dangerous Occurrences Regulations 1995 (RIDDOR).	Ensures that accident books are monitored and completed. Certain aspects are reportable under RIDDOR.	Accident books should be kept. Any reportable occurrences should be notified to the Health and Safety Executive.
Equality Act 2010.	In the case of disability, service providers are under a duty to make reasonable adjustments to their workplaces/settings to overcome barriers experienced by disabled people.	Adaptation to allow all service users to be included in creative and therapeutic activities.

As well as these laws, there may be specific policies that relate to the setting (such as the confidentiality **policy**) that you should observe. There may also be other codes of practice which relate to specific roles or duties you may have.

Key terms

Legislation: This is law that has been passed by Parliament.

Regulation: This is an enforceable guideline that must be followed in an organisation.

Policy: This is a set of statements that outlines values and principles within an organisation. It may include instruction as to how to carry out actions to achieve the policy requirements.

Needs of the individual or group

Service users may have a variety of needs, which may mean they could benefit from creative and therapeutic activities. These needs can be remembered as PIES.

Physical

Studied ☐

Physical needs are to do with the body. A person may have had a stroke, which could have left them with a weakness in one side of their body. Or they may have had an accident which has caused them to lose a limb. Any activities that exercise the body would count as physical.

Intellectual (cognitive)

Studied ☐

Intellectual needs are to do with the brain, thinking or learning new skills. Intellectual needs may include activities that relieve boredom. They can also help to prevent memory loss. Any activities that stimulate the brain or get people thinking are ideal for meeting intellectual needs. A service user may have lost the ability to speak, or a child may learn new words.

Emotional

Studied ☐

Emotional needs are to do with how we feel about ourselves or our ability to express emotions. A service user may have poor self-esteem or may be depressed, or he or she may be bereaved or separated from loved ones.

Social

Studied ☐

Social needs are to do with friendship groups and working with other people. A service user could be new to the area or have few friends.

Factors affecting choice of activity

When choosing, planning and implementing an activity, it is crucial to consider the needs of service users. You could find this out by asking them directly or by speaking to carers or family. You can then start to develop activities that will have maximum benefits for the individual service user. There are also a number of factors that you should consider during this process.

Setting

Studied ☐

Your first consideration would be where is the activity going to take place? This is an important factor, as a physical activity requiring a large area may not be appropriate in a small dining area, for example. Other important factors include seating arrangements and checking there is sufficient space for service users and equipment.

Potential benefit

Studied ☐

When selecting activities for the service users, we should make sure they are going to enjoy them. However, therapeutic and creative activities are carried out because they provide a range of benefits. Also, skills can be regained, improved and developed, depending on the age and type of service user you are planning for.

Age

Studied ☐

This is an important factor to consider. The activity should be appropriate for the age and developmental stage of children and should meet those needs, not only physically but also intellectually. Older service users should not be stereotyped into activities because of age, but safety should be considered at all times.

Intellectual ability

Studied ☐

There may be a range of intellectual abilities in your group, which will affect your choice of activity. This may be a very general activity in order to include all service users; also you will need to make sure that they are not bored by the activity, nor find that it is too challenging.

Physical ability

Studied ☐

The physical ability of service users will determine the types of activities you may wish to choose. Consider some of the following questions:

1. What stage of development are children at?
2. Does any equipment need to be adapted?
3. Is the environment safe?
4. Do any service users have physical restrictions?
5. Are you trying to enhance small physical skills or gross physical skills?

Communication skills

Studied ☐

The communication skills of service users may influence your choice of activities. For example:

1. Is a hearing loop required or hearing appliances?
2. Do instructions need to have enlarged print?
3. Do instructions need to be in Braille?

Gender

Studied ☐

Most activities should be enjoyed by all genders to promote inclusion, but there could be a cultural reason that may affect who takes part in the activity. For example, a sporting activity that involves showing parts of the body (e.g. swimming) may exclude some females because of their religion.

P4
P5
M3
D3

Culture

Studied ☐

Consider the cultural background of all your service users to ensure that you do not exclude someone whose beliefs or traditions may prevent them from taking part in the activity.

Health and fitness of the individual(s)

Studied ☐

Remember that all your activities should be adapted to suit the abilities of your service users to support inclusion. This will require you to check your service users' needs and match your resources to them. Some of the questions you may consider are:

1. What developmental stage is the service user at?
2. Which developmental area are you focusing on?
3. Is the service user developing, regaining or maintaining particular skills?

Availability of resources and facilities

Studied ☐

The availability of resources and facilities will affect your choice of activity. (See below for more information about resources and facilities.)

Time and cost restrictions

Studied ☐

The time of day is a factor to consider when choosing activities. For example, a photography session that requires light should be carried out in the morning or early afternoon. The length of the activity should be considered. Do you have enough time to complete the activity? You may have to repeat it several times for large groups. Is the activity too long? Will the service users be bored? Consider the concentration span of the service users.

Cost has a big implication on choice of activities and can be restricting. Cost should be considered in planning; for example, visiting a garden centre may not be costly but transport, meals and extra staff may make the activity more costly.

Planning

When planning creative and therapeutic activities, health and safety considerations are an important part of selecting suitable and appropriate resources. Consider the following:

- Is there enough space?
- Is there sufficient seating for all service users?
- Is the space and equipment accessible by all participating service users?
- Do you have enough material resources?
- Do you need other health and social care workers with you to support the activity and service users?

For example, if you are cooking with 20 children, do you have enough oven space for all their cakes and biscuits?

Risk assessment

Before carrying out any activity it is crucial to consider any health and safety implications. This is to ensure the health and well-being of service users, staff, other people and the general environment. You may carry out a risk assessment, which looks at what hazards there may be, what may occur as a result of this hazard and then what measures are in place to reduce the possibility of this occurrence.

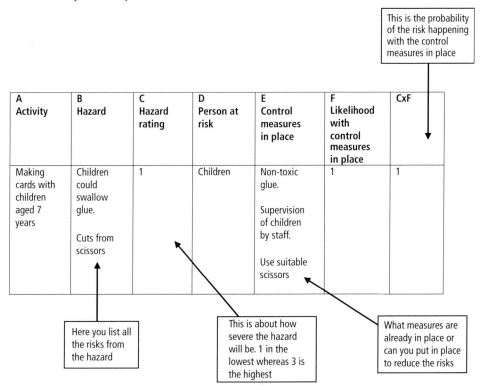

A Activity	B Hazard	C Hazard rating	D Person at risk	E Control measures in place	F Likelihood with control measures in place	CxF
Making cards with children aged 7 years	Children could swallow glue. Cuts from scissors	1	Children	Non-toxic glue. Supervision of children by staff. Use suitable scissors	1	1

This is the probability of the risk happening with the control measures in place

Here you list all the risks from the hazard

This is about how severe the hazard will be. 1 in the lowest whereas 3 is the highest

What measures are already in place or can you put in place to reduce the risks

Table 12.02 Example of a risk assessment

Resources

Appropriate equipment

Use of appropriate resources and equipment will not only avoid accidents and injuries, but also will allow the activity to run smoothly. For example, gardening without trowels and forks would be unsafe and not enjoyable, as would photography without film or memory cards.

Below is a range of equipment you may require when carrying out activities with your service users.

P4

P5

Figure 12.02 Examples of resources used in creative and therapeutic activities

Specialist resources

Service users who have a disability may need some of the following items to ensure they can participate:

- easy grip tools or equipment
- hearing loops/talking books
- non-slip mats
- computers with touch screens or pads
- alternative written instructions in Braille, a different language, in large print

Figure 12.03 Equipment that can be used to support service users

Real life connection

Activities coordinator

An activities coordinator may work independently in a care home or may work as part of a team in a retirement home or hospital. An activities coordinator working as part of a team may work with occupational therapists, nurses, a psychiatrist and art therapists.

The arts have an important therapeutic role, for example in helping people to communicate and to express themselves through art, music, drama, dance or other creative ways. People can also gain greater self-awareness, confidence and self-esteem, as well as simply taking part in an activity with others that gives them great pleasure and satisfaction.

Academic qualifications may not be needed (but may well be an advantage), although a good general education with numeracy and literacy skills is likely to be required, as some paperwork may be involved as part of the role.

Skills required will depend upon the role, but you are likely to need:

- an interest and ability in art, crafts, drama, music (some posts may seek applicants with sport or cookery skills, or an interest and ability in gardening)
- creativity and imagination
- a caring and encouraging attitude
- good communication skills
- patience.

Check your understanding

Read the following case studies and then discuss what factors may need to be considered when planning and implementing these activities.

Case study 1

Amy is an activities coordinator and is planning to take 10 elderly service users from Pear Tree Residential Care Home for a morning's shopping trip. They all have varying mobility problems but are keen to go out. The care home is situated fairly close to an indoor shopping mall.

Case study 2

Stephen and Joanna are care assistants at a local private nursery and would like to plan a baking activity with 24 pre-school children. They will be baking to support a local charity event.

Case study 3

Nikita is an occupational therapist and works at the local hospital. She provides a weekly session for a group of young adults who have learning difficulties; this week she is planning a yoga session.

Key learning points

Risk assessment
Revised

This is a process carried out prior to commencing a therapeutic or creative activity to ensure safety.

Resources
Revised

This refers to the equipment required to carry out the activity appropriately.

Specialist resources
Revised

Equipment which may be adapted to ensure all service users can take part in the activity.

Needs
Revised

This refers to the specific area for which a service user requires assistance and support; for example, physical, cognitive, social or emotional.

Model assignment

This assignment will assess the following learning aims:

A explore different creative and therapeutic activities used in health and social care and their benefits

B understand how professionals support and encourage individuals who take part in creative and therapeutic activities

C be able to plan and implement appropriate creative and therapeutic activities in a health and social care setting.

Scenario

As a new health and social care student you have been asked to investigate two different settings where you intend to spend a period of work experience. You should produce an information leaflet about each setting. Examples of settings could be:

1. A residential care home

2. A pre-school

Task 1

In each leaflet you need to describe **at least three** suitable creative and therapeutic activities for the service users (include pictures if you wish). They can be group or individual activities.

Included in the leaflet should be an outline of the benefits of each activity (remember PIES).

Case study

Task 2

Read the following case study and then write a report;

Rainbow Day Care Centre offers a range of creative and therapeutic activities to young adults who have learning difficulties. One of the centre's roles is to promote independence. Each week the centre carries out the following activities:

● Monday – painting and drawing

● Tuesday – cooking

● Wednesday – singing and music

● Thursday – drama

● Friday – board games

Each afternoon the service users are engaged in reading activities or watching DVDs.

Assess the suitability of these activities for the service users described. What would you recommend to improve the range of activities available and why?

Booklet

Task 3

Pear Tree Retirement Village offers care at varying levels to elderly service users and it employs a range of professionals who are responsible for carrying out creative and therapeutic activities.
In a booklet for family members:

1   Describe the role of professionals involved in planning and implementing creative and therapeutic activities at the retirement village.

2   Using the following examples, compare and contrast (similarities and differences) the role in planning and implementing activities of:
   ● Activities coordinator at the retirement village
   ● Occupational therapist at the local children's hospital.

3   Evaluate (advantages and disadvantages) how the professional support given when conducting creative and therapeutic activities impacts on the service users.

Task 4

During your work placement you need to select, plan, implement and review a creative and therapeutic activity with an individual or group. Collect evidence in the form of plans, witness testimonies, and reflections as evidence for this task.

1   Describe the factors which may affect the selection, planning and implementation of your activity.

2   Complete the following chart while planning and carrying out your activity.

Setting name	
Activity	
Date	
Time/duration	
Service user group	
Service user number	
Specific needs	
Resources needed	
Health and safety considerations, including risk assessment	
Physical benefits	
Intellectual benefits	
Emotional benefits	
Social benefits	

Outline of activity, including your role and what you hope to achieve

Assessment of activity
Ask yourself the following questions:
- Was the setting/environment suitable?
- Did I have sufficient time?
- Did I have enough resources?
- Was health and safety adequate?
- Did the service users participate and enjoy the activity?
- Did I meet all service users' needs?
- Was it the correct activity?
- Did I achieve what I set out to do?

Evaluation of activity – use the following questions to help you:
Ask yourself the following questions Which of these will help you to formulate your evaluation?
- Would I do this activity again?
- How might I change it?
- Did I enjoy it?

Remember: Prior to carrying out your activity, make sure you have consent from your setting's supervisor, manager or teacher to ensure health and safety considerations are made and consent is obtained from service users if required.

Unit 13

The Health and Social Care Sector

This unit requires placement of a minimum of 25 hours in a health or social care setting. In this unit we look at the skills and professional standards needed to work in this sector and the structure of the services and jobs within it.

Learning aims

In this unit you will:

✓ develop an understanding of the skills and professional standards required of health and social care workers

✓ investigate service provision and job roles in the health and social care sector

✓ undertake a work placement within the health and social care sector and reflect upon performance.

Assessment criteria

Level 2 Pass	Level 2 Merit	Level 2 Distinction
Learning aim A: Develop an understanding of the skills and professional standards required of health and social care workers		
2A.P1 Describe the skills and professional standards required to work in the health and social care sector.	**2A.M1** Explain how the skills and professional standards required in the health and social care sector enable successful working with service users, with reference to a selected placement.	**2A.D1** Assess the importance of skills and professional standards required to work in the health and social care sector.
Learning aim B: Investigate service provision and job roles in the health and social care sector		
2B.P2 Describe the different types of provision in health and social care.	**2B.M2** Explain the different characteristics of different types of health and social care provision, using selected examples.	**2B.D2** Assess the different characteristics of different types of health and social care provisions.
2B.P3 Describe three different roles of health and social care workers.	**2B.M3** Compare and contrast the characteristics of three selected job roles in the health and social care sector.	**2B.D3** Assess own suitability for three selected job roles within the health and social care sector.
2B.P4 Describe the purpose of provision and the benefits to service users of a selected health and social care setting.		
Learning aim C: Undertake a work placement within the health and social care sector and reflect upon performance		
2C.P5 Demonstrate work related skills to address work-related tasks within the health and social care sector.		
2C.P6 Describe the skills learned and understanding gained while on work placement.	**2C.M4** Discuss own performance on work placement, describing strength and areas for improvement, giving recommendations for future development.	**2C.D4** Analyse own strengths and areas for improvement on work placement, justifying recommendations for future development.

Skills needed in the health and social care sector include:

- teamwork
- communication with colleagues and service users
- observation of service users
- planning activities.

Teamwork

Recording and reporting information accurately, following instructions, and time management are important when working with others. No one person can adequately give all the care that a person requires. A team approach is needed and that can only happen if people on the team share information. In previous units we saw the importance of the values that underpin care: maintaining dignity, empowerment, promoting independence, respecting diversity, culture and beliefs and maintaining confidentiality. Empathy or understanding how someone might feel, and a caring disposition are essential qualities for carers. Carers who lack empathy and a caring disposition cannot care effectively. The Nursing and Care Quality Forum report of May 2012 recommends

'making sure nurses are recruited for their caring nature and compassion as well as their knowledge and skills'. www.dh.gov.uk/health/2012/05/nursing-forum

Communication with colleagues and service users

In Unit 3 we looked at communication with colleagues and service users: verbal and non-verbal skills, conversation, active listening, and alternative forms of communication such as British Sign Language, Makaton, picture cards, Lightwriters, and assistive software. A carer may not know how to use all these alternative forms of communication, but must be willing to learn whatever is needed to help the service user to communicate.

Observation of service users

Observation is an essential skill. Observation of service users and their behaviour to identify improvement or deterioration in ability or health status is vital. Here are two examples of how observation leads to better care.

Observation leads to better care and can save lives

Mr Zaid who we met in earlier chapters, gets agitated when he needs the toilet. He cannot communicate his needs because he has dementia. An observant carer will notice when he starts to get agitated, and could help him to the toilet, thus preventing incontinence, and preserving his dignity.

Sometimes observation skills can save lives. Mrs Khan is diabetic. Sue the manager noticed that Mrs Khan was very irritable, drowsy, trembling and complained of headache. Sue checked Mrs Khan's blood sugar and found it was low. Mrs Khan was hypoglycaemic and about to go into a coma. Sue quickly dissolved a spoonful of sugar in a glass of water and gave it to Mrs Khan to drink, then called the doctor.

Organisational skills

Organisational skills are needed for planning appropriate activities that match the ability of service users, for providing resources and for planning and displaying work. In Unit 12 you can see this is important. Here is an example of the skills needed.

Planning for an activity that requires few resources

Jenny, an activities coordinator at Poppydene care home, plans a sing along because everyone can join in if they wish, or they can just listen. This requires few resources – she uses the CD player and a CD of their favourite songs, with some word sheets for those who have forgotten the words. She does not even have to be able to sing!

Check your understanding

Match start and endings.

1. Teamwork involves _____
2. A recent study called for _____
3. Observing service users is important for _____
4. Organisational skills are needed for _____
    a. …planning activities for service users.
    b. …sharing information with others on the team so that care really does meet the needs of service users.
    c. …nurses to be recruited not just for their academic ability but also for their caring attitude.
    d. …recognising if someone is getting better or getting worse.

A.2 Professional standards

In Units 2, 7 and 8 we looked at professional standards. Check back and look at the work you may have done for these units. Professional standards relate to three areas:

● your own behaviour
● your responsibilities
● maintaining competence.

Your own behaviour

This includes professional conduct, timekeeping, personal hygiene, dress code, positive attitude, values, and confidentiality. Professions have codes of conduct to guide their members, telling them how to behave.

The nursing and midwifery code states that nurses and midwives must 'Be open and honest, act with integrity and uphold the reputation of your profession'. www.nmc-uk.org

The General Social Care Council publishes useful guidance on behaviour. According to this, the 'professional boundary' is the 'boundary between what is acceptable and unacceptable for a professional both at work and outside work'. It covers 'behaviour which has a negative impact on a service user(s) and/or which undermines public trust and confidence in social care services'. www.gscc.org.uk

If a nurse or social worker is consistently late for an appointment with service users, is smelly and dressed in dirty clothes he or she would not gain the trust or confidence of service users. One who breaks confidentiality would not be trusted and one who does not show respect or value individuals would not be a good professional.

Your responsibilities

Your responsibilities include professional relationships, identifying and meeting the individual needs of service users, managing the service, maintaining service users' safety, and safeguarding activities. In Unit 8 we looked at the responsibilities that carers have for safety and safeguarding, for confidentiality and for meeting the individual needs of service users.

Nurses, midwives and social workers assess the needs of individuals and record this in a care plan. The plans are reviewed and adapted to meet the changing needs of service users. We saw in Unit 8 how Sue the manager completed a risk assessment for the care home and reviewed it, but learned that safety is everyone's responsibility. As part of safeguarding, the care of Mr Zaid, who has dementia, was assessed for risk and the risks of his violent behaviour were reduced.

Maintaining competence

Maintaining competence means updating and maintaining skills and professional standards. It is the responsibility of every professional. Nurses have to keep a current portfolio of what updating they have done. Continuous professional development is required by all professions. The Social Work Reform Board set out the Professional Capabilities Framework (PCF) which focuses on capabilities such as communication skills. www.education.gov.uk/swrb

Possible consequences of not keeping up to date and maintaining professional standards can be disastrous. Two cases from Nursing and Midwifery Council hearings illustrate this. A midwife who does not keep up to date and cannot read a graph of a baby's heartbeat correctly is not competent. The baby may be showing distress but the midwife fails to recognise it. This poses a risk to mother and to baby. A nurse who cannot correctly use computer records enters the immunisations given to a baby incorrectly and the baby then does not get the immunisation he should. Both these are real cases. You can read more on www.nmc-uk.org/Hearings/

The murder of baby Peter and the murder of Victoria Climbie, both vulnerable children, are two high-profile cases where social workers have not maintained professional standards and children have died.

Check your understanding

Match the start with the correct sentence ending:

1. Teamwork _____
2. Communication skills _____
3. Professional standards _____
4. Updating _____
    a. ...is essential to remain competent and safe.
    b. ...is important in health and social care.
    c. ...include the use of verbal and non-verbal skills.
    d. ...influence a carer's behaviour all the time.

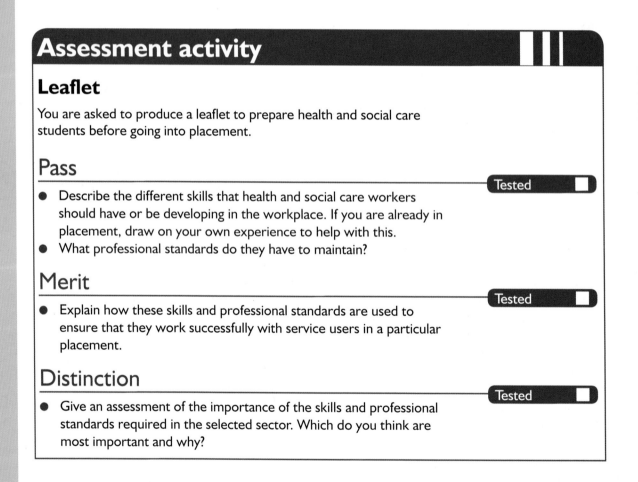

Key learning points

Skills required for working in the health and social care sector

Revised ☐

These include teamwork, communication skills, observation skills and the organisational ability to plan.

Professional standards

Revised ☐

These govern a person's own behaviour, his or her responsibilities and the requirement for current occupational competence.

Assessment activity

Leaflet

You are asked to produce a leaflet to prepare health and social care students before going into placement.

Pass

Tested ☐

- Describe the different skills that health and social care workers should have or be developing in the workplace. If you are already in placement, draw on your own experience to help with this.
- What professional standards do they have to maintain?

Merit

Tested ☐

- Explain how these skills and professional standards are used to ensure that they work successfully with service users in a particular placement.

Distinction

Tested ☐

- Give an assessment of the importance of the skills and professional standards required in the selected sector. Which do you think are most important and why?

Learning Aim B

B.1 The different types of provision relating to health and social care, and their characteristics

In Unit 11 we saw that there are three types of provision:

- statutory or state provision
- private or independent provision
- voluntary, not-for-profit provision, sometimes called the third sector.

Characteristics of types of provision

Statutory

Studied ☐

Statutory services for health include GP services, midwifery, surgery, general medicine, nursing, health centres, National Blood Service and Air Ambulance.

Private or independent

Studied ☐

Private hospitals, some dentists, and physiotherapy clinics are in the private independent sector. The government sometimes buys these services from the private sector; for example, to reduce waiting lists for surgery it buys space in theatres in private hospitals, or it pays private dentists to provide some dental care. Social care services, too, are often bought in by the state from private providers in the independent sector. These services include residential care for older people, or for people with learning disabilities, and residential care for young people with complex needs. Domiciliary care is usually offered by private organisations. Warden-assisted complexes and sheltered housing are offered usually in the private sector. Many builders such as McCarthy and Stone specialise in building retirement properties, in which older people can live as independently as possible.

Figure 13.01 A private retirement village

Voluntary or not for profit

The voluntary or not-for-profit sector provides a lot of social care. The NHS sometimes buys services from the voluntary sector but often the voluntary sector provides services for free. MIND and SANE, two charities supporting those with mental health issues, offer counselling, as do Alcoholics Anonymous and Macmillan Cancer Support. The British Heart Foundation provides advice on diet and exercise. The National Blood Service collects blood from donors and supplies it to hospitals as a free service. In some countries people have to buy blood if they need a transfusion and some people who are poor sell their blood. In this country blood is free for those who need it, thanks to this voluntary service. The Air Ambulance service is also a charity that provides an emergency ambulance service to areas where an ordinary ambulance may have difficulty or experience delay in reaching.

The Citizens Advice Bureau provides a very important social care service, offering advice for people who may be struggling with money or legal problems. The Salvation Army provides night shelters, while day care is offered by voluntary organisations such as Age UK. The National Society for the Prevention of Cruelty to Children runs Childline – a telephone helpline for children – and works closely with social services to protect children.

Some not-for-profit organisations provide social housing and residential accommodation for vulnerable people. Friendship Housing is one such organisation that operates in the Midlands.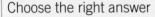
www.fch.org.uk/care-support/supported-livng

Check your understanding

Choose the right answer

1. The Air Ambulance is a...   not-for-profit/private/statutory organisation.
2. The Blood Transfusion service is a...   not-for-profit/private/statutory organisation.
3. Macmillan Cancer Support is a...   not-for-profit/private/statutory organisation.

B.2 Job roles within health and social care settings

Working in health and social care is physically demanding, which is why care workers need to be fit. It is emotionally demanding too. Sometimes the people you look after die and this can be very upsetting, but as a carer you have to empathise with relatives while still staying calm. As a care worker, you are a role model and in a position of trust.

In this section we look at:

- job roles
- working in health and social care
- purpose and benefits.

Job roles

Roles that require a professional degree

Studied ☐

Many jobs require a professional degree. The four branches of nursing – mental health, general, children, and learning disability – require a three-year degree. Midwives (a separate profession to nursing); physiotherapists; occupational therapists; dieticians; clinical psychologists and social workers also undertake a degree in order to qualify in their profession.

Doctors study for five years in university and then two more years before further training and taking exams to specialise as a general practitioner or as a consultant. For all these professions, there is a requirement to continue updating throughout their career, to prove their ongoing competence. Doctors have to prove they are competent to continue practising by being tested every five years. Nurses have to keep a file of their continuous professional development and this may be called in at any time.

Counsellors usually train part time, often as a second or third career after teaching or nursing. Some take a higher degree in a specialist area of counselling. Jobs are often in the voluntary sector and part time. New regulation of counsellors means that it is now becoming recognised as a profession.

Non-graduate roles

Studied ☐

Some jobs do not require degrees as an entry qualification. Healthcare assistants, social work assistants, social care support workers, housing officers, key workers, family support workers, day care officers, community development workers, activity coordinators and youth workers often train on the job while working for vocational qualifications.

UNIT 13 The Health and Social Care Sector

Working in health and social care

In general, the longer the training, the higher the salary is likely to be. Newly qualified doctors undertaking GP training earn between £44,000 and £69,400 per year, whereas care assistants with much less training earn from £12,000 to £16,000 per year.

Professionals such as nurses and doctors are required to register with their professional body, which regulates their conduct and deals with complaints. The General Medical Council, General Dental Council and Nursing and Midwifery Council are professional bodies regulating their professions. In case of complaint, the professional body holds a hearing and may take away the person's registration if he or she is found guilty of misconduct. This means that person is no longer allowed to practice that profession.

Purpose and benefits

Providing access to treatments and services

Studied ☐

Most job roles have specific purposes. A doctor will examine a patient, diagnose a condition and prescribe medication. A nurse will not diagnose. Although some nurses may have specialist training to enable them to prescribe specific drugs, nurses in general do not prescribe. A midwife deals with pregnant healthy women during their pregnancy, through delivery and for ten days afterwards, when the health visitor takes over. A social worker plans care but does not deliver it. A care assistant may deliver personal care such as washing and help with the toilet and have a little involvement in planning.

Safeguarding

Studied ☐

Everyone who works in health and social care has a duty to safeguard service users, and to promote the best quality of life they can for them.

Benefits to service users

Studied ☐

The benefits of care for service users may be physical, for example when a nurse helps a patient to walk after hip surgery. The benefits may be intellectual such as when a speech therapist helps a patient learn to speak again after a stroke, or they may be emotional, for example when a counsellor helps a bereaved widow come to terms with loss. Benefits may be social, for example, when a support worker helps people with learning disabilities to plan and enjoy a holiday. All care aims to give people an increased sense of independence.

Figure 13.02 Examples of healthcare professionals

Check your understanding

Match the start with the correct sentence ending:

1. Statutory health provision _____

2. Statutory social care provision _____

3. Private health care _____

4. Private social care _____

5. Voluntary sector health care _____

6. Voluntary sector social care _____

    a. …includes social workers.

    b. …includes most dentists, opticians, and private hospitals.

    c. …includes privately owned care homes and private foster care organisations.

    d. …includes Macmillan Cancer Support and British Heart Foundation.

    e. …includes Age UK and Mencap.

    f. …includes hospitals, GPs, antenatal care, regional specialist hospitals and district nursing.

P3

P4

M3

D3

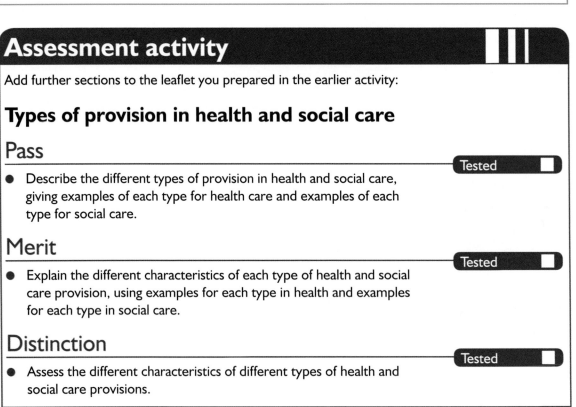

Key learning points

Types of provision in health and social care

Revised ☐

There are three different types of provision in health and social care. These are: statutory provision; private or independent sector provision; and voluntary or not-for-profit provision.

Services provided in health and social care

Revised ☐

Different services are provided in health and in social care.

Job roles

Revised ☐

There is a wide variety of job roles within health and social care settings. Some job roles involve university level training and joining a professional body.

Some training is short and can be given on the job.

Assessment activity

Add further sections to the leaflet you prepared in the earlier activity:

Types of provision in health and social care

Pass

Tested ☐

- Describe the different types of provision in health and social care, giving examples of each type for health care and examples of each type for social care.

Merit

Tested ☐

- Explain the different characteristics of each type of health and social care provision, using examples for each type in health and examples for each type in social care.

Distinction

Tested ☐

- Assess the different characteristics of different types of health and social care provisions.

UNIT 13 The Health and Social Care Sector

Roles of health and social care workers

Pass

- Describe three different roles of health and social care workers.

Merit

- Compare and contrast the characteristics of three selected job roles in the health and social care sector.

Distinction

- Start a placement diary and assess your own suitability for three selected job roles within the health and social care sector.

Benefits to service users

Pass

- Describe the purpose of provision and the benefits to service users of a selected health and social care setting.

P2

P3

P4

M2

M3

D2

D3

While you are in placement there are several skills you will need to demonstrate. These include:

- communicating with others, e.g. line manager, colleagues, service users
- working with others, including colleagues and relatives of service users
- completing tasks within agreed timescales
- following instructions
- following health and safety practices
- maintaining confidentiality, adhering to Data Protection Act
- asking for help and guidance when necessary
- placement expectations: active participation, following placement policies and procedures including absence, agreed working hours and limits of role.

Skills needed for effective care

Many of the skills you need for work have been explained in other units. Communication with others, completing tasks and following instructions are vital if care is to be effective. All placement providers expect people to follow health and safety practices, wearing suitable clothing and footwear and making sure that unauthorised people do not have access to vulnerable clients, and that service users are kept safe.

Confidentiality is expected whether you are a volunteer or a paid employee.

Expectations of placement providers

Placement providers have expectations. They are doing you a favour by allowing you into their workplace, and in turn they expect active participation. If you stand around looking bored you will not develop skills for work. Placement providers expect you to follow policies and procedures such as telling them if you are going to be absent or late and working to agreed working hours, rather than expecting to keep to school or college times. They expect you to know the limits of the role and ask if you are not sure.

Check your understanding

Choose one option to complete the sentence.

1. If you are ill you need to:
   a   let your placement know
   b   stay in bed and go back to sleep.
2. When you are at placement if you do not know what to do, should you:
   a   get your phone out and text friends?
   b   ask what you can do to help?
3. A senior carer asks you to do something you do not know how to do. Should you:
   a   go ahead and give it a go?
   b   ask them to show you how?
4. Your school or college hours end at 4.15pm but your placement ends at 5pm. Should you:
   a   leave at 4.15 p.m. saying you have done your hours?
   b   stay until 5 p.m. and appreciate the chance to gain more experience?

C.2 Reflective practice and evaluation

There are three factors in this section:

- reflective practice
- ways of reflecting on practice
- what to reflect on.

Reflective practice

This means understanding how to reflect on your own work and its importance for future learning, setting goals and working towards them and identifying strengths, achievements and areas to improve.

Using the skills audit shown in Table 13.01 ask a senior person at your work placement to comment in general on your skills in each area, and then complete the remaining columns yourself.

Table 13.01 Skills audit

Skill	Supervisor comments	Own comment, e.g. satisfactory OR need to improve	How you will improve this skill and by when
Communicating with others, e.g. line manager, colleagues, service users			
Working with others, including colleagues and relatives of service users			
Completing tasks within agreed timescales			
Following instructions			
Following health and safety practices			
Maintaining confidentiality, adhering to Data Protection Act			
Asking for help and guidance when necessary			

Ways of reflecting on practice

Include checklists, supervisor reports, one-to-one interviews with placement supervisor, and feedback from teacher and peers.

You will need to recall actions on a daily basis, using a diary to record your own performance. Reflect on how you work with service users, participation with placement staff, solving problems, and recalling actions that happened during the day. If your school or college uses a virtual learning environment, you may be able to keep an electronic diary.

You may wish to use a format to guide your reflection. Here is one way to reflect:

- What happened?
- How did you feel?
- How did other people react? Why do you think they did or said that?
- What would you do differently if it happened again?

Observation records have greater validity than witness statements, as they directly record an assessment decision. When you have been to your placement a few times and feel confident, ask the senior person if they would observe your skills and give written feedback on each of these skills in a specific situation. You may wish to use a similar format to the one shown in Table 13.02 on the next page.

What to reflect on

There is a lot to reflect on so you need to be selective. Key areas for reflection are: working with service users, participation with placement staff and solving problems. Try to reflect on at least two of these situations. Recall actions that happened during the day each day and this will improve your performance.

Check your understanding

Match the start with the correct sentence ending:

1. Work skills include _____
2. Work skills improve _____
3. Reflective practice means _____
4. Feedback from others can _____
   a. ...being realistic about your strengths and weaknesses.
   b. ...communication, teamwork, following instructions, keeping confidentiality and asking for help.
   c. ...if we reflect on what we have done and how to improve.
   d. ...help you improve.

Table 13.02 Format suitable for an observation record

Observation record	
Edexcel BTEC Level 2 First Certificate and Extended Certificate in Health and Social Care	
Unit 13: The Health and Social Care Sector	
2C.P5	Demonstrate work-related skills to address work-related tasks within the health and social care sector
Learner name	
Description of activity undertaken, e.g., organising and leading a quiz in a day centre	
How the activity meets the requirements of the grading criteria: ● communicating with others e.g. service users ● working with others ● completing tasks on time ● following instructions ● following health and safety practices ● maintaining confidentiality ● asking for help and guidance when necessary	
Learner comment:	
Learner signature: **Date:**	
Assessor signature: **Date**:	
Assessor name: **Assessor job role:**	

Real life connection

Social worker

Social workers work with service users to enable them to help themselves. They maintain professional relationships with service users, acting as guides, advocates or critical friends. Service users may be ex-offenders, drug addicts, and people on the fringes of society. Social workers work to support individuals, families and groups within the community, in the service user's home or in schools, hospitals or other places. They also work closely with other health and social care staff.

In order to become a social worker, a person has to take a degree in social work. Applicants for the degree must have voluntary work experience as well as academic entry requirements for university. There is a shortage of social workers.

Key learning points

Specific skills we need for work
Revised ▢

These are: communication, an ability to work with others, completing tasks on time, following instructions and health and safety practices, maintaining confidentiality and asking for help and guidance when necessary.

Ways of improving skills
Revised ▢

We improve skills through reflecting on what we have done, evaluating our own performance and planning how to do better.

P5

P6

Assessment activity

Your skills

Pass
Tested ▢

1   Complete a skills audit – you may wish to use the format given in Table 13.01 in this unit.

Pass
Tested ▢

2   Ask a supervisor in the workplace to observe you in an activity and then complete your observation record.

Pass/Merit/Distinction
Tested ▢

3   During your placement keep a daily diary of events. State what happened, what others did, what you did and why. Record what you did well and also what you would do differently if it happened again. Explain why you would change. Include a section on what you have learned from the situation.

M4

References

www.beacon4blind.co.uk/services-and-resources/activities/it-suite/

www.nmc-uk.org/Nurses-and-midwives/Standards-and-guidance1/The-code/The-code-in-full/#standard

www.gscc.org.uk/cmsFiles/Conduct/GSCC_Professional_Boundaries_guidance_2011.pdf

www.education.gov.uk/swrb/

www.nmc-uk.org/Hearings/Hearings-and-outcomes/May-2012/

https://nationalcareersservice.direct.gov.uk/advice/planning/jobprofiles/Pages/counsellor.aspx

D4

Model assignment

This assignment will assess the following learning aims:

A develop an understanding of the skills and professional standards required of health and social care workers

B investigate service provision and job roles in the health and social care sector

C undertake a work placement within the health and social care sector and reflect upon performance.

Scenario

You are asked to advise a friend on careers in health and social care. You research some information and prepare a short report to help your friend understand the skills and professional standards needed by health and social care workers.

Section 1

Develop an understanding of the skills and professional standards required of health and social workers.

- Identify the skills and professional standards required to work in the health and social care sector.
- Describe the skills and professional standards required to work in the health and social care sector.
- Explain how the skills and professional standards required in the health and social care sector enable successful working with service users, with reference to a selected placement.
- Assess the importance of skills and professional standards required to work in the health and social care sector.

Section 2

To help both yourself and your friend to decide about careers, you investigate service provision and job roles in the health and social care sector and summarise your findings.

- Give three examples of each of the different types of provision and services in either health or social care.
- Describe the different types of provision in health and social care.
- Explain the different characteristics of different types of health and social care provision, using selected examples.
- Assess the different characteristics of different types of health and social care provisions.

- Identify three different roles of health and social care workers.
- Describe three different roles of health and social care workers.
- Compare and contrast the characteristics of three selected job roles in the health and social care sector.
- Assess own suitability for three selected job roles within the health and social care sector.
- Outline the purpose of provision of a selected health and social care setting.
- Describe the purpose of provision and the benefits to service users of a selected health and social care setting.

Section 3

Finally, to help you decide your future career, you undertake a work placement within the health and social care sector and reflect upon performance.

Using your reflective journal and observation checklists you:

- Demonstrate work-related skills to address a work task within the health and social care sector.
- Demonstrate work-related skills to address work-related tasks within the health and social care sector.
- Identify the skills learned and understanding gained while on work placement.
- Describe the skills learned and understanding gained while on work placement.
- Discuss own performance on work placement, describing strength and areas for improvement, giving recommendations for future development.
- Analyse own strengths and areas for improvement on work place-ment, justifying recommendations for future development.

Unit 14

The Early Years Sector

This unit looks at the basic structure of the early years sector, how activities are used to promote children's development in early years settings and how to plan for activities. We look at the skills that early years workers need, how to reflect on your performance during work placement and how to make recommendations for future improvement.

This unit requires placement of a minimum of 25 hours in an early years setting. In this unit we look at the basic structure of the early years sector and the different types of services for children and their families across statutory, private and voluntary provision. You will also learn about different job roles available in the sector and the training or qualifications needed.

Learning aims

In this unit you will:

✓ develop an understanding of the skills and professional standards required of early years workers.

✓ explore planning experiences and activities for children in early years settings.

✓ investigate service provision and job roles in the early years sector.

✓ undertake a work placement in the early years sector and reflect on your experience.

Assessment criteria

Level 2 Pass	Level 2 Merit	Level 2 Distinction
Learning aim A: Develop an understanding of the skills and professional standards required of early years workers		
2A.P1 Describe the skills and professional standards required to work in the early years sector.	**2A.M1** Explain how the skills and professional standards required in the early years sector enable successful working with adults and children, with reference to a selected case study.	**2A.D1** Assess the importance of skills and professional standards required to work in the early years sector.
Learning aim B: Explore planning experiences and activities for children in early years settings		
2B.P2 Describe different activities and experiences suitable for children in two different age groups.	**2B.M2** Explain why selected activities and experiences are appropriate for different age groups.	**2B.D2** Evaluate appropriateness of selected activities for children in different age groups.
2B.P3 Produce a plan for an activity that would be suitable for children in a selected age group.		
Learning aim C: Investigate service provision and job roles in the early years sector		
2C.P4 Describe different types of provision and services in early years.	**2C.M3** Explain the characteristics of different types of early years services, using selected examples.	
2C.P5 Describe three different roles of early years workers who give care to children.	**2C.M4** Compare and contrast the characteristics of three selected job roles in the early years sector.	**2C.D3** Assess own suitability for three selected job roles within the early years sector.
Learning aim D: Undertake a work placement in the early years sector and reflect on your experience		
2D.P6 Demonstrate work-related skills to address different work-related tasks.		
2D.P7 Describe the skills learned and understanding gained while on work placement.	**2C.M5** Discuss own performance on work placement, describing strength and areas for improvement, giving recommendations for future development.	**2C.D4** Analyse own strengths and areas for improvement on work placement, justifying recommendations for future development.

A.1 Skills required when working in the early years sector

Some of the skills needed to work in early years include:

- communicating with children
- building effective working relationships with children
- developing effective working relationships with colleagues
- supporting children with additional needs.

Communicating with children

Communicating with children includes: talking with children of different ages, effective listening with children, asking questions which help to encourage the child's language skills, writing for children (including use of lowercase and uppercase letters), reading to and with children.

Here is an example of how this happens in practice.

Communicating with babies and two-year-olds

Samrah is on placement in the baby room today. She knows that in the pre-linguistic stage babies make babbling sounds. As she gives a baby a bottle feed, Samrah talks to the baby, making eye contact. Afterwards the baby makes 'ooo' sounds.

Next time Samrah is in placement she is with two-year-olds. Peter is two years old and can say 'Me want juice'. Samrah responds by asking 'Apple juice or orange juice?' Later he draws a picture and tells her it is a cat, so she writes 'cat' for him, in lowercase letters. He chooses a picture book about cats and she reads it to him.

Building effective working relationships with children

Children are very aware of relationships even if they cannot talk about them and they learn to trust familiar faces. Children learn when they are happy and having fun. Respecting children and working with all children irrespective of needs and abilities helps to build effective working relationships. Observing children's behaviour and skills during play, telling colleagues what you have observed, knowing when to intervene to ensure safety and/or extend the children's play and knowing how to empower children to develop independence are part of what an early years practitioner does.

Here is another example from Samrah's placement.

Maintaining trust and a working relationship

Jamie is three years old and recently got a new little brother. Since the birth of the baby, Jamie's behaviour has changed. He snatches toys from other children and hits them if they try to keep hold of the toy. Other children are beginning to avoid him. Samrah is on placement. She sees him go to a little girl and snatch the doll she is dressing. Samrah tells the practitioner in charge, who then talks to Jamie and comforts the little girl. Jamie gives the doll back. Samrah then takes him to the water play area, where he pours water from a jug into a plastic bottle. He splashes a bit, but Samrah wipes the splashes and lets him play. Soon he is sharing his toys with the little girl who has come over to join the fun.

Developing effective working relationships with colleagues

This involves being part of a team, communicating with colleagues, recording and reporting information accurately, following instructions, and managing your time. In the examples above, we see that Samrah works as part of a team, communicating when Jamie was aggressive. She reported the situation, stating the facts, and she did not exaggerate. The nursery nurse recorded Jamie's behaviour so that it could be monitored. Samrah followed instructions to take Jamie to a different play area. Samrah knows the importance of time management; as the children have to wash their hands before snack time, she needs to tell them in good time to tidy up.

Supporting children with additional needs

Additional needs may be physical, mental, learning or behavioural needs. Physical needs such as not being able to hear may cause learning difficulties. A child who does not hear the teacher tell him or her to tidy up may be thought uncooperative. Jamie has additional behavioural and emotional needs as he adjusts to not being the baby of the family. His needs are temporary, but genetic disorders such as Down's syndrome and developmental disorders such as Autistic spectrum disorder are permanent and may have a long-term impact on a child's development. Accidents may cause permanent mobility problems or brain damage and have a long-term impact on a child who was previously developing normally. Whatever additional needs a child has, it is important to see each child as a unique individual and assess him or her as a whole person.

Figure 14.01 Children may need support

Check your understanding

Are the following statements true or false?

1. Communicating with children is important for their social development. It is possible to communicate with a baby who cannot yet speak. True or false?

2. To build effective working relationships with children you need to care about their welfare. True or false?

3. To develop effective working relationships with colleagues you must be reliable, hardworking and trustworthy. True or false?

4. Additional needs may be physical, mental, learning, or a behavioural need. A child may have more than one learning need at the same time. True or false?

UNIT 14 The Early Years Sector

346

A.2 Professional standards

In Units 2, 7 and 8 we looked at professional standards. Check back and look at the work you may have done for these units. Professional standards relate to three areas:

- own behaviour
- responsibilities
- maintaining competence.

Own behaviour

Your professional conduct, timekeeping, personal hygiene, dress code, positive attitude, values, and respect for confidentiality are part of what it means to be a professional. Someone who is always late for work, has poor personal hygiene, dresses inappropriately, is always grumbling and putting others down, who does not care about the children and gossips about them and their parents is not the type of person who should work in early years.

Early Years Professional Status is awarded to graduates who are leading in the area of practice from birth to the end of the Early Years Foundation Stage, and expected standards of behaviour are published by the Teaching Agency. www.education.gov.uk

Responsibilities

Responsibilities cover professional relationships, managing children's behaviour, identifying and meeting individual needs of children, maintaining children's safety, and implementing the policy for safeguarding children. In Unit 8 we looked at the responsibilities that workers have for safety, for safeguarding, for confidentiality and for meeting individual needs.

When Samrah intervened to stop Jamie bullying the little girl she was implementing the safeguarding policy, but there is much more to safeguarding children. Workers are screened through the Criminal Records Bureau to prevent unsuitable people having contact with children. From December 2012 it is planned that the Criminal Records Bureau will become the Disclosure and Barring Service (DBS) and checks will continue to make sure that people who work in early years are screened.

Although the early years sector does not have a professional regulating body, maintaining skills and professional standards is very important and is overseen by the Teaching Agency. The Nutbrown Review, 'Foundations for Quality – the independent review of early education and childcare qualifications' published by the government in June 2012, has nineteen recommendations for improving the professional practice of people working in early years. The government are considering these recommendations, including bringing in a new early years specialist route to Qualified Teacher Status from September 2013.

Maintaining skills and professional standards

Professional standards are important. In early years, the consequences of not maintaining professional standards are that child abuse may happen because no one recognises it. Even though we have CRB checks and Ofsted inspections, unsuitable people do get to work in the early years sector.

One example of the consequences of not maintaining professional standards can be seen in the Vanessa George Serious Case Review held by Plymouth Safeguarding Children Board, where a worker abused young children in a nursery environment. Poor communication with outside agencies, poor management and a lack of training for staff set up an environment where abuse could happen. Child protection policies were rarely followed. www.nurseryworld.co.uk/news/1040320/BIG-ISSUE-Vanessa-George-nursery-abuse-case

In 'The Early Years: Foundations for life, health and learning: An Independent Report on the Early Years Foundation Stage to Her Majesty's Government' by Dame Clare Tickell, one of the recommendations is: 'the need to upskill the workforce, to commit to promoting a minimum level 3 qualification and to maintain the ambitions for a graduate led sector.' http://media.education.gov.uk

Check your understanding

Match the start with the correct sentence ending:

1. Building effective working relationships with children includes _____
2. Communication with children includes _____
3. Building effective working relationships with colleagues includes _____
4. Supporting children with additional needs includes _____

   a. …talking with children of different ages, effective listening, asking questions which encourage the child's language skills, writing for children (including use of lowercase and uppercase letters) and reading to and with children.

   b. …respecting children, working with all children, observing children, telling colleagues what you have observed, knowing when to intervene to ensure safety and/or extending the children's play and knowing how to empower children to develop independence.

   c. …assessing a child's individual physical, cognitive, emotional and social abilities and planning activities to develop skills.

   d. …being part of a team, communicating with colleagues, recording and reporting information accurately, following instructions and time management.

Key learning points

Skills needed for working in the early years sector

Revised

Workers in the early years sector need to: communicate with children; build effective working relationships with children; develop effective working relationships with colleagues; and support children with additional needs.

Professional standards

Revised

These govern a person's own behaviour, his or her responsibilities and the requirement for current occupational competence.

Assessment activity

Leaflet

You are asked to produce a leaflet to prepare students before going into placement.

Pass

Tested

- Describe the different skills and professional standards that early years workers should have in the workplace. If you are already in placement, draw on your own experience to help with this.
- What professional standards do they have to maintain?

Merit

Tested

- Use a case study to explain how skills and professional standards are used by early years workers to work successfully with adults and children.

Distinction

Tested

- Assess the importance of skills and professional standards required in the selected sector. Which do you think are most important and why?

Learning Aim B

B.1 Importance of providing suitable experiences and activities

In this section we look at:

- different age groups of children
- appropriate experiences
- different activities.

Different age groups of children

The age groups of children we work with are:

- babies: birth to 1 year
- toddlers: 1 to 3 years
- pre-school children: 3 to 5 years
- school-aged children: 5 to 8 years.

Birth to 1 year

Studied ☐

Personal, social and emotional development, communication and language, and physical development are the essential foundations for healthy development; and these are laid down in this early period. Children who have the love and care of family members at this stage develop and continue to do so, but those children who are neglected at this stage lag behind in later development.

Toddlers 1 to 3 years

Studied ☐

In terms of personal and social development, there is growing self-confidence and self-awareness. By 36 months, children separate from their main carer with support and encouragement from a familiar adult and begin to recognise danger and know who to turn to for help. They are aware that some actions can hurt or harm others. They respond to the feelings and wishes of others.

Children seek out others to share experiences and play alongside others. Physically, children gain increasing control of their whole bodies and are becoming aware of how to negotiate the space and objects around them. Children can communicate their physical needs for things such as food and drink and can let adults know when they are uncomfortable. Children listen with interest when adults read stories to them and speaking develops. Children can identify action words by pointing to the right picture, for example 'Who's jumping?'. They understand simple questions and are developing understanding of basic concepts (e.g. big/little).

Pre-school children 3 to 5 years

Children can select and use activities and resources with help. They talk about their own needs and feelings. They are confident to talk to other children. They are aware that some actions can hurt others' feelings. They can adapt their behaviour to different events.

Children can play in a group. Physically they maintain balance when they concentrate.

Children can recognise and express their own need for food, exercise, the toilet, rest and sleep. They can put on a jumper and coat with little assistance and can fasten big buttons. Children listen to others one to one or in small groups when the conversation interests them.

They respond to instructions containing positional language, for example 'over' and 'under', and can identify objects by their use. They attempt to answer 'why' and 'how' questions using words like 'because'. Children use talk, actions and objects to connect ideas and recall past experiences. They can retell a simple past event in the correct order, and can talk about things that will happen. They question why things happen and can give explanations.

School-aged children 5 to 8 years

Personal, social and emotional development, communication and language and physical development are identified as prime areas of learning. These continue to develop alongside the skills of literacy, mathematics, expressive arts and design, and understanding the world as a child enters education.

(*Source:* The Early Years: Foundations for Life, Health and Learning – Tickell, 2012.)

Appropriate experiences

Appropriate experiences require suitable materials and resources to give children the opportunity to experiment indoors and outdoors. Babies learning to walk require a safe environment with furniture corners protected and no loose mats indoors. Outdoors they need a safe surface in case they fall. In both indoor and outdoor environments they need something or someone to hang on to for support. Five-year-olds need a variety of experiences to refine coordination, for example cycling outdoors, and drawing indoors.

Different activities

Different activities require suitable materials and resources to encourage a child's sensory development, imagination and creativity, and to meet their physical needs. A baby's eyesight develops as he or she learns to focus on a mobile. A musical toy will help a baby to recognise sounds. As the baby starts on solid food he or she experiences different tastes. Nursery rhymes and songs will stimulate language skills; painting will stimulate imagination and creativity. Crawling and exploring safe surroundings encourages physical development.

Five-year-olds have the same needs for sensory development, but are now refining their skills. They will sing songs, and tell a story. They will know colours and be able to paint a more complex picture, explaining what the picture is about. They may use puppets or dolls to tell a story and take part in role play such as 'house' or 'shop' and other imaginative games. Physically, a five-year-old will be able to learn to cycle and swim.

Check your understanding

Match the start and ending to make the right sentence:

1. Three prime areas of learning are _____

2. Four other areas of learning are _____

3. By 36 months _____

4. By 5 years they _____

     a. …literacy, mathematics, expressive arts and design, and understanding the world as a child.

     b. …children separate from their main carer with support and encouragement from a familiar adult.

     c. …demonstrate friendly behaviour, initiate conversations and form good relationships with peers and familiar adults.

     d. …personal, social and emotional development; communication and language and physical development.

B.2 Role of the early years practitioner

The early years practitioner's job is to provide suitable experiences and activities for children of different ages. Practitioners must assist in the planning and preparation of activities, making resources available, making sure the environment is safe but giving opportunities for risk-taking. Their role includes working with children during experiences and activities, checking the suitability of the placement setting for the needs and interests of the child.

Two examples show how we provide different activities and resources for children of different ages.

Planning activities for a 3-month-old

Ryan, an early years worker, knows that in the baby stage from 0–1 year old, babies are learning about the world through their senses. They have short attention spans. He plans activities for Mikey, who is 3-months-old. Mikey has a bottle feed at about 10 a.m. and then likes to play in the baby gym for a short while. It is clean, soft and made from padded cloth, which forms the sides and base. Ryan observes that Mikey likes to look at the red toy dangling from the side of the baby gym. Ryan moves the toy and squeezes it so that it makes a noise. Mikey turns his head to listen, which shows that his sense of hearing is developing. Mikey also likes to kick his legs when he is lying in the gym, exercising his muscles ready for learning to walk. Mikey can hold his head up and can roll over now. Ryan ensures the baby gym is on a mat on the floor so that if Mikey rolls, he will not come to any harm. When Mikey gets tired he cries; then Ryan picks him up, sings a lullaby and gently rocks Mikey to sleep.

Next day Ryan has to cover for a sick colleague, and he is working with pre-school children aged 3 to 5 years. He plans different activities for this age group.

Activities for a three-year-old

Zafar is a particularly active three-year-old. If he is bored he runs around, disrupting everyone. Ryan plans activities that will help Zafar's sensory development, imagination and creativity and meet his physical needs. Zafar loves to play with water, especially in the outdoor water play area. Ryan ensures there are jugs for pouring, and also small plastic watering cans so that Zafar can water the garden. Zafar loves this. He also likes the pedal tricycles in the garden. By the time it is snack time, he is ready for a less energetic activity, and happily goes to the dressing-up box, where he finds his favourite fireman's helmet. After playing fireman he goes to the painting corner and paints a big red fire truck. He tells Ryan that he wants to be a fireman. They finish the morning with a story about a big red fire truck.

Check your understanding

1. The role of the early years practitioner includes _____
2. A suitable activity for babies birth to 1 year is _____
3. A suitable activity for toddlers 1 to 3 years, is _____
4. A suitable activity for pre-school children 3 to 5 years is _____
5. A suitable activity for school-aged children 5 to 8 years is _____

    a. …lying in the cot and kicking.

    b. …planning experiences and activities for children, ensuring safety while allowing some appropriate risk taking and working with children during experiences and activities.

    c. …riding a bike with stabilisers.

    d. …riding a bike.

    e. …riding a tricycle.

Key learning points

Children's learning

Children learn better when they have appropriate experiences and activities.

Role of the early years practitioner

Revised

Early years practitioners plan experiences and activities for children and ensure safety while allowing some appropriate risk taking.

Age groups of children in early years

Revised

Different age groups of children need different activities.

Age groups are: babies birth to 1 year; toddlers 1 to 3 years; pre-school children 3 to 5 years; and school-aged children 5 to 8 years.

P2

P3

Assessment activity

Folder of activities

Make a folder of activities suitable for different age groups. You will need to separate your folder into different sections for each age group:

- babies birth to 1 year
- toddlers 1 to 3 years
- pre-school children 3 to 5 years
- school-aged children 5 to 8 years.

Produce a plan for one activity for each age group and say why it is appropriate for that age group.

Try out three of these different activities with children at your placement and state for each what worked and what could be improved.

- Identify an activity or experience suitable for children in a selected age group.

Pass

Tested

- Describe different activities and experiences suitable for children in two different age groups.

Merit

Tested

- Explain why selected activities and experiences are appropriate for different age groups.

Distinction

Tested

- Evaluate the appropriateness of selected activities for children in different age groups.

With guidance, produce a plan for an activity that would be suitable for children in a selected age group.

Pass

Tested

- Produce a plan for an activity that would be suitable for children in a selected age group.

M2

D2

Learning Aim C

C.1 The different types of provision for children and their families and their characteristics

In Unit 11 we saw that there are three types of provision:

- statutory
- private
- voluntary.

Most provision is inspected by Ofsted and reports are published on the Ofsted website. www.ofsted.gov.uk/inspection-reports/find-inspection-report

Providers who want to offer childcare for children aged from birth to the 31 August following their fifth birthday (the early years age group) **must** register on the Early Years Register. They must deliver the Early Years Foundation Stage (EYFS) – a framework for the education and welfare of young children.

People who want to provide childcare for children older than the early years age group but under eight years old must register on the compulsory part of the Childcare Register.

All nurseries, pre-schools and childminders are required to give parents a written summary of a child's progress at the age of two, based on a progress check focused on the prime areas of children's development set out in the Early Years Foundation Stage.

Statutory provision

This is provided by the state (government) and is usually free or subsidised because it is paid for out of taxes. It includes nursery, schools, and services for children with specific needs, children's centres and Sure Start centres.

Children's centres and Sure Start centres offer support for speech and language and emotional development and extra opportunities for physical and literacy development. They focus on the relationship between parent and child; model good relationships by staff between themselves and parents; and support parenting actively from pregnancy to encourage parents to think about their relationship with the developing baby.

The Early Support Programme for parents and carers of disabled children aged 5 and under includes support for health, education, and social care. It is available through the local council.

Private provision

This is privately owned provision and is paid for by the people who use the service. Private provision aims to make a profit from the business. Examples include private nurseries, private schools, out-of-school clubs, afterschool clubs, breakfast clubs, crèches, childminders, nannies, pre-schools and holiday clubs (home and abroad).

Voluntary or not-for-profit provision

This aims to just cover expenses, not make a profit. Often these are paid for by donations from charities. Examples of voluntary provision include youth groups and crèches. The BBC Children in Need campaign supports many HomeStart projects across the country, which provides playgroups, activities and trips for children. www.bbc.co.uk/programmes/b008dk4b/profiles/cin-whoyouhelp-homestart.

Check your understanding

Choose the right answer.
1. Sure Start is a...   not-for-profit/private/statutory organisation.
2. A childminder is a...   not-for-profit/private/statutory organisation.
3. HomeStart is a...   not-for-profit/private/statutory organisation.

C.2 Job roles in the early years sector

There is a wide range of jobs in the early years sector including, for example, nursery workers, room supervisors, nursery managers, childminders, nannies, teachers, learning support assistants, play workers and hospital play specialists.

The training and qualifications for these jobs have changed. The old nursery nurse NNEB qualification was phased out and replaced by a variety of qualifications such as BTEC Level 3 National Diploma in Children's Play, Learning and Development. The Children's Workforce Development Council (CWDC) maintained a list of qualifications considered full and relevant until it was disbanded in April 2012. The Teaching Agency has taken over some of its work and is moving towards a graduate workforce, with leaders in Early Years taking a Master's degree in Early Years to gain Early Years Professional Status.

CWDC introduced a Certificate and Diploma in September 2010 as the recommended basic qualification; however, the Nutbrown Review, published in June 2012, recommends keeping many training programmes. Professor Nutbrown set out recommendations on the training for early years workers. Three key recommendations are:

'Level 3 qualifications should become the minimum standard for the workforce, including those for childminders who work with the EYFS framework.

Level 2 English and mathematics should be entry requirements to level 3 early education and child care courses.

An early years specialist route to Qualified Teacher Status, specialising in the years from birth to seven, should be introduced, starting from September 2013.'

The review did not support a requirement for licensing practitioners. www.education.gov.uk/nutbrownreview

Salary scales vary with the job role. A selection from the National Careers Website shows a special needs teaching assistant may earn £12,000 a year for a 40-hour week; a nursery nurse may earn £10,000 a year for variable hours. A hospital play specialist with a foundation degree may earn £13,000 or more per year for 37.5 hours per week.

At the other end of the pay scale, a graduate teacher with qualified teacher status will have a starting salary of £21,588 per year.

https://nationalcareersservice.direct.gov.uk/Pages/Home.aspx

Check your understanding

1. There are three types of provision: _____
2. Private provision aims to make _____
3. Jobs in this sector have _____
4. Qualifications are changing and the trend is for _____
5. Voluntary provision includes _____
   a. ...low pay.
   b. ...a better skilled workforce.
   c. ...crèches.
   d. ...profit as a business.
   e. ...statutory, private and voluntary.

Key learning points

Types of provision

Revised

There are three types of provision: statutory, private and voluntary.

Funding

Revised

Statutory provision is paid for by the government. Private provision is paid for by the people who use the service. Voluntary provision is usually paid for by donations from charities.

Aims

Revised

Private provision aims to make a profit as a business whereas statutory and voluntary provisions do not.

Jobs in the early years sector

Revised

There is a wide range of jobs in this sector but most are low paid.

Training and qualifications

Revised

There are several courses at the moment that offer qualifications in early years. Training and qualifications are changing but the trend is for a higher-skilled workforce.

Assessment activity

Add sections about early years provision and jobs in the sector to the leaflet you have prepared.

Provision

- Find three examples of early years provision in your local area, drawing examples from each type of provision. Explain how the provision differs and what service each offers.

Pass

Tested ☐

- Explain what statutory, private and voluntary provision means, and then describe some of the different types of services that are available in each sector.

Merit

Tested ☐

- Give an example of statutory, private and voluntary provision in early years, and explain the characteristics of each using examples.

Job roles

Pass

Tested ☐

- Describe three different job roles of early years workers who give care to children.

Merit

Tested ☐

- Compare and contrast the daily tasks, training, qualifications and salary ranges of three different workers in the early years sector. Choose a range of roles, for example, a childminder, a teacher and a nursery nurse. Describe the daily tasks that each might do and compare salary ranges for each role.

Distinction

Tested ☐

- Assess your own suitability for the job roles you have selected. Base this assessment on your skills, qualities and likely educational achievement.

While you are in placement there are several skills you will need to demonstrate. These include:

- communicating with others; for example, line manager, colleagues, children
- working with others, including colleagues and primary carers
- completing tasks within agreed timescales
- following instructions
- following health and safety practices and safeguarding practices
- asking for help and guidance when necessary
- maintaining confidentiality, adhering to Data Protection Act.

Skills required on placement

Communicating with others

`Studied` ☐

This is a basic skill for working in the early years sector. Communication is a two-way process. The line manager needs to know if there is a problem, and colleagues will also need to know.

Working with others

`Studied` ☐

Earlier in the unit we met Ryan on placement. He works closely with other workers so everyone knows who is doing what. He knows who is responsible for the water play area and when the children have break time. The manager at the nursery knows each family well and knows the families where children are at risk.

Completing tasks within agreed timescales

`Studied` ☐

Each placement has a timetable and a routine. This is to ensure that all children have access to activities according to their needs. Ryan knows when the children have to finish activities and be ready for home time.

Following instructions

`Studied` ☐

Ryan knows that it is important to follow instructions. Children have to wash their hands before eating and after messy play to avoid getting sick. Ryan knows that water on the floor can cause slips and falls, so he does not mind being asked to mop the floor.

Following health and safety practices and safeguarding practices

Studied ☐

At Ryan's placement there are strict policies about who can collect children at the end of the day. This is to safeguard children. Sometimes parents separate and only one parent has access to the child. At Ryan's placement there is a list of who collects which child and a procedure for what to do if the person expected does not arrive.

Asking for help and guidance when necessary

Studied ☐

Ryan feels confident enough to say if he is not sure what to do. At his placement, the staff are always keen to explain what to do and to teach others. Ryan knows the safest thing to do is to ask for help if he is not sure.

Maintaining confidentiality, adhering to Data Protection Act

Studied ☐

Ryan knows how important it is to maintain confidentiality. He does not talk about the children outside work, and he is aware not to discuss children with other parents.

Placement providers' expectations

Active participation

Studied ☐

They are doing you a favour by allowing you into their workplace, and in turn they expect active participation. If you stand around looking bored you will not develop skills for work.

Follow placement policies and procedures

Studied ☐

Placement providers expect you to follow policies and procedures including those for absence and agreed working hours. Tell your provider if you are going to be absent or late but, better still, do not be late and do not miss sessions. Your placement provider may expect you to work to agreed working hours, rather than to school or college times. You will also be expected to know the limits of your role and ask if you are not sure.

Check your understanding

1. List seven skills you need to show in placement.
2. Give an example of how you can show each one.

Reflective practice

Reflective practice means understanding how to reflect on your own work and its importance for future learning, setting goals and working towards them and identifying strengths, achievements and areas to improve. Use the following skills audit shown in Table 14.01 and ask a senior person at your work placement to comment *in general* on your skills in each area, and then complete the remaining columns yourself:

Table 14.01 Skills audit

Skill	Supervisor comments	Own comment e.g. satisfactory OR need to improve	How you will improve this skill and by when
Communicating with others, e.g. line manager, colleagues, children			
Working with others, including colleagues and primary carers			
Completing tasks within agreed time-scales			
Following instructions			
Following health and safety and safe-guarding practices			
Maintaining confidentiality, adhering to Data Protection Act			
Asking for help and guidance when necessary			

Ways of reflecting on practice

Ways of reflecting on practice include

- checklists
- supervisor reports
- one-to-one interviews with placement supervisor
- feedback from teacher and peers.

Observation records have greater validity than witness statements, as they directly record an assessment decision. When you have been to your placement a few times and feel confident, ask the senior person if he or she would observe your skills and give written feedback on each of these skills in a *specific* situation, for example, supervising a painting activity for three children aged three. You may wish to use a similar format to the one shown in Table 14.02.

Table 14.02 Format suitable for an observation record

Observation record
Edexcel BTEC Level 2 First Certificate and Extended Certificate in Health and Social Care
Unit 14: The Early Years Sector

2D.P6	Demonstrate work-related skills to address different work-related tasks in the early years sector.

Learner name
Description of activity undertaken

How the activity meets the requirements of the grading criteria – skills to be demonstrated, how they are shown:

- communicating with others, e.g. children
- working with others including colleagues and primary carers
- completing tasks on time
- following instructions
- following health and safety and safeguarding practices
- maintaining confidentiality, adhering to Data Protection Act
- asking for help and guidance when necessary

Learner comment:
Learner signature:
Date:
Assessor signature:
Date:
Assessor name:
Assessor job role:

You will need to recall actions on a daily basis, using a diary to record your own performance.

Real life connection

Early years teacher

Early years, or nursery, teachers work in pre-school, nursery and reception classes with children aged between three and five. They develop and implement work schemes and lesson plans based on the early years foundation stage (EYFS).

In England and Wales, **qualified teacher status (QTS)** is needed. You will need a degree in education or a degree and a Postgraduate Certificate in Education (PGCE) with an early years specialism. GCSE (A–C) passes in English, maths and science (or equivalent qualifications) are also needed, with an enhanced Criminal Records Bureau check.

Salary - £21,588 to £31,552

What to reflect on

There is a lot to reflect on so you need to be selective. Key areas for reflection are: working with children, participation with placement staff and solving problems. Recall actions that happened during the day each day and this will improve your performance.

Check your understanding

Match the start with the correct sentence ending.

1. Work skills include
2. Work skills improve
3. Reflective practice means
4. Feedback from others can
    a. ...being realistic about your strengths and weaknesses.
    b. ...communication, teamwork, following instructions, keeping confidentiality and asking for help.
    c. ...if we reflect on what we have done and how to improve.
    d. ...help you improve.

Key learning points

Skills needed to work in the early years sector

Revised

There are specific skills we need for work. They are: communication, an ability to work with others, completing tasks on time, following instructions and health and safety practices, maintaining confidentiality and asking for help and guidance when necessary.

Improving skills

Revised

We improve skills through reflecting on what we have done, evaluating our own performance and planning how to do better.

Assessment activity

Reflect on your experience

Undertake a work placement in the early years sector and reflect on your experience. Complete a work placement diary which covers the 25 hours you are on work placement.

1   In your diary you need to include a record of:
    - daily activities you completed on placement.
    - the different activities and experiences that the placement gives for the children and how these can support development.

2   Ask a supervisor in the workplace to observe you in a specific activity and then complete your observation record.
    - Demonstrate work-related skills to address a work-related task.
    - Demonstrate work-related skills to address different work-related tasks.

3   Complete a general skills audit – you may wish to use the format shown in Table 14.01 in this unit.
    - Identify the skills learned and understanding gained while on work placement.
    - Describe the skills learned and understanding gained while on work placement.

4   During your placement keep a daily diary of events. State what happened, what others did, what you did and why. Record what you did well and also what you would do differently if it happened again. Explain why you would change. Include a section on what you have learned from the situation.
    - Discuss own performance on work placement, describing strength and areas for improvement, giving recommendations for future development.
    - Analyse own strengths and areas for improvement on work placement, justifying recommendations for future development.

References

http://media.education.gov.uk/assets/files/pdf/r/eyps%20standards%20from%20september%202012.pdf

www.education.gov.uk/publications/eOrderingDownload/Review%20of%20early%20education%20and%20childcare%20qualifications%20-%20Interim%20report.pdf – Nutbrown Review

www.education.gov.uk/nutbrownreview – Foundations For Quality -The independent review of early education and childcare qualifications, Final Report June 2012

https://nationalcareersservice.direct.gov.uk/Pages/Home.aspx

http://media.education.gov.uk/MediaFiles/B/1/5/%7BB15EFF0D-A4DF-4294-93A1-1E1B88C13F68%7DTickell%20review.pdf – The Early Years: Foundations for Life, Health and Learning: An Independent Report on the Early Years Foundation Stage to Her Majesty's Government, Dame Clare Tickell, 2011

Model assignment

This assignment will assess the following learning aims:

A develop an understanding of the skills and professional standards required of early years workers
B explore planning experiences and activities for children in early years settings
C investigate service provision and job roles in the early years sector
D undertake a work placement in the early years sector and reflect on your experience.

Scenario

You are helping a friend find out about the early years sector and decide to make a booklet to help him to develop an understanding of the skills and professional standards required of early years workers.

Section 1

- Describe the skills and professional standards required to work in the early years sector.
- Explain how the skills and professional standards required in the early years sector enable successful working with adults and children, with reference to a selected case study.
- Assess the importance of skills and professional standards required to work in the early years sector.

Section 2

You decide to explore planning experiences and activities for children in early years settings, so you add more information to your booklet.
- Describe different activities and experiences suitable for children in two different age groups.
- Explain why selected activities and experiences are appropriate for different age groups.
- Produce a plan for an activity that would be suitable for children in a selected age group.
- You talk to some parents and nursery nurses and decide to evaluate the appropriateness of selected activities for children in different age groups.

 P1
 P2
 P3
 P4
 P5
 P6
 P7
 M1
 M2
 M3
 M4
 M5
 D1
 D2
 D3
 D4

Section 3

You decide to find out more about early years provision and investigate service provision and job roles in the early years sector.

- Describe different types of provision and services in early years.
- Explain the characteristics of different types of early years services, using selected examples.

You then decide to find out about job roles.

- Describe three different roles of early years workers who give care to children.
- Compare and contrast the characteristics of three selected job roles in the early years sector.
- Assess own suitability for three selected job roles within the early years sector.

Section 4

At this point you begin to consider whether there could be a career for you in this area and decide to undertake a work placement in the early years sector and reflect on your experience.

- Demonstrate work-related skills to address different work-related tasks.
- Describe the skills learned and understanding gained while on work placement.
- Discuss own performance on work placement, describing strength and areas for improvement, giving recommendations for future development.
- Analyse own strengths and areas for improvement on work placement, justifying recommendations for future development.

At the end of this you have decided whether or not you would like to work in early years.

Answers

Unit 1, Learning aim A: Check your understanding, page 13

1. c
2. a
3. d
4. b

Unit 2, Learning aim A: Check your understanding, pages 42–43

1. j
2. l
3. b
4. k
5. e
6. h
7. c
8. f
9. d
10. g
11. i
12. a

Unit 2, Learning aim B: Check your understanding, page 51

1. b. Sometimes people have unrealistic choices. A person with dementia may express the wish that they want to go home, but it would be unsafe to let them go out alone, and there may not be enough staff free to take them out. Duty of care and safeguarding mean that sometimes people cannot have everything they want.
2. a. It is not enough to meet physical needs for food, fluid, hygiene. Effective care includes social, emotional and intellectual needs. A team quiz can meet all three, providing a social event where all take part, enjoy and learn.
3. b. See what happened to Mr Jones earlier in the chapter.
4. a. A carer working alone is not able to give the best care. Knowing something about the person, such as what health needs they have, can help you provide more effective care. Working as part of a team information care be shared to give better care.
5. a. People who are involved in planning their own care feel valued, respected and are likely to have high self-esteem and well-being.

Unit 3, Learning aim A1: Check your understanding, page 61

Verbal communication	Non verbal communication
Pronouncing words correctly	Use of jargon
	Use of gestures
Use of jargon	Use of touch and personal space
Formal language	Eye contact
	Facial expressions

Unit 3, Learning aim A2: Check your understanding, page 64

1. **Braille** is a writing system which enables blind and partially sighted people to read and write through **touch**.
2. An interpreter is someone who converts **spoken** language into signs.
3. **Children** may have an object of reference like a toy to help them **settle** into nursery.
4. Bliss **symbols** are a system of meaning-based symbols which can be used by people with severe difficulties in speaking.
5. **Makaton** is a language programme using signs and symbols to help people to communicate.
6. A **translator** changes the written word into other forms.
7. **Minicom** is a device used for those who have a hearing problem.
8. An **advocate** is a person who will speak or act on behalf on a **vulnerable** person.

Unit 3, Learning aim B: Check your understanding, page 70

Case study 1

1. Adapting the environment – reduce background noise; use of electronic devices, e.g. telephone amplifiers, hearing loops; human aids; staff should speak clearly and not use jargon.
2. Lip read; use technological aids; ask staff and clients to repeat themselves if he does not understand; ask people to use written communication.
3. The wrong message may have been sent; Christopher does not do what he has been asked; he misses out on important information about clients.

4. Christopher may not be attending to their individual needs; clients may feel he is not listening to them; they may become frustrated and upset.
5. Use of technological aids; effective use of the communication cycle; staff could use more non-verbal skills.

Case Study 2
1. Not communicating with Yasser; teacher may not be able to support Yasser's needs; Yasser may feel left out.
2. Lonely; low self-esteem.
3. Use non-verbal communication skills; use signs; use basic sign language; use human aids such as interpreters or translators.
4. Human aids.
5. They could use the basic English that they can speak at home; encourage him to use this language by praising.

Unit 4, Learning aim A1: Check your understanding, page 81
1. d
2. c
3. b
4. a

Unit 4, Learning aim A2: Check your understanding, page 84
1. b
2. c
3. a
4. e
5. d

Unit 4, Learning aim B: Check your understanding, page 91
1. True
2. True
3. True
4. True
5. True

Unit 4, Learning aim C: Check your understanding, page 99
1. b
2. a
3. d
4. c

Unit 5, Learning aim A2: Check your understanding, page 116
1. handwashing
2. drugs
3. obesity

4. vaccination
5. government
6. treatment
7. exercise
8. smoking
9. lifestyle
10. habits

Unit 5, Learning aim B: Check your understanding, page 125
1. d
2. a
3. e
4. c
5. b

Unit 6, Learning aim A1: Check your understanding, page 137
1. True
2. False
3. True
4. True
5. True
6. False
7. True
8. False
9. False
10. True
11. True
12. False
13. False
14. True
15. True
16. True
17. True

Unit 6, Learning aim A2: Check your understanding, page 142
1. Diabetes
2. Water
3. Scurvy
4. Coronary heart disease
5. Obesity

Unit 6, Learning aim B1: Check your understanding, page 145
1. e
2. c
3. a
4. f
5. b
6. d

Unit 6, Learning aim B2: Check your understanding, page 148

1. d
2. c
3. f
4. a
5. e
6. g
7. b

Unit 7, Learning aim A1: Check your understanding, page 158

1. non-discriminatory
2. discrimination
3. non-discriminatory
4. discriminatory

Unit 7, Learning aim A2: Check your understanding, page 161

1. c
2. e
3. b
4. a
5. f
6. h
7. d
8. g

Unit 7, Learning aim B1: Check your understanding, page 168

1. b
2. c
3. a

Unit 7, Learning aim B2: Check your understanding, page 170

1. c
2. a
3. b
4. e
5. d
6. f

Unit 8, Learning aim A1: Check your understanding, page 180

1. The Human Rights Act 1998
2. The Mental Health Act 2007
3. The Equality Act 2010
4. The Mental Health Act 2007
5. The Mental Health Act 2007

Unit 8, Learning aim A2: Check your understanding, page 184

1. c
2. a
3. b

Unit 8, Learning aim B1: Check your understanding, page 190

A. Step 1 Identify the hazards
   Step 2 Decide who might be harmed and how
   Step 3 Evaluate the risks and decide on precautions
   Step 4 Record your findings and implement them
   Step 5 Review your assessment and update if necessary
B. Protecting people from harm
C. Control of substances harmful to health
D. Gloves and aprons
E. Everyone
F Toilets, washing facilities, drinking water, first aid facilities
G. The Health and Safety at Work Act 1974.

Unit 8, Learning aim B2: Check your understanding, page 193

1. b
2. e
3. a
4. c
5. f
6. d
7. g

Unit 10, Learning aim A3: Check your understanding, page 248

1. h
2. g
3. e
4. d
5. a
6. f
7. b
8. c

Unit 10, Learning aim A4: Check your understanding, page 252

1. The circulatory and the respiratory system work together to transport **inspired** oxygen to all cells and **expired** carbon dioxide out of the body.

2. The muscular and nervous system work together to enable the body to **move**.
3. The digestive and endocrine system work together to allow insulin to absorb glucose from the **diet**.
4. The endocrine and **reproductive** system work together to allow **hormones** to regulate the menstrual cycle in **females** and sperm production in **males**.

Unit 10, Learning aim B1: Check your understanding, page 265
1. e
2. d
3. a
4. c
5. f
6. b

Unit 11, Learning aim A2: Check your understanding, page 281
1. b
2. c
3. e
4. d
5. f
6. a
7. h
8. i
9. g
10. k
11. j
12. m
13. l

Unit 11, Learning aim B1: Check your understanding, page 286
1. a
2. d
3. b
4. e
5. c

Unit 12, Learning aim C1: Check your understanding, page 316

Case study 1
- Possible factors could include age, mobility, transport, time, helpers.

Case study 2
- Possible factors could include time, cost, location, helpers, equipment.

Case Study 3
- Possible factors could include communication, cost, space, helpers, health considerations.

Unit 13, Learning aim A1: Check your understanding, page 323
1. b
2. c
3. d
4. a

Unit 13, Learning aim A2: Check your understanding, page 325
1. b
2. c
3. d
4. a

Unit 13, Learning aim B1: Check your understanding, page 328
1. not for profit
2. not for profit
3. not for profit

Unit 13, Learning aim B2: Check your understanding, page 331
1. f
2. a
3. b
4. c
5. d
6. e

Unit 13, Learning aim C1: Check your understanding, page 335
1. a
2. b
3. b
4. b

Unit 13, Learning aim C2: Check your understanding, page 337
1. b
2. c
3. a
4. d

Unit 14, Learning aim A1: Check your understanding, page 346
1. True
2. True
3. True
4. True

Answers

Unit 14, Learning aim A2: Check your understanding, page 348

1. b
2. a
3. d
4. c

Unit 14, Learning aim B1: Check your understanding, page 352

1. d
2. a
3. b
4. c

Unit 14, Learning aim B2: Check your understanding, page 354

1. b
2. a
3. e
4. c
5. d

Unit 14, Learning aim C1: Check your understanding, page 357

1. Statutory
2. Private
3. Not for profit

Unit 14, Learning aim C2: Check your understanding, page 359

1. e
2. d
3. a
4. b
5. c

Unit 14, Learning aim D1: Check your understanding, page 362

1. Communicating with others, e.g. line manager, colleagues, children
   Working with others, including colleagues and primary carers
   Completing tasks within agreed timescales
   Following instructions
   Following health and safety practices and safeguarding practices
   Asking for help and guidance when necessary maintaining confidentiality, adhering to Data Protection Act
2. Check with a friend and then your tutor.

Unit 14, Learning aim D1: Check your understanding, page 365

1. b
2. c
3. a
4. d

Index